BUILDING CRAFT SERIES

JOINERY

BUILDING CRAFT SERIES

BRICKWORK	*By* W. B. McKAY
CARPENTRY	*By* W. B. McKAY
JOINERY	*By* W. B. McKAY

BUILDING CONSTRUCTION
By W. B. *and* J. K. McKAY

Volumes One, Two, Three and Four
(*These are also available as two separate books
in hard covers*)
Volumes One and Two together
Volumes Three and Four together

BUILDING CRAFT SERIES

BY

W. B. McKAY

M.Sc.Tech., M.I.Struct.E.

Former Registered Architect and Chartered Structural Engineer
and Head of Department of Building and Structural Engineering
in the Faculty of Technology, Manchester University

Revised by J. K. McKAY

B.A., B.Sc.Tech., A.R.I.B.A., C.Eng., M.I.Struct.E., F.F.B.

WITH DRAWINGS BY THE AUTHORS

LONGMAN

LONGMAN GROUP LIMITED
London
*Associated companies, branches and representatives
throughout the world.*

Longman
1724-1974

First Published .	.	1946
Seventh Impression	.	1963
Second Edition .	.	1965
Second Impression	.	1967

Second Edition © J. K. MᶜKAY 1965
Third Edition 1974

ISBN 0 582 42518.2
Library of Congress Catalog Card
Number 73-86516

Set in IBM Press Roman 10 on 11 point.

Printed in Great Britain by
Lowe & Brydone (Printers) Ltd., Thetford, Norfolk

PREFACE TO THE FIRST EDITION

IN the book on Carpentry, which forms part of this Building Craft Series, the broad differences between carpentry and joinery were explained. It included a chapter on the classification, structure, growth, felling, conversion, seasoning, preservation, defects, characteristics and uses of timbers, another chapter on plywood and one on drawing.

As this volume on Joinery is complementary to the one on Carpentry, these three chapters have not been repeated here. Moreover, as the machines used in the conversion of logs and the hand tools employed by the woodworker were described in the book on Carpentry, it has only been necessary here to consider the machines used in the preparation of timber (see Chapter One).

Reasons for introducing the subject of plywood and other laminated materials were given in the preface to the book on Carpentry. In the present book will be found applications to flush doors, solid-balustraded stairs, floor covering, etc.

It is a pleasure again to record the author's indebtedness to Mr J. R. Holland and Mr. E. Spencer, especially in connection with the sections on setting out and woodworking machinery.

W. B. McK.

PREFACE TO THE THIRD EDITION (METRIC)

THIS new edition, in metric terms, incorporates the latest amendments.

J. K. McK.

CONTENTS

CONTENTS

Note: Unless otherwise stated all the dimensions on the drawings are given in millimetres.

CHAPTER ONE

WOODWORKING MACHINERY

Machines employed in the preparation of timber, including those for sawing, planing, thicknessing, matching, mortising, tenoning, dovetailing, mitreing, sand-papering and sharpening. Various forms of circular saws and rotary cutters.

HAND tools, including portable hand tools, used by the carpenter and joiner and some of the heavier machines employed in the conversion of timber have been described in the book on *Carpentry*.

The considerable use now made of machinery has revolutionized the woodworking section of the building industry. Machines have speeded up output and reduced costs, and comparatively little hand labour is needed in the well-equipped workshop, as practically all woodworking processes normally required can be done by machinery.

The machines which are used in the preparation of timber (such as those employed for sawing baulks into planks, deals,[1] etc., planing surfaces, and mortising and tenoning members which are to be framed together to form doors, windows, etc.) will now be considered. These machines are power driven, electricity being the chief motive power. The power may be transmitted from its source either by shafting or, preferably, by a separate motor attached to each machine or group of machines. The shafting (steel rods) is suspended by hangers fixed to the roof or ceiling. Rotary motion is imparted to the shafting by belting which passes over pulleys connected to the shafting and the motor, and the motion of the shafting is transmitted by a belt to the machine. Shafting is gradually being dispensed with as machines with individual motors are installed; such are known as *motorized machines*.

The following are some of the machines which are used in the preparation of timber: (1) Circular saw bench, (2) band sawing machine, (3) planing and surfacing machine, (4) surface planing and thicknessing machine, (5) panel planing and thicknessing machine, (6) moulding machine, (7) spindle moulder, (8) planing and matching machine, (9) mortising machine, (10) tenoning machine, (11) double-dimension saw bench, (12) dovetailing machine, (13) lathe, (14) mitreing machine, (15) sand-papering machine, (16) universal woodworker, and (17) sharpening machines.

---

[1]*Baulks* are square in cross-section of size exceeding 150 mm by 150 mm.
  Planks are from 50 to 150 mm thick and at least 275 mm wide.
  Deals are pieces of softwood which are from 50 to 100 mm thick by 225 to under 275 mm wide.
  Other converted timbers are defined in the book on "Carpentry", p. 16.

9

1. CIRCULAR SAW BENCH OR CIRCULAR SAWING MACHINE (see Fig. 1).—This consists of a vertical circular saw, such as that shown at A, Fig. 2, protected by a guard to which a riving knife is attached, and a metal guide or fence. The spindle of the saw is mounted on a frame having a flat metal table. The saw varies from 225 to 1 500 mm in diameter, and the table or bench is from 750 to 2 400 mm long and 600 to 1 200 mm wide. The revolving saw runs in a slot in the table. The fence, which is parallel to the saw, can be readily adjusted, the distance between its face and the saw being regulated to the width to which the timber is to be sawn. Some machines have fixed tables; others can be raised and lowered (called "rising and falling tables") with fences which can be canted through 45°, the latter being useful for bevelling (sloping cuts).

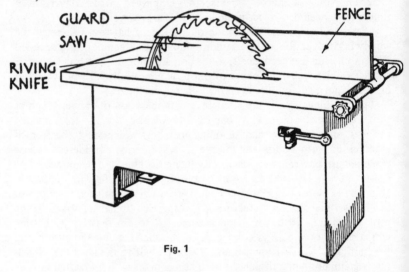

GUARD · SAW · RIVING KNIFE · FENCE

Fig. 1

CIRCULAR SAW BENCH

This machine is extensively employed for general sawing purposes, such as sawing baulks into planks, deals, etc. (known as *deep-cutting*), or into smaller scantlings (called *flat-cutting*), ripping, edging and cross-cutting. Each piece of timber is pressed against the fence (unless it is to be cross-cut), which has been adjusted to the required distance from the saw, and fed towards the rotating saw; the pressure is maintained as the timber slides forward on the table during the cutting operation. The riving knife, which is immediately behind the saw, widens the cut in the timber and thus prevents pressure on the saw.

CIRCULAR SAWS are made of crucible cast-steel plates. The common form, shown at A and P, Fig. 2, and known as a *plate saw*, is a disc of uniform thickness or gauge throughout, the thickness depending upon the size of the saw and the character of the wood to be sawn. Thus, the normal thickness of a saw of 610 mm diameter is 2·5 mm for hardwoods and 2·7 mm for softwoods, whilst the thickness of a 762 mm saw is 2·4 mm for hardwoods and 2·5 mm for softwoods. They are conveniently divided into *rip saws* (those which cut with the grain) and *cross-cut saws* (which cut across the grain). As the fibres of the wood are parallel to the plane of the saw during ripping and perpendicular during cross-cutting, and as timbers vary in hardness, it follows that the shape

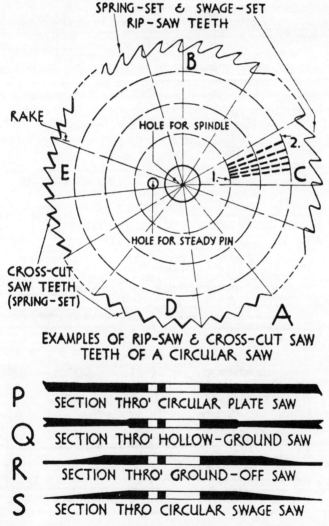

SPRING-SET & SWAGE-SET RIP-SAW TEETH

RAKE

HOLE FOR SPINDLE

HOLE FOR STEADY PIN

CROSS-CUT SAW TEETH (SPRING-SET)

EXAMPLES OF RIP-SAW & CROSS-CUT SAW TEETH OF A CIRCULAR SAW

P SECTION THRO' CIRCULAR PLATE SAW

Q SECTION THRO' HOLLOW-GROUND SAW

R SECTION THRO' GROUND-OFF SAW

S SECTION THRO CIRCULAR SWAGE SAW

NOTE: THE THICKNESS OF THE SAWS SHOWN AT "P." "Q." "R" & "S" IS EXAGGERATED

Fig. 2

of the teeth differ in accordance with the work for which the saw is to be used.

Sketches of teeth of a rip saw are shown at B and C, Fig. 2, and those of a cruss-cut saw are indicated at D and E. The names of the various parts are indicated on the enlarged elevations G and M, Fig. 3. The *hook* or *rake* is the inclination of the *front* or *face* of a tooth; in all ripping saws the cutting *point* of a tooth is forward to form a *forward hook* (see G and M, Fig. 3); the teeth of cross-cut saws have usually a *backward rake* (see E and D, Fig. 2) and occasionally no hook. The *gullet* (G and M) must be sufficiently well rounded to remove the sawdust rapidly during the cutting operation.

SET.—The setting of the teeth of hand saws to produce the cut or *kerf* in the timber of greater width than the thickness of the blade is referred to in the companion volume *Carpentry*. A similar clearance or set must be given to the body of a circular saw so as to eliminate friction, otherwise the timber would bind on the saw, generating heat and causing the saw to wobble. This clearance must be equal on each side if "pulling" to one side is to be avoided. Teeth are either (*a*) spring set or (*b*) swage set.

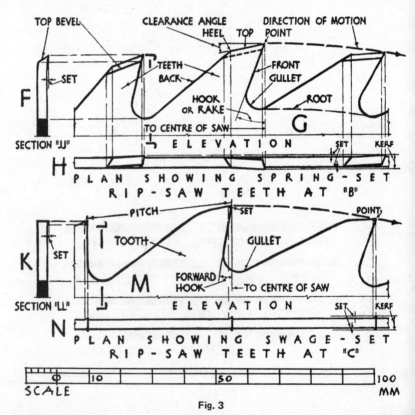

Fig. 3

(a) *Spring Set or Side Set.*—In this type the points of the teeth are bent over to the right and left alternately. Only the extreme points are sprung over, as shown at F and H, Fig. 3. The amount of set depends upon the nature of the timber. In general, hardwoods require less set than softwoods, and the set is increased when wood of a woolly and binding character is to be sawn. As a rule the set required for a 900 mm diameter saw is about 0·38 mm for cutting hardwoods and 0·4 mm for sawing softwoods. The tool used for bending the points of the teeth is called a *saw set.* This is a small steel tool, having several notches of various widths on each of its two edges, and provided with either one or two handles. When setting, the notch in the tool corresponding to the thickness of the saw plate is fitted over the point of the tooth and bent over in the required direction as slight pressure is applied on the handle of the tool. Another tool, called a *set gauge,* is used to measure and ensure the uniform projection of the teeth on each side of the saw. This is a small piece of steel having a straight edge which is notched at the end by an amount equal to the required set. When applying the set gauge, its straight edge is held square along the centre line of the saw, and the point of the tooth should just touch the notched top of the gauge; any adjustment of the tooth is made by the saw set.

The top of each tooth of a rip saw is sharpened with a slight bevel, called the *top bevel* (see F and G, Fig. 3). This enables the outer and higher extreme point to lead in the saw cut. The front of each rip-saw tooth has little or no bevel, but both the front and back of cross-cut teeth are bevelled on alternate sides.

Spring-set teeth are often used for ripping and cross-cutting. Setting of the teeth can be done by the automatic saw sharpening machine described on p. 27.

(b) *Swage Set.*—The point of each tooth when swage set is pressed out so that it slightly extends an equal distance on each side of the saw (see K and N, Fig. 3). Thus, each tooth clears both sides of the saw, whereas in spring set every other tooth clears one side and the alternate teeth the other. Two tools are used for swaging or spreading the teeth, *i.e.,* the *swage* and the *side dresser* or *swage shaper.* The former consists of a block of steel having a slot to admit the saw blade, and an internal anvil and eccentric die; the top of the tooth is pressed against the anvil, and a handle is turned causing the die to apply pressure on the face of the tooth as it spreads out the point. The side dresser ensures a uniform width across the points of the saw; this steel tool has two metal dies between which the point of each tooth is squeezed, the finished width being determined by an adjustable steel plate which rests on top of the tooth.

Swage set is preferred for rip saws, log band saws and re-saws.[1] A faster feed can be employed when a saw is swage set and not spring set.

The above cross-cut and rip saws are of uniform thickness. Another form of circular cross-cut saw, known as a *hollow-ground saw,* is of

[1] Horizontal and vertical log band mills and the band re-sawing machine are described in *Carpentry.*

uniform thickness at the centre (for the diameter of the collar see below) and, after being reduced, gradually increases in thickness towards the rim (see Q, Fig. 2). It is used for accurate work. The teeth require no set.

The *ground-off* saw and the *swage saw* or *bevelled saw* are two other types of circular saw which are not of uniform thickness throughout. Both are thinner at the rim than at the centre, the ground-off saw (see R, Fig. 2) having a thin parallel rim of 25 to 45 mm width and increasing in thickness by a slight concave taper on one side only, and the swage saw (S, Fig. 2) is tapered on one side from the rim towards the edge of the collar. They are either spring set or swage set. Both produce thin clean saw kerfs, and are used for cutting boards from 2 to 9 mm thick and the swage saw for sawing boards up to 20 mm thick.

TENSIONING.—A saw after continuous use becomes stretched at the rim. If not attended to it will fail to cut true and will run noisily. Therefore, in order to obtain efficient performance, it is essential to examine the saw and recondition it when necessary. This correction is obtained by a process of hammering known as *tensioning*. The process is usually confined to the middle half of the saw, and the *radial hammering* method is one of several which produces satisfactory results. Thus, if concentric circles are chalked off, as shown by thin broken lines at A, Fig. 2, light hammering (by a round-faced or *dog-head hammer*) is performed, working from the outside to the inside, *i.e.*, from "2" to "1", as indicated by the thick broken lines. The saw is hammered on an anvil, and both sides of the saw are dealt with in this manner. This expands the metal over this area and counteracts the expanding effect at the rim when the saw revolves at a high speed.

A saw to be tested for tension is laid horizontally on a table or anvil and is raised at one edge. A metal straight-edge is placed on the saw, extending from the centre to the circumference. If correctly tensioned, the ends only of the straight-edge should touch the saw, and there should be a space between with a maximum at the centre. The whole saw is tested in this manner and the clearance between the saw and straight-edge should be uniform. Absence or deficiency of tension is indicated when the surface of the saw between the ends of the straight-edge touches, or almost touches, the edge, and also if the saw shows "round" under the straight-edge.

Improper treatment of the saw whilst in operation may produce bright or blue coloured bulges on the surface, known as *lumps* or *blisters*. The exact shape of these is determined by the straight-edge and marked; the saw is placed on the anvil and the lumps are removed by the gentle application of a round-faced or *cross-face hammer*.

A circular saw is fitted on the spindle of the machine between two collars (one being "fast" and the other "loose") and secured by a nut; a *steady pin* projects from the face of the fixed collar and engages in the small hole in the saw (see A, Fig. 2). The saw runs in a slot in the table (see p. 10). A *packing* must be placed in the slot on each side of the saw between it and the table. A good type of packing consists of a thin strip of wood round which spun yarn, afterwards oiled, is wound; this is about 25 mm wide, and its length extends from the collar to just short of the base of the teeth. The packing must just be sufficiently tight for the purpose, excessive thickness being reduced by hammering on the wrapping. Correct packing prevents deflection of the saw and ensures steadiness.

SPEED.—The speed of a circular saw depends upon its type, size and class of wood to be sawn. The most effective *rim speed* (that at the circumference of the saw) for general purposes is 3 000 m per min. The rim speed, divided by the circumference of the saw, gives the number of revolutions. Thus, for a 0·6 m diameter saw the revolutions per minute are 1 592 (3 000 ÷ πd), and for a 0·9 m saw, 1 061 revs. per min.

2. BAND SAWING MACHINE (see Fig. 4).—This is similar to, but

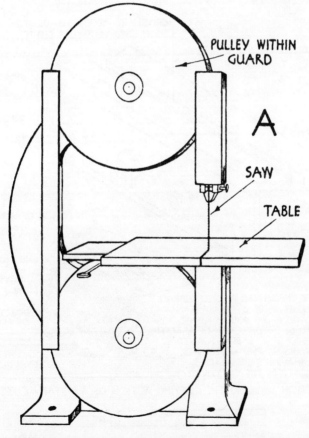

PULLEY WITHIN GUARD

A

SAW

TABLE

BAND SAWING MACHINE

Fig. 4

much lighter than, the vertical log band mill[1] in that the band saw is strained over two pulleys placed one above the other. The diameter of the pulleys is 760, 915, 1 070 or 1 220 mm, a useful size for general purposes being the 915 mm machine. The saw blade varies in width from 6 to 40 mm. The timber is hand-fed on a 915 mm square table which is about 915 mm above the floor. This machine is used for shaping pieces by straight or circular cuts. The table may be canted and locked in position when required for bevel cutting.

PLANING AND MOULDING MACHINES.—There is a big similarity between these two classes of machines, as the function of both is to reduce each sawn piece of timber to accurate size and produce a smooth and true finish to one or more surfaces. The planing machine shaves or planes *flat* surfaces, and, as implied, the moulding machine forms a *moulded* surface. Planing is achieved by steel knives or cutters. There are two kinds of cutters, *i.e.*, (*a*) rotary and (*b*) fixed.

(*a*) *Rotary Cutters.*—This type consists of knives bolted in a steel block,

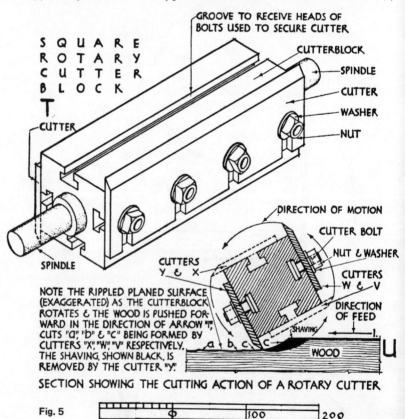

GROOVE TO RECEIVE HEADS OF
BOLTS USED TO SECURE CUTTER

SQUARE
ROTARY
CUTTER
BLOCK

CUTTERBLOCK

SPINDLE

CUTTER

WASHER

NUT

CUTTER

DIRECTION OF MOTION

CUTTER BOLT

NUT & WASHER

CUTTERS
Y & X

CUTTERS
W & V

SPINDLE

DIRECTION
OF FEED

NOTE THE RIPPLED PLANED SURFACE
(EXAGGERATED) AS THE CUTTERBLOCK
ROTATES & THE WOOD IS PUSHED FOR-
WARD IN THE DIRECTION OF ARROW "I",
CUTS "a", "b" & "c" BEING FORMED BY
CUTTERS "X", "W", "V" RESPECTIVELY.
THE SHAVING, SHOWN BLACK, IS
REMOVED BY THE CUTTER "Y".

SHAVING

WOOD

SECTION SHOWING THE CUTTING ACTION OF A ROTARY CUTTER

Fig. 5

SCALE   100   200
                                       MM

[1] This machine is described in *Carpentry*.

called a *cutterblock,* fixed on a rotating spindle, the latter being mounted on bearings. Cutterblocks are either square or circular in section.

A *square cutterblock* is shown at T, Fig. 5, and has either four knives or cutters, one bolted on each face, or two knives mounted on a pair of opposite faces. A square cutterblock, with knives omitted, is shown in position at B, Fig. 7. A diagrammatic view showing the cutting action of rotary cutters (in this case fixed above the timber) is shown at U, Fig. 5. As the cutterblock rotates at a high speed, the projecting edges of the knives cut shavings or chips from the advancing wood. The portion of wood, shown black, indicates the chip which would be removed by knife "Y" as it rotates. It will be seen that the planed surface is composed of waves or ripples (see sand-papering machines, pp. 25 and 26); the quality of the surface is improved as the number of knives or the speed of the spindle is increased.

Circular cutterblocks are shown at D and E, Fig. 6, and C, Fig. 7. Each carries two (as shown) or more knives. The cutterblocks are placed horizontally in some machines (see E and H, Fig. 6), vertically in others (see B, Fig. 7), and certain machines, such as moulding machines (see p. 19), have both horizontal and vertical cutterblocks. The cutting action of the knives of a circular cutterblock is shown at E, Fig. 6.

(b) *Fixed Knives or Cutters.*—These are fixed on certain machines, *i.e.*, the planing and matching machine (p. 21), at the bottom and sides. They shave the wood and produce a superior finish on the surfaces. The result is similar to that produced by the hand plane (illustrated at J, Fig. 154, in *Carpentry*), but as the knives are fixed, the timber must be pressed against them as it is guided rapidly past. The speedier the feed the better the finish.

Most planing machines are designed to perform additional labours, including moulding, thicknessing, grooving, beading, chamfering, etc. (see below). Whilst a combined moulding and planing machine is an advantage in a workshop having a small mixed output, it is desirable to have an independent moulding machine when the output is large. Three reasons for this are: (a) The fast feed speed required on a planing machine is not desirable on a moulder when the mouldings are required to have fine surfaces; (b) a common cutterblock cannot be conveniently used for both surfaces, and (c) the feed rollers best for flat planing are not of the type most desirable for working mouldings.

3. PLANING AND SURFACING OR PLANING AND JOINTING MACHINE (see H, Fig. 6).—This consists of back and front tables, a cutterblock and an adjustable fence. The overall length of the tables varies from 1 800 to 3 050 mm, the larger type of machine being capable of planing timber of a maximum width of 770 mm. An enlargement of the cutterblock, containing two knives, is shown at D and a section is shown at E. The tables can be adjusted by the handwheels to enable the back table to support the timber and the front table to regulate the depth of the cut. The section E shows a piece of timber partially planed as the cutterblock rotates in the direction of the arrow at a speed of 4 000 revs per min. The

cutterblock has a guard (not shown) to protect the operator. The fence can be canted for chamfering (see p. 64) and bevelling. This simple hand-fed machine is used for planing, surfacing, jointing, bevelling, rebating (see p. 42) and chamfering. If a face and edge of a piece of timber are to be planed, it is first placed flat and pressed against the table (or held

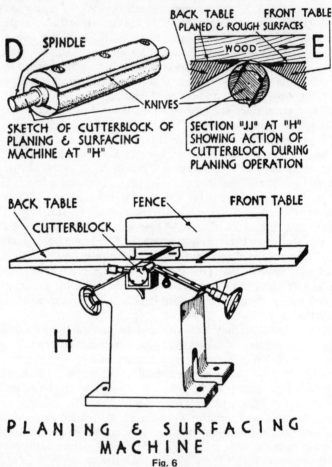

SKETCH OF CUTTERBLOCK OF PLANING & SURFACING MACHINE AT "H"

SECTION "JJ" AT "H" SHOWING ACTION OF CUTTERBLOCK DURING PLANING OPERATION

PLANING & SURFACING MACHINE

Fig. 6

down by two springs similar to those shown at B, Fig. 7) and passed over the rotating cutter. The piece is then edged in a similar manner with the dressed face against the fence.

This machine can also be obtained with a mechanical feed. This feed unit is superimposed over the table and consists of two endless travelling chains having projecting steel points. These points grip the timber and guide it forward over the cutterblock. The maximum rate of feed is 17 m per min.

4. SURFACE PLANING AND THICKNESSING MACHINE.—The object of
this machine is to reduce the timber to a parallel thickness in addition to
planing its surfaces. It resembles the machine at H, Fig. 6, with the
addition of a second table, situated below the back and front tables. The
bottom table can be raised or lowered as required, the vertical distance
between the upper surface of the bottom table and the edge of the knife
in the cutterblock (when immediately below its centre) being equal to
the required finished thickness of the timber. If a piece of timber is to be
thicknessed and planed on all four sides, an edge and one face are first
planed on the top table, as explained on p. 18, after which the piece is
placed with the dressed face resting on the bottom table, and the upper
face is dressed by the cutterblock as the timber is fed mechanically by
the rollers. The second edge is finally dressed in a similar manner, a
process known as *widthing*. The maximum size of timber which can be
dealt with is 770 mm by 225 mm and the maximum rate of feed is 16 m
per min.

5. PANEL PLANING AND THICKNESSING MACHINE.—One form of this
powerful machine consists of a table, a cutterblock having three, four or
six knives, a mechanical feed of rollers, pressure bars to hold the timber
firmly down on the table and a *chipbreaker* to break up and discharge the
chippings. One of the heavier types is capable of dealing with timber
of 915 mm maximum width and up to 225 mm thick. The cutterblock,
being above the table, planes the upper face and reduces the thickness of
the timber. The maximum rate of feed is 30 m per min.

Another form of this machine is provided with two cutterblocks, a
bottom one (at table level) near the front and a top cutterblock near the
back. Two surfaces can be dealt with at the same time, and thus the
machine acts as a double surfacer. In addition, two side vertical cutterblocks can be fitted near the back end of the machine; it thus acts as a
four-cutter planing and thicknessing machine and is capable of planing all
four sides at once.

6. MOULDING MACHINES.—There are several types of machines used
for forming moulded surfaces. The cutterblocks are provided with
cutters shaped according to the moulded section of timber to be produced. A moulding of complicated design will require more than one
cutter to form it. Moulding machines may have either four, five or six
rotary cutterblocks. Thus, a *six-cutter* has the following at intervals.
commencing near the feed end: A bottom cutterblock, two side cutterblocks (one at each side), a top cutterblock, a second top cutterblock or
profile head, and a second bottom or end cutterblock or *beading head*
near the back end; this is suitable for large mouldings. A *five-cutter* is
similar but without either one of the bottom or top cutterblocks; the
side cutterblocks may either precede or be between the two top cutterblocks. A *four-cutter* has bottom and top cutterblocks and two side
cutterblocks.

The feed is by means of two pairs of rollers (the first being fluted)
through which the timber is guided or propelled; the rollers are driven

by gearing controlled by a three, four, six or nine speed gearbox, depending upon the type of machine. The timber is pressed against the table and/or fence by *pressures,* such as smooth rollers or pads, over or adjacent to the various cutters. A chipbreaker is provided. The maximum size of timber which can be dealt with varies; thus, one type of six-cutter can deal with sections up to 380 mm by 150 mm, whilst another is designed to take a maximum size of 305 mm by 100 mm; the capacity of some four-cutters is limited to 100 mm by 50 mm stuff.

There is a big variation in the feed-speeds; thus, one six-cutter machine has a range of speeds up to 50 m per min, whilst some four-cutters have a maximum feed-speed of 15 m per min only. The speed depends upon many factors, such as the size, kind and quality of the timber, number of cutters, quality of finish required, power available, etc. As mouldings of high finish are usually required, it is customary to feed the machines at much lower speeds than the maximum, otherwise ridges or "ripple marks" (see U, Fig. 5) will be more pronounced.

The latest type of "high-speed" planing and moulding machine, which can be built up with either four, five or six rotary cutterblocks in addition to fixed knives, has six rates of speeds varying from 7 to 60 m per min. The fixed knives, which produce a high quality finish, consist of two bottom knives and two side knives, and are situated between the first cutterblock and the side cutterblocks. It is necessary to use an *automatic feeding table* in order to obtain the maximum output from this high-speed machine. This may be 6 m long by 610 to 760 mm wide, and has six grooved bottom rollers at intervals along its length, with two top rollers at the planing machine end. It has a fence along one side and a sloping board along the other, on to which the pieces of timber are dropped and from which they slide on to the rollers to be delivered to the moulding machine. The feed table is connected to the feed mechanism of the moulding machine, and its speed is in excess of that of the machine.

7. Spindle Moulder or Vertical Spindle Moulding Machine (see B, Fig. 7).—This is a useful machine for forming mouldings on straight, curved or irregularly shaped lengths of timber; it is also used

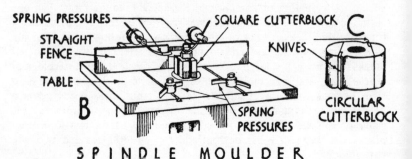

SPRING PRESSURES — SQUARE CUTTERBLOCK C

STRAIGHT FENCE —

KNIVES

TABLE —

B

SPRING PRESSURES

CIRCULAR CUTTERBLOCK

SPINDLE MOULDER

Fig. 7

for planing, edging, recessing, tonguing, grooving, tenoning, dovetailing and jointing. The cutterblock may be circular, as shown at C, or square, as shown at B. It has a pair of straight fences and a pair of *ring* or circular fences, all of which can be moved and fixed in position on the table to suit the timber. Two adjustable spring pressures are fixed to the straight fences for holding the timber to the table and against the fences. The spindle speeds are usually 3 000, 4 500 and 6 000 revs per min. It can rotate in either direction to suit the grain of the wood. A guard, not shown, is fitted over the cutter spindle to protect the operator. This machine is hand-fed and is known as a *single-spindle moulder.* Another type has two cutter spindles and is hence called a *double-spindle moulder.* Both types can be mechanically fed when large outputs are required, the maximum speed-rate being 15 m per min.

8. PLANING AND MATCHING MACHINE.—This very powerful machine, which is at least 6 m long and 1·3 m wide, is designed to produce large and speedy outputs of accurately machined floor boarding, match-boarding (see p. 48), skirtings, etc. The maximum output from the latest type can exceed 120 m of tongued and grooved floor boarding per minute, and the maximum size of timber which the largest can deal with is 380 mm by 150 mm. It is provided with either four, five or six rotary cutter-blocks. It has, in addition, either two, three or four horizontal fixed knives in a box immediately after the first bottom cutterblock for producing a first-class finish to the face; side fixed knives may also be fixed next to the side cutterblocks. They are positioned as described for moulding machines (p. 19).

The cutterblocks fixed on the side vertical spindles which form the tongue and groove on the edges of floor and match boarding are called the *tonguing head* and *grooving head* respectively. The tonguing head has either six or eight cutters; each alternate cutter forms the edge and upper portion of the tongue during rotation, and the remaining cutters form its lower portion. The grooving head has either eight (four for edging and four for grooving) or twelve (six edging and six grooving) cutters; the straight-edging cutters plane the edge of the boarding and alternate with the projecting grooving cutters or *bits.*

For tongued and grooved and single or double vee-jointed match boarding (see L and M, Fig. 27) the cutters of both the tonguing and grooving heads are shaped to form the necessary chamfers. The bead at the tongued edge of the tongued and grooved and single beaded match-ing (see N, Fig. 27) is formed by the second horizontal bottom cutter-block or beading head of the six-cutter machine; if the matching is double beaded (see O, Fig. 27) the second bead is shaped by the second top cutterblock. Other labours on the edges, such as are required for the boards shown at Q, V and W, Fig. 42, *Carpentry,* are formed by suitably shaped cutters in the side cutterblocks.

One type of machine is fitted with eight feed rolls (460 mm in diameter), two pairs immediately before the first cutterblock and two pairs before the side cutterblock. It has suitable side pressures. A shaving breaker is mounted below the fixed knives to reduce the long shaving to small particles. An automatic feeding table, described on p. 20, must be provided.

The rates of feed vary. Thus, one machine has twelve distinct rates of feed varying from 6 to 110 m per min. Another has nine rates varying from 20 to 140 m per min. Those used for production work only have minimum and maximum speeds of 60 and 160 m per min.

A four-cutter planing and matching machine will be suitable for flooring, plain matching and simple moulded skirtings. Thus, for tongued and grooved boarding, the sawn boards are successively (1) planed on the lower face by the bottom cutterblock, (2) given a high finish by the fixed blades (although these are not always provided), (3) planed and grooved on one edge by the grooving head, and tongued and reduced to the correct width by the tonguing head, and (4) finally reduced to the required thickness by the top cutterblock. Five and six cutter machines are necessary for beaded matching, more elaborate moulded skirtings, etc.

9. MORTISING MACHINES (see K, Fig. 8).—These are used for mortising the framing of doors, windows, etc. The two cutting tools chiefly used are the *hollow chisel* and the *chain cutter*.

The hollow chisel mortiser, as shown at F, consists of a chisel in the form of a tube, square in section, and an auger bit which revolves within the chisel. The normal size of the chisel is up to 25 mm square (40 and 50 mm square chisels are used in the heavier machines), and its lower edge has a fine cutting edge. The chisel is attached to a spindle and works with an up-and-down movement, and the stroke can be varied to give any depth of mortise down to 200 mm.

A chain cutter is an endless chain with links having cutting teeth on the outside. The chain travels vertically at a high speed over a top sprocket (cogged) wheel fixed to the spindle and a bottom guide wheel forming the lower end of a tension bar. The width of the chain varies from 6 to 40 mm and is capable of forming a mortise of 150 mm maximum depth.

The movement of the chisel is controlled by the hand lever. The timber is fixed to the table by one or two adjustable cramps. The table can be raised and lowered by a central screw when operated by handwheel "3"; it can be moved either backwards or forwards by a screw operated by handwheel "2", and longitudinally over the slide by operating handwheel "1".

Handwheels "2" and "3" are manipulated until the table is correctly positioned, *i.e.,* the position of the mortise marked on the cramped timber is brought immediately under the chisel, which has been lowered until it almost touches the wood. Once the table has been set it is not necessary to alter its transverse position and height, provided all the timber is of the same scantling and the size and relative position of the mortises are common.

Mortising is performed by the simplest type of hand-lever machines by lowering the lever; this drives the chisel through the wood. The lever is raised; handwheel "1" is manipulated by the free hand to give the necessary short lateral movement of timber, and the lever is again lowered. This is repeated until the mortise has been completed. If the machine is of the automatic type, the reciprocal feed motion of the chisel is controlled by the hand lever having automatic knocking-off and

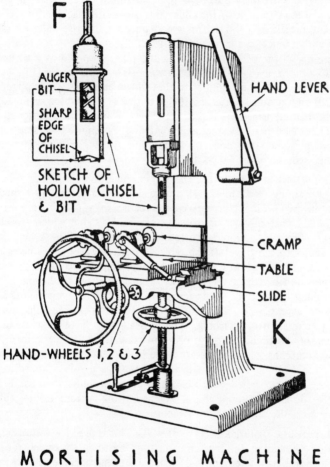

F

AUGER BIT

SHARP EDGE OF CHISEL

SKETCH OF HOLLOW CHISEL & BIT

HAND LEVER

CRAMP

TABLE

SLIDE

K

HAND-WHEELS 1, 2 & 3

MORTISING MACHINE
Fig. 8

adjustable stops; mortises of uniform length are thus formed rapidly. In one type of automatic machine the feed of the chisel is operated by a foot lever, and the movement of the chisel continues automatically until the foot is released from the pedal of the lever.

In some machines the head carrying the hollow chisel can be quickly substituted for the chain cutter head. The mortising chisel shown at K may be fitted with a chain cutter attachment in addition to the hollow chisel. Alternatively, a *boring* attachment, consisting of a spindle carrying a rotating auger, can be fitted. A boring machine is a form of mortiser, it being used to form circular holes for dowelling (p. 70), etc. The auger, like the hollow chisel, has a vertical movement and is controlled by a hand lever. Some multiple-boring machines carry four or more spindles which operate simultaneously by a hand lever or foot treadle. A boring machine may also be of the horizontal type, the auger spindle being placed at the side of the table; this is a useful machine for recessing and slot mortising (p. 43), for which purpose the rise and fall tables, fitted with a fence, can be moved horizontally.

Another form of vertical boring machine is known as a *router* or *recessing machine* or *overhead spindle moulder*. This consists of a bench, a vertical cutter spindle similar to that shown at B, Fig. 7 (see pp. 16, 17 and 20) and another cutter spindle or boring tool mounted on an adjustable horizontal arm overhanging the table. The overhead cutter spindle is used for housing, recessing and trenching, as required for stair strings (to accommodate the ends of treads and risers — see pp. 196–201), shelving, recessed door panels, etc.

10. TENONING MACHINE.–The single and double tenoning of members of framing (see pp. 42–45 and p. 58) is performed by a machine which has two horizontal rotary cutterblocks, two vertical rotary scribing (see p. 62) cutterblocks, a cross-cut saw and a table which travels on rollers. The two tenoning cutterblocks, one below the other, are at right angles to the travel of the table and carry two or four knives each; they can be adjusted both vertically and horizontally to suit the required thickness and length of the tenons. A cutter is fitted to the end of each cutterblock to sever the fibres across the grain and form clean cuts at the shoulders (see p. 42). The two vertical cutterblocks are adjustable for both top and bottom scribing. The cross-cut saw is adjustable and cuts the end of the timber prior to or after being tenoned and scribed. The sawing, tenoning and scribing are done in sequence at each travel of the table, the scribing being the last operation as a rule. An adjustable *drunken saw* (so called because it appears to wobble when rotating) is used for double tenoning; this is attached to the bottom scribing spindle and replaces the bottom scribing block.

11. DOUBLE-DIMENSION SAW BENCH.–This is used for various classes of work (including ripping, cross-cutting, mitreing, grooving, rebating, bevelling and cutting compound angles) requiring accuracy in sawing to dimensions. The 1 100 mm by 1 000 mm table can be canted to 45°. A revolving frame carries two saws (usually a rip saw and a hollow-ground cross-cut saw); that required for use is raised to the required height by turning a wheel; this operation lowers the other saw. The main fence can be accurately adjusted in any position and can be canted to 45° or swivelled to 30°. The front portion of the table can be moved laterally as required for cross-cutting, etc., and carries a mitreing and cross-cutting fence which is set to the required angle on reference to a graduated arc marked on the table or fence.

A *single-dimension saw bench* is similar to the above, but carries only one saw. This saw can be interchanged.

12. DOVETAILING MACHINE.—Dovetailing of timber for drawers and similar work is performed by an automatic single spindle dovetailing machine consisting of a vertical or horizontal rotary cutting spindle, mounted on a slide, and a travelling table to which the timber is cramped. The movement of the table conforms with the reciprocating motion of the spindle as the latter enters and leaves the wood to form dovetails at the required spacing. One type of multiple spindle dovetailing machine for repetition work has a table (which accommodates two boards to be jointed at right angles to each other) fitted with an automatic mechanism for spacing the dovetails at the required pitch, and a complete dovetail joint is formed as the table moves past a series of cutters.

13. LATHE.—This is used for wood turning, examples being turned balusters (see p. 181), moulded newel caps and drops (p. 183), legs of furniture, etc. The essential components are a fast *headstock* and a loose *tailstock*. These may be fixed on a wood bench or on a metal bed supported on legs. The headstock, usually fixed on the left-hand side, carries a short horizontal revolving spindle having a forked chuck to grip the timber and a three or four speed pulley. The tailstock is at the opposite end of the bench or bed and has a sliding horizontal spindle (carrying a tail centre which slightly penetrates and supports the end of the timber), operated by a handwheel; it can be moved and locked in any position along the bench.

The piece of wood to be turned is fixed horizontally between the stock. The shaping of the wood is performed by a chisel or gouge of suitable shape which is fitted in a tool-holder and held against the wood as it revolves at a high speed; the cutting tool is held stationary or traverses the length of the timber as required during the shaving process. The tool, fixed in a holder and provided with an adjustable slide, may be used for turning long pieces; this is fitted to a sliding carriage which traverses the length of the bed.

For hand turning the tool is held and manipulated by hand, supported by a rest, various sizes and shapes of chisels and gouges being used in the process.

14. MITREING MACHINE.—This machine, used for cutting mitres and squaring edges of timbers, is not power driven. It consists of a pedestal which supports a table and a knife which is operated by a hand lever. The timber is placed on the table, with one edge against a pivoting fence which has been adjusted to the required angle according to a graduated arc marked on the table, and the edge is cut by the knife on a downward stroke of the lever. Hand mitreing is described in *Carpentry*.

15. SAND-PAPERING MACHINE OR SANDER.—Planed surfaces, especially if they have been prepared by rotary cutters, are uneven, due to the presence of a series of ridges (see U, Fig. 5, and p. 17). In order to eliminate these ripples and give a smooth finish it is necessary to apply an

abrasive paper (glass or sand-paper) to the surfaces. The hand application of this abrasive is referred to in *Carpentry*. This slow and tedious process is gradually being superseded by the machine. There are three classes of sanders, *i.e.*, (*a*) drum, (*b*) belt and (*c*) disc.

(a) *Drum or Cylinder Sanders.*—One type, suitable for large outputs, consists of three horizontal drums which have a combined rotary and oscillating motion. Sand-paper is fixed to each drum, coarse grade paper being used to cover the first drum, medium grade the second and fine grade the third. These drums are superimposed over the feed mechanism, which may consist of a travelling endless belt or eight rollers. The timber is placed on the belt or feed rollers and suitable pressure bars or rollers ensure that it comes into close contact with the abrasive. The minimum rate of feed is 8 m per min. One or more hoods are fitted over the drums and are connected by a pipe to an exhaust fan which extracts the dust from the machine.

A smaller machine is provided with either one or two drums.

(b) *Belt Sander.*—This comprises a travelling table, 2·5 m long, and a 150 or 200 mm wide endless belt above, which passes over two pulleys and travels the full length of the table. The timber is placed on the table, and the belt, with abrasive paper attached, is pressed down for close contact by means of a pad. This machine is suitable for medium outputs.

A smaller machine consists of a 2 100 mm by 610 mm table with two vertical rollers near the ends, on which a 200 mm wide belt travels. The timber is laid on the table and pressed against the belt by hand.

(c) *Disc Sander.*—One type consists of a pillar which supports a short revolving spindle at each end of which is a disc which varies from 500 mm to 915 mm in diameter. A small table, which can be canted, is fixed opposite to each disc and the work is held against it during rotation.

A combined machine, known as a *disc and bobbin sander,* carries a disc with a table, as described above, and a vertical spindle called a bobbin. The latter operates in the centre of a table and has a vertical reciprocating and rotary motion. Both tables can be canted. The bobbin, which is covered with abrasive paper, is useful for curved work.

16. UNIVERSAL WOODWORKER OR GENERAL JOINER.—This is a general utility machine capable of satisfying the requirements of smaller establishments where different classes of work are dealt with and the output is insufficient to justify the provision of separate machinery.

One type of machine consists of two sections. The front half comprises a horizontal rotary cutterblock, front and back tables, and adjustable fence (somewhat similar to those shown at ʜ, Fig. 6) for planing, surfacing, chamfering and jointing timber up to 305 mm wide. In addition, a vertical rotary cutter spindle, arranged to rise and fall as required, is fitted in the middle of the front table and thus resembles ʙ, Fig. 7; this is used for moulding circular and irregularly shaped pieces of timber up to 90 mm thick. A further addition consists of a small rise and fall table in front of this half-section for hollow chisel mortising, boring and slot mortising; the chisel is fixed horizontally to the end of the horizontal cutterblock and overhangs the small table; the timber is fixed by a vertical cramp to the table, which can be moved longitudinally and transversely; the chisel is replaced by either the boring bit or slot mortising auger as required.

The back half of the machine consists of a rise and fall table, fence and a spindle to which is attached either a circular saw or a horizontal rotary cutterblock. The maximum size of saw is 610 mm diameter and will saw up to 225 mm deep; cross-cutting, mitreing and dimension sawing may be performed, as a steel plate to carry the timber and adjustable fence can be fitted to slide in a groove along the edge of the timber. When required for tonguing, grooving, thicknessing and moulding, the saw is replaced by a horizontal cutterblock (125 mm long) carrying suitable knives. The table is lowered to bring it to the desired level below the cutterblock when the timber is to be moulded and thicknessed; the timber is first surfaced on one side and edge, and then thicknessed or moulded on the upper and opposite side; a power feed apparatus and pressures are provided for this purpose. The cutterblock is replaced by a suitable tenoning cutterblock for forming tenons, the maximum length of which is 125 mm; the timber is fixed transversely by a cramp to a plate and passed horizontally under the rotary cutter to form the upper portion of the tenon; the table, with plate and timber still attached, is then raised to the required height above the cutter over which the timber is passed to cut the opposite side of the tenon. Tonguing and grooving are performed when the cutterblock, with suitable cutters attached, is rotated against the timber, which is fixed to the table at a suitable height. For sand-papering, the cutterblock is replaced on the spindle by a small drum covered with sand-paper, and the operation is performed with the table adjusted at a suitable height.

17. SHARPENING MACHINES.—There are many machines for conditioning saws, cutters, etc. These include:—

Automatic Saw Sharpening Machine.—This is used for sharpening circular saws, the sharpening and gulleting (recutting the gullets to the correct shape — see G and M, Fig. 3) being done by a grinding machine which automatically grinds the whole profile of each tooth at one operation. The teeth can be ground square across or at any desired bevel. The grinding wheel, 200 or 300 mm in diameter, is fitted to a spindle which is provided with a rise and fall movement and may be canted to suit the hook or rake (see G and M, Fig. 3) of the saw teeth. The shape of the teeth is governed by a cam operating the rise and fall of the grinding wheel. Cams are varied in their shape to suit different sizes of teeth and are easily interchanged. The saw is fed forward under the grinding wheel by a feed pawl or finger which engages against the face of the tooth being ground. The stroke of the pawl is adjustable to suit different pitches of teeth and positioning of the face of the tooth under the grinding wheel. The saw is mounted on a spindle fitted with a self-centering cone to suit the variation in diameter of the spindle hole in the centre of the saw (see

A, Fig. 2). This spindle is adjustable both vertically (to suit the diameter of the saw) and horizontally, according to the varying rakes of saw teeth. The rate of feed is from 15 to 30 teeth per minute, according to the pitch of the teeth.

A similar machine is used for sharpening band saws. The saw during the grinding operation is stretched horizontally and passes round two pulleys as it automatically progresses forward to bring each tooth (or alternate teeth) under the frame holding the grinding wheel.

Automatic Cutter Grinder.—This is used for grinding and shaping cutterblock and planing knives. A knife is fixed horizontally to a travelling table which traverses to and fro under a rotary emery wheel which grinds the knife to the required bevel. In another type of machine the knives are not removed from the block, the spindle of which is supported at each end of a table which travels longitudinally during the grinding operation.

Mortise Chain Cutter and Hollow Chisel Grinder.—This is a small machine conditioning the two cutting tools named. It is fixed to and driven by the mortising machine (Fig. 8). The chain cutter is passed on to a sprocket mounted on a horizontal slide along which it passes to and fro under a specially shaped rotary emery wheel as the cutting teeth are ground. The machine also carries a cone emery wheel for sharpening hollow chisels.

Grindstone.—This is a cylindrical disc, 900 to 1 200 mm in diameter and 150 mm thick, of Derbyshire grit or similar hard natural stone, which is mounted on a spindle that is rotated during the grinding operation. A finer stone disc, which gives a keener edge, may also be mounted on the spindle in addition to the coarse disc. These rotate in troughs containing water when wet grinding is required to prevent overheating. This machine is useful for general grinding, especially large hand tools.

A suitable machine for grinding smaller hand-cutting tools, such as chisels, gouges and planing irons, consists of a frame supporting a rotary spindle which carries four or six emery or sandstone (or both) discs which are 300 mm in diameter and of varying thickness. A water tap is fixed above each disc and a trough is provided below.

Further descriptions of the application of certain of the machines mentioned in this chapter appear on pp. 44, 85 and 91 (doors), 134 and 154 (windows), and 198 and 199 (stairs).

CHAPTER TWO

FLOOR FINISHES

Floor coverings, including wood boards, wood blocks, plywood, parquetry,
cork, rubber and thermoplastic tiles. Plank floors.

BOARDED and joisted floors are dealt with in the book on Carpentry,
Chapter Four. That chapter includes a description of (1) the joints
between floor boards, (2) methods of laying floor boards, and (3) double
boarded floors. Such description will not be repeated here (with
exception of a few references), although it should be understood that
the fixing of floor boards is the work of the joiner.

Double and triple floors of timber construction are also detailed in
Carpentry. Timber triple floors especially are now practically
obsolete, fire-resisting floors being employed in which any timber used
is that for coverings only. The following brief description of fire-
resisting floors is provided in order that a comparison may be made
between them and those entirely of timber construction.

FIRE-RESISTING FLOORS.—A part plan of a typical floor of a building
of steel-framed construction is shown at A, Fig. 9, the steel members
being indicated by single lines. The floor consists of three sets of steel
beams, *i.e., filler* or *primary, secondary* and *main beams*. The filler
beams, usually spaced at not more than 770 mm centres, are encased in
concrete and are supported on the secondary beams. The latter are
secured to the main beams by means of steel angle cleats and rivets or
bolts. The main beams are either riveted or bolted to vertical members
called steel *pillars* (or columns). The secondary beams, main beams and
pillars are also encased in concrete. The sizes of the various steel
members depend upon the load to be supported, span, method of
fixing, etc. Details of this floor are shown at B and C, Fig. 9, and the
isometric sketch in Fig. 10.

In lieu of filler beams encased in concrete, the floor may consist of
hollow concrete or fireclay blocks or beams supported on the concrete
haunches of steel beams. One example of such a floor is shown at C,
Fig. 15. The steel bars are provided to resist tension and shear stresses.

Another type of fire-resisting floor is shown at B, Fig. 14. This
portion of a reinforced concrete floor is called a *slab*. It somewhat
resembles that shown at A, Fig. 9, with *transverse bar* reinforcement at
close spacing in lieu of filler beams. Another set of bars, called
distributing or *secondary bars* are placed at a greater distance apart
immediately over and wired to the transverse bars.

29

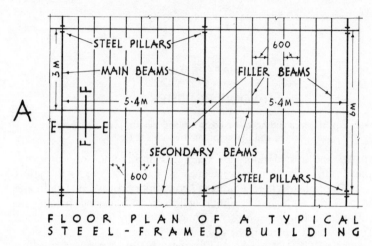

FLOOR PLAN OF A TYPICAL
STEEL-FRAMED BUILDING

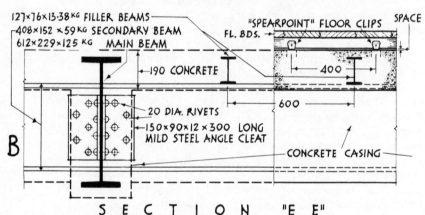

SECTION "EE"

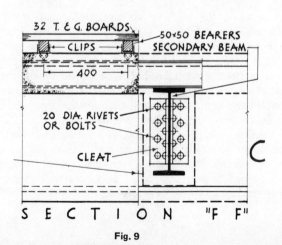

SECTION "FF"

Fig. 9

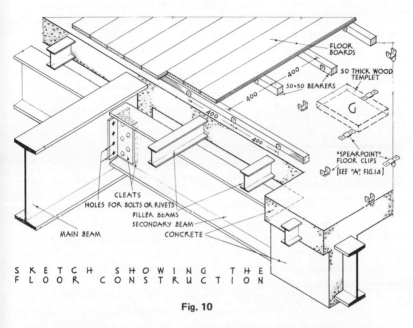

SKETCH SHOWING THE
FLOOR CONSTRUCTION

Fig. 10

FLOOR FINISHES — There is a wide range of floor finishes and only those fixed by a joiner are described here. Many other types are described in the book *Building Construction,* Vol. 3, by the same authors. The following floor finishes are described here: (1) Wood boards, (2) wood blocks, (3) plywood, (4) parquetry, (5) cork.

1. WOOD BOARDS.—A description of this flooring appears in the companion book *Carpentry.* As there stated Douglas fir, pitch pine, red pine, redwood, sitka spruce, western hemlock and whitewood are softwoods used for floor boards; the hardwoods used for the same purpose include English, American, Tasmanian and Japanese oak, maple, birch, beech, elm, gurjun, iroko and teak. Rift or quarter sawn narrow boards

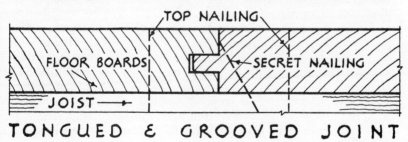

TONGUED & GROOVED JOINT

Fig. 11

are preferred for first-class work. Tongued and grooved boards (which are generally top nailed and only occasionally secret nailed—see Fig. 11) are chiefly employed, although hardwood flooring which is to be secretly nailed (see *Carpentry*) is occasionally splayed, rebated, tongued and grooved (see Fig. 12). The planing and matching machine, described on p. 21, is employed for producing speedy outputs of such boards.

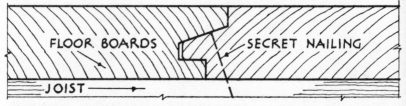

SPLAYED, REBATED, TONGUED & GROOVED JOINT

Fig. 12

A floor is usually covered with boards of the same width. An attractive flooring is, however, obtained by the use of hardwood boards of varying widths, called *random widths*; these must be well seasoned to the correct moisture content (see *Carpentry*) if excessive shrinkage of the wider boards especially is to be avoided.

A double boarded floor (see *Carpentry*), now much favoured, consists of a sub-floor of 25 mm square edged (or t. and g.) softwood boarding, laid diagonally as shown at G, Fig. 18, and covered with 50 to 75 mm wide hardwood boards which are only 10 mm thick. This thin and narrow covering, which has a very attractive appearance when of selected timber, is known as *strip flooring*. The boards are t. and g. at the edges and ends, and are usually secret nailed. One advantage of a double boarded floor is that plastering can be completed and allowed to dry before the top flooring is laid, and thus a common cause of damage to the finished floor is eliminated.

The description of flooring which appears in *Carpentry* is restricted to that fixed to wood joists. The following refers to concrete floors which are finished with wood boards that are fixed to either (1) *fillets* or *bearers* partially embedded in the concrete, or (2) bearers secured by *floor clips* to the concrete.

(1) The top surface of the concrete must be level throughout. The fillets are placed on the concrete at 400 mm centres and kept temporarily in position by nailing cross battens to them. More concrete is then placed in position to within about 12 mm of the top of the fillets, as shown in Fig. 13. One or both sides of the fillets are splayed and are thus keyed into the concrete; an economy results if only one side is splayed, as a pair of fillets can be obtained from a 115 mm by 75 mm scantling.

Special precautions must be taken to prevent the fillets (and the boards subsequently) from becoming affected by dry rot. The concrete must be dry, the fillets must be well seasoned and should be treated with a preservative (see *Carpentry*), if the floor is at ground level the concrete must have a properly constructed d.p.c. beneath it.

(2) A more recent method of securing the bearers is to anchor them to the concrete by means of floor clips. One of several patent floor clips

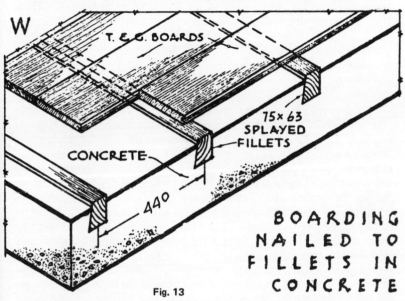

W

T. & G. BOARDS

75 × 63 SPLAYED FILLETS

CONCRETE

440

BOARDING NAILED TO FILLETS IN CONCRETE

Fig. 13

is the "Spearpoint". It is shown at A, Fig. 14, and is made of 1·5 mm thick mild steel, which is galvanized to prevent corrosion. It is in one piece, having two spear-shaped flanges or legs which are inserted into the

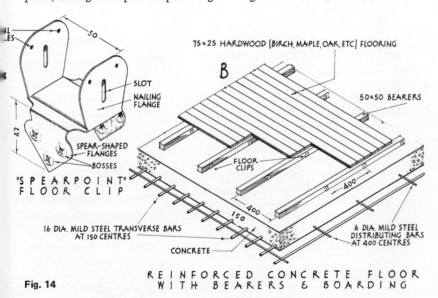

SLOT

NAILING FLANGE

50

SPEAR-SHAPED FLANGES

BOSSES

42

"SPEARPOINT" FLOOR CLIP

75 × 25 HARDWOOD (BIRCH, MAPLE, OAK, ETC) FLOORING

B

50 × 50 BEARERS

FLOOR CLIPS

400

400

150

16 DIA. MILD STEEL TRANSVERSE BARS AT 150 CENTRES

6 DIA. MILD STEEL DISTRIBUTING BARS AT 400 CENTRES

CONCRETE

Fig. 14

REINFORCED CONCRETE FLOOR WITH BEARERS & BOARDING

concrete, a cross-piece, and two upper nailing flanges or ears between which the wood bearers are fixed. The projecting holed bosses in the legs assist in increasing the bond between the concrete and metal. These clips are obtainable with the ears bent down and in four sizes, *i.e.*, for 38, 50, 75 and 100 mm wide bearers; the usual size employed for the average floor is that designed to receive 50 mm square bearers. The clips are spaced in rows at 400 mm centres, and at 400 mm centres along the rows (see B).

These clips are fixed in the following manner: The legs of the clips are pressed into the concrete within about half an hour after it has been laid and levelled, and before its plasticity has disappeared. Either a plank or a templet (consisting of two long boards with top cross-pieces nailed at intervals) is used to ensure accurate spacing of the clips in true alignment and the prevention of damage to the surface of the concrete by the workmen. The ears, being horizontal when the clips are inserted, lie flat on the surface of the concrete and thus present no obstruction to wheeling, etc. operations which are usually carried out when the concrete has hardened (see G, Fig. 10). The plank or templet is marked along its edges at 400 mm intervals, and the fixers standing upon it press the clips into the concrete at the divisions. The broken lines at G, Fig. 10, represent a portion of a templet, the width of which equals the distance between the edges of the extended ears in adjacent rows. The clips are sometimes staggered. When the concrete has hardened, the ears are prised by the claw of the hammer until they are vertical (see B and C, Fig. 9, and Figs. 10 and 14). The bearers are placed in position between the ears and first nailed through the slots; they are then levelled and, if necessary, packed with small wedges between the underside of the bearers and the surface of the concrete, which may be somewhat irregular. The bearers are finally nailed through the top holes, and the floor boards are then nailed in the usual manner.

Complete circulation of air round the bearers is assured, as the central portion of each clip is slightly above the concrete (see B, Fig. 9), and thus this method of fixing is an improvement upon that in which partially embedded fillets are employed (p. 32). It is emphasized that the concrete must be dry before the bearers are fixed; the latter should be sound, well seasoned and, preferably, treated with preservative before being fixed (p. 32).

The Bull Dog clip is also of 1·5 mm sheet metal and is of H-section (see D, Fig. 15). These clips are fixed at the same distance apart and in a somewhat similar manner to Spearpoint clips. Before insertion, the two ears are folded over (see C, Fig. 15), and they are not raised until the floor is ready to receive the bearers; unimpeded use of the floor for walking, wheeling, etc. is thus permitted. Two nails are driven through the upper holes of each ear into the bearers. End joints between the bearers should coincide with the clips, and the lower hole in each ear is to allow an additional nail being driven through at the bearer end,

A further development is the "acoustic" type of floor clip. This has a pad of rubber or other insulating material fixed on the cross-piece. The bearers thus rest upon the pads, and a reduction in the transmission of sound through the floor results.

Hardwood boards in narrow widths are shown fixed to the bearers at B, Fig. 14, and C, Fig. 15. Softwood boards are used for cheaper work.

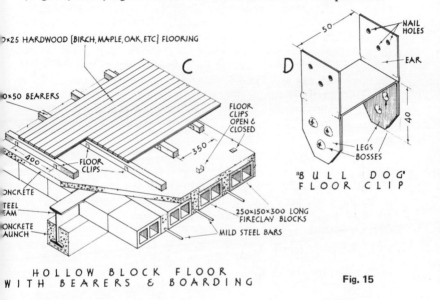

HOLLOW BLOCK FLOOR
WITH BEARERS & BOARDING

Fig. 15

PLANK FLOOR (see Fig. 16).—This floor was once adopted for

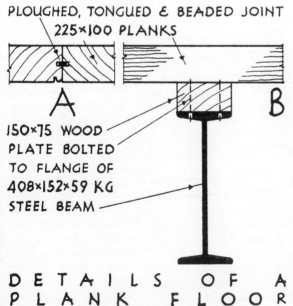

DETAILS OF A
PLANK FLOOR

Fig. 16

buildings of the warehouse or factory type. It consists of 75 or 100 mm thick planks which are supported at intervals by steel beams. Wood members, called *sleeper plates,* are bolted to the top flanges of the steel beams (see B); the bolts are from 12 to 19 mm diameter and are spaced at about 900 mm apart, staggered (*i.e.,* those on the left are midway between those on the right). The planks, which are nailed to the sleeper plates, are ploughed, tongued and beaded as shown in the cross-section at A; 25 mm by 9 mm hardwood tongues or "slip feathers" are inserted in the ploughs or grooves; the lower edges of the planks may be beaded, as shown (see also N, Fig. 27), or chamfered (see L, Fig. 27) in order to make less objectionable the appearance if the planks shrink and the joints open. The thickness of the planks depends upon the span (distance between the steel beams) and the weight to be carried. Thus, for example, if the load on the floor does not exceed 488 kg/m^2 the thickness may be 75 mm provided the span does not exceed 2·7 m, and 100 mm thickness for spans up to 3·7 m; if the load is up to 976 kg/m^2 the allowable distance between the steel beams is 1·85 m for 75 mm thick planks and 2·7 m for 100 mm planks. This floor is easily constructed.

2. WOOD BLOCKS.—These are of softwoods (such as redwood, Douglas fir and pitch pine) or hardwoods (*i.e.*, oak, maple, birch and teak). They should be quartered (rift-sawn) to ensure the maximum resistance to wearing action and the minimum expansion and contraction, and they should be carefully kiln-dried to the required moisture content (see *Carpentry*). The nominal sizes of the blocks vary from 225 to 300 mm long by 50 to 75 mm wide by 25 to 38 mm thick. One of many

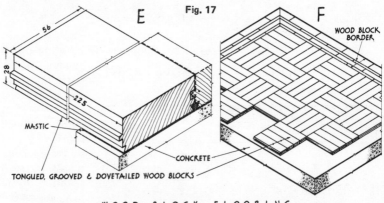

WOOD BLOCK FLOORING
ON CONCRETE SUB-FLOOR

types is shown at E, Fig. 17, the edges being tongued, grooved and dovetailed; the ends are sometimes t. and g. The dovetail groove provides a good key for the hot mastic, and the interlock provided by the t. and g. tends to prevent the loosening of the blocks and the development of an uneven surface. A simpler joint consists of the dovetail groove only. The blocks are laid to various designs; those shown in the sketch at F, Fig. 17, are laid to the basket-weave pattern. The blocks forming the borders may be arranged simply in one or two rows next to the walls, or one or more narrow strips may be introduced (see F), etc., the border blocks may be stained a different colour to that of the general flooring, or a contrast may be afforded by the use of one or more rows of blocks of different timbers; they are usually mitred at the corners as shown.

A bituminous material or mastic is used as an adhesive to secure the blocks to the concrete, the surface of which must be truly level. The latter should be well brushed to remove the dust, and if the surface is then given a good coat of creosote, adherence of the mastic to the sub-floor will be assisted. The blocks are dipped to about half their thickness into a vessel containing the hot mastic and then bedded level on the concrete; when the blocks are pressed down, the mastic rises in the dovetail grooves. As the work of covering proceeds, each block is brought to the correct level as tested by a straight-edge and spirit level.

It is very essential that the building in which the blocks are to be fixed is as dry as possible, otherwise the seasoned blocks will absorb moisture and may swell to such an extent as to cause the floor(s) to rise in the centre. The concrete must be thoroughly dry before the blocks are laid, otherwise the mastic will not adhere to it. A good test for determining the dryness of the concrete sub-floor is as follows: A square of approximately 300 mm side of the sub-floor is covered with crystals of calcium chloride; a sheet of glass is placed over them and its edges are sealed with putty (see p. 126); if the crystals are unaffected after three days, the laying of the wood blocks can proceed; otherwise this should be delayed, as the dissolving of the crystals indicates the presence of moisture in the concrete.

After the floor has been completed the surface of the blocks is planed (large surfaces being usually dressed with an electrically driven portable machine planer), scraped, sand-papered, waxed and polished.

Wood block flooring is sometimes laid on a cheap wood sub-floor. The surface of the latter is generously covered with the adhesive, a portion at a time; each block is then tapped into position and further secured with panel pins which are subsequently punched below the surface, and the small holes stopped with special putty or wood mastic, coloured to conform to that of the wood. The surface is finally planed, scraped, etc.

3. PLYWOOD (see Fig. 18).—This is a cheap covering of good appearance, consisting of squares and narrow strips (for borders) cut from boards of 3-ply (described in Chapter Two of *Carpentry*). The stock sizes of the squares are 225, 300, 450 and 900 mm and from 5 to 10 mm thick; the thicker the surface veneer the better. Oak, birch, walnut, maple and ash plywoods are suitable for this purpose. The plywood can be obtained with the top veneer stained as required for its full thickness. The squares are usually laid with the grain alternating, or woods of contrasting colours can be effectively employed.

The covering is laid on a sub-floor of 25 mm square-edged boards laid diagonally (see *Carpentry*) as shown at G; alternatively, the sub-floor may consist of sheets of 15 or 19 mm softwood (such as Douglas fir) plywood, a common size being 1 220 mm wide and 2 135 to 2 440 mm long, depending upon the spacing of the joists (see sub-floor in Fig. 19);

(these sheets should be well nailed at the edges and at 300 mm intervals along each joist. Each square and strip of the covering should be well

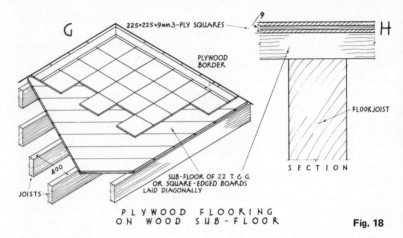

225×225×9MM 3-PLY SQUARES

PLYWOOD
BORDER

FLOORJOIST

SECTION

JOISTS

SUB-FLOOR OF 22 T. & G.
OR SQUARE-EDGED BOARDS
LAID DIAGONALLY

P L Y W O O D   F L O O R I N G
O N   W O O D   S U B - F L O O R

Fig. 18

glued and panel pinned in the centre and at about 100 mm intervals round the edges, although the adhesive is sometimes omitted. The pins are punched and the holes stopped as described on p. 37.

This is rather a noisy covering. The "drumming" can be minimized if strips of felt or similar insulating material are laid on the joists before the sub-floor is fixed.

4. PARQUET OR PARQUETRY.—There are two kinds, *i.e.* (*a*) ordinary and (*b*) inlaid.

(*a*) *Ordinary Parquetry* consists of thin, small pieces of richly decorative hardwood (chiefly oak and teak) which are hot glued and panel pinned to a softwood boarded or plywood sub-floor, the pins being punched and the holes stopped as described on p. 37. The thicknesses are 6, 9 and 12 mm, the former being used in most cases and the latter when likely to be subjected to heavy traffic. The pieces are square-edged and arranged according to pattern; sometimes timbers of various colours are made to conform to elaborate designs.

It is advisable to introduce a layer of 5 mm plywood between the softwood boarded sub-floor and the parquetry. The plywood boards are nailed to the sub-floor, the joints between them are filled with wood mastic or putty, planed off and sand-papered, and the parquetry is then fixed. The object of this intermediate layer is to afford a perfectly level surface for the thin covering and prevent any movement (expansion and shrinkage) and cupping of the softwood boards being transmitted to the parquetry. Of course, this intermediate layer is not required if the sub-floor is formed of the thicker plywood boards (such as is shown in Fig. 19) and if the joints between the latter are sealed.

(*b*) *Inlaid or Plated Parquet* (see Fig. 19) is considered to be the best form of this class of covering, and consists of a surface veneer of richly figured and coloured hardwood which is glued under great pressure to a

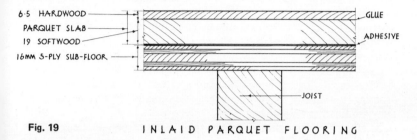

Fig. 19   INLAID PARQUET FLOORING

softwood backing. The veneer varies from 5 to 9 mm in thickness and the backing is either 19 or 25 mm thick. It is cut into slabs of various shapes and sizes, blocks 300 to 600 mm square being common. These are glued and pinned to the softwood boarded or plywood (as shown) sub-floor already described; the pins are punched and the holes stopped.

Parquet flooring is surfaced and polished as before described.

Although cork coverings are usually fixed by specialists, the following brief description is given, as wood sub-floors are sometimes required to receive them.

5. CORK.—This is used for both public and domestic buildings. It is noiseless, non-slip even when highly polished, resilient, durable if properly treated, and has an attractive appearance. It is obtained in the form of (*a*) tiles and (*b*) carpet.

(*a*) *Cork Tiles* are in stock sizes, varying from 100 to 610 mm square and 6 to 14 mm thick; colours range from light brown to dark chocolate; they may be square-edged or their edges may be tongued and grooved.

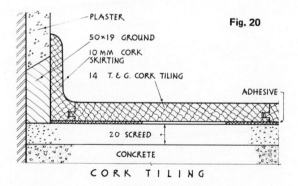

CORK TILING

They are laid on both wood and concrete floors. If the former, soft-wood boards or plywood sheets (as already described) are used, free from surface irregularities, and usually covered with a special felt paper to prevent any movement in the timber affecting the tiles, which are fixed with a special bituminous mastic and panel pinned at the corners. If, as shown in Fig. 20, a concrete floor is to be covered, the screed (composed of 1 part cement to 3 parts sand and applied to produce a level surface) must be dry and free from dust; a bituminous or resin adhesive is used. Skirtings, of various sections and lengths, are made of this material; these are fixed to grounds, as shown (see also Chapter Thirteen), and their vertical joints are usually made to coincide with those of the border strips or squares.

After laying, square-edged tiles are surfaced with a planing or sand-papering machine; tongued and grooved squares do not require this. They are finally wax polished.

Briefly, tiles are made from the thick bark of certain trees (which grow in Portugal and countries bordering the Mediterranean), which after removal is boiled, scraped, ground, pressed, heated and cut to the required shape and size.

(b) *Cork Carpet* differs from cork tiles in that the granules of cork when heated with linseed oil, etc. are compressed by rolling on to a backing of canvas, and is obtainable in 1·8 m wide rolls which vary from 13 to 30 m long.

BATTENED DOORS

Battened doors, including ledged and battened, ledged braced and battened, framed ledged and battened, and framed ledged braced and battened. Frames and methods of fixing. Preparation and hanging of doors. Hardware.

THE various types of doors include battened, panelled, transomed, glazed, flush and semicircular, etc. headed. These will be described, the former being dealt with in this chapter.

External doors are usually secured or "hung" by metal *hinges* to solid wood *frames*, and internal doors are generally hung to wood *casings* or *linings* (see p. 73).

The B.S. for doors deals with the door leaf, its frame and attached ironmongery defined as a door set. It specifies: (*a*) the co-ordinating size which is the size of the opening into which the door and frame fit, (*b*) the overall size of the door and frame, and (*c*) the door leaf size. It enumerates standards of dimensional and functional performance for (1) Category A doors for residential buildings, and (2) Category B doors for other buildings. The various standard tests which the door set has to satisfy include: strength, surface finish, twist, resistance to wear and deformation, etc.

The B.S. gives the following widths for external doors: 726, 826, 926, and 1 126 mm, and for internal doors: 726 and 826 mm. Both types are 2 040 mm high and 40 mm thick, the latter is little enough for good class external doors which ought to be 45 mm thick. The following kinds of doors are specified: flush panelled with and without glazed panels; doors made with stiles cut from 100 mm by 50 mm timber and with solid or glazed panels, double-leaf doors and doors with fanlights (these are described as ceiling height sets).

FRAMES.—A simple door frame consists of three members, *i.e.*, two uprights or *posts* which are secured at the top to a cross-piece or *head*; a frame for a door with fanlight above (see Chapter Five) has an additional horizontal member between the door and fanlight called a *transome*.

The sizes of these members vary, but 100 mm by 75 mm and 75 mm by 50 mm are common. These are *nominal* or *stuff* sizes, *i.e.*, those of the pieces when the members have been sawn; after being dressed or *wrought* (*i.e.*, planed and sand-papered) the sizes are reduced and are known as *net* or *finished* sizes. The usual allowance for work which is given a smooth finish (as for painted work) is 1·7 mm for *each* dressed surface plus about 0·8 mm for sand-papering each surface.

The head usually projects from 50 to 100 mm beyond the posts, and these projections, called *horns*, assist in making the frame secure when it is built into the wall. These horns may be splayed, as shown by thick broken lines in the isometric detail in Fig. 21 and at S, Fig. 25, and covered with splayed bricks to preserve the face appearance of the brickwork. A 12 to 16 mm deep recess or *rebate* (or *rabat*) is formed round the frame to receive the door. An alternative but less satisfactory check for the door is formed by *planting* (nailing) a 12 or 19 mm thick bead or *stop* on both posts and head, the beads being mitred at the angles (see Fig. 23).

FRAME JOINTS.—The head and posts of a frame are morticed (or mortised) and tenoned together, variations of the joints being: (*a*) closed mortice and tenon,(*b*) haunched mortice and tenon, (*c*) draw pinned slot mortice and tenon, and (*d*) double tenon.

(a) *Closed Mortice and Tenon Joint* (see Fig. 21).—The head is morticed to receive the tenon on the post. The mortice and tenon must be correctly proportioned if failure of the joint is to be avoided, and the following are accepted rules:—

(1) Thickness of tenon should equal one-third that of member.

(2) Width of tenon should not exceed five times this thickness or a maximum of 125 mm, whichever is the *less*. Thus, the maximum width of a 12 mm thick tenon would be 5 x 12 mm = 60 mm, and the maximum width of a 32 mm thick tenon would be 125 mm and *not* 5 x 32 mm = 160 mm.

The "thickness" and "width" of a tenon are indicated in Fig. 21, and the "width" and "length" of a mortice are shown in Fig. 22.

Wide tenons should be avoided, as they (1) may shrink excessively, causing them to leave the wedges (see below), which thus become loose, (2) tend to bend when the joint is wedged, resulting in the splitting of the morticed members, and (3) require wide mortices which are apt to weaken the members.

These joints are *glued and wedged*, glue (see p. 244) being applied to the tenon and *shoulders* (or abutments at the bottom or *root* of the tenon—see Fig. 21), and the tenon is inserted into the mortice. Wedges, as shown, are dipped into the glue and driven in between the edges of the tenon and the mortice to secure the joint. Note that the mortice is slightly enlarged and bevelled to receive the wedges. Oak *pins* or *dowels,* 9 to 19 mm diameter, are sometimes used in addition to wedges. This is called a *pinned joint*, and examples of it are shown in Fig. 33. A hole is first bored through the head and tenon, and the pin is driven in after it has been dipped in glue.

(b) *Haunched Mortice and Tenon Joint* (see Fig. 22).—This joint is adopted when the frame is not built in as the work proceeds. Horns are not required, and therefore the width of the tenon is reduced, except for about 12 mm from the shoulders (p. 43), otherwise wedging would not be possible. This abbreviated portion or stump is called the *haunch* or *haunchion,* and its object is to increase the strength of the tenon at its root and prevent twisting of the post. The stub mortice made to receive

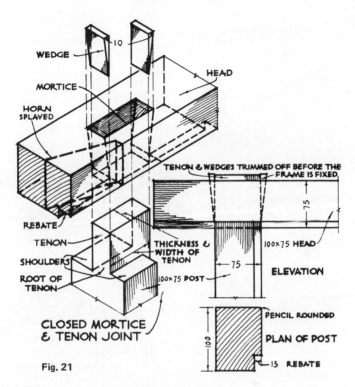

Fig. 21

the haunch is called the *haunching*. The horns are not removed until the wedging has been completed, otherwise the driving in of the wedges would split the narrow portion of the head above the haunch.

(c) *Draw-pinned Slot Mortice and Tenon Joint* (see Fig. 23).—This joint is sometimes used for large frames. The mortice is continued to the end of the head. A hole is bored through the *cheeks* (sides) of the mortice, the tenon of the post is inserted, a point J on a 45° line from the centre of the hole is pricked on the tenon, the post is removed, with J as centre a hole is bored through the tenon, the latter is again placed in correct position between the cheeks, and finally the dowel is glued and driven into the holes to draw the shoulders of the joint together and the side of the tenon against the inner end of the mortice.

(d) *Double Tenon Joint* (see K, Fig. 33).—This joint, which, as implied, consists of double tenons, is usefully employed between members of large size, it being more effective than a single tenon in bringing the shoulders of the tenon tight up against the adjacent member. At any joint the combined thickness of two tenons should equal that of one single tenon.

PREPARATION OF FRAME.—If, as is general, the various labours (such as planing, rebating, morticing, tenoning, etc.) are performed by machinery, the timber is dressed and rebated by the planing and surfacing machine (H, Fig. 6—p. 17), one end of each post is tenoned by the

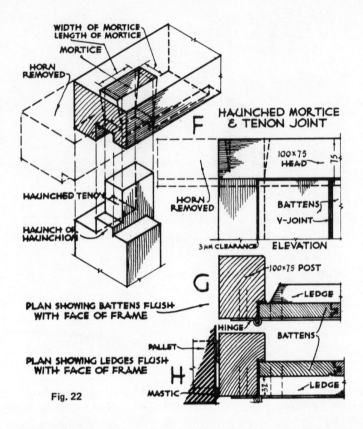

WIDTH OF MORTICE
LENGTH OF MORTICE
MORTICE
HORN REMOVED

HAUNCHED MORTICE & TENON JOINT

F

100×75 HEAD   75

HORN REMOVED

BATTENS
V-JOINT

3 MM CLEARANCE   ELEVATION

HAUNCHED TENON

HAUNCH OF HAUNCHION

100×75 POST

G

LEDGE

HINGE

BATTENS

PLAN SHOWING BATTENS FLUSH WITH FACE OF FRAME

PALLET

PLAN SHOWING LEDGES FLUSH WITH FACE OF FRAME

H

MASTIC

LEDGE

Fig. 22

tenoning machine (p. 24), and the ends of the head are morticed by the mortising machine (K, Fig. 8). It is usual for the mortices to be machined square, and the wedge-room (as required in examples Figs. 21 and 22) is obtained by hand application of the chisel. Holes for dowels (see Fig. 23) are formed by the auger of the mortising machine (see pp. 22 and 23).

If hand prepared, it is usual to obtain dressed timber which has already been machine planed and rebated. Otherwise, the rebating is done by hand by one of several methods. Thus, after the rebate has been marked to the required width down the post by means of a marking gauge (4, Fig. 151, *Carpentry*), as explained on p. 88, a small (say 38 mm by 19 mm) length of wood, called a *fence,* is lightly nailed or screwed flat on the unrebated portion of the surface of the post and along the mark; this serves as a guide for the rebate plane (5, Fig. 154, *Carpentry*), which is applied until the required depth of rebate has been reached. Mortices are formed with a firmer chisel (see *Carpentry*) when they are wider than 16 mm, or a mortise chisel (see *Carpentry*) for narrower mortices; the mortices, having been previously marked on the head by means of the mortise gauge (6, Fig. 151, *Carpentry*), are cut as described on p. 89.

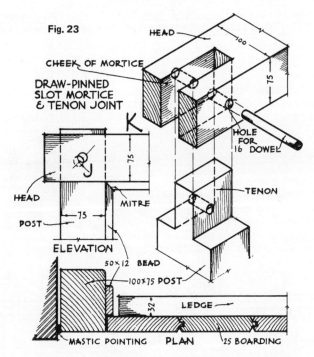

Fig. 23

HEAD

CHEEK OF MORTICE

DRAW-PINNED
SLOT MORTICE
& TENON JOINT

HOLE
FOR
16 DOWEL

HEAD

MITRE

TENON

POST

75

ELEVATION

50×12 BEAD

100×75 POST

LEDGE

MASTIC POINTING   PLAN   25 BOARDING

After "gauging" the ends of the posts, the tenons are cut by the rip and/or tenon saw (see *Carpentry*), as explained on p. 89. Finally, the sides of the tenons and the insides of the mortices are glued, the tenons are inserted in the mortices, the cramp is applied and the glued wedges are tightly driven in (see description on p. 90). If the joints are draw-pinned, as shown in Fig. 23, the holes are formed, as shown, with a 12 or 16 mm auger (see *Carpentry*).

To prevent distortion of a frame before it has been fixed in position, a temporary piece of wood is nailed across the lower ends of the posts. The horns are splayed (Fig. 21) or removed (Fig. 22) before the frame is fixed.

METHODS OF FIXING FRAMES.—A door frame may be fixed in position either (*a*) during the construction of the walling, or (*b*) after the walling has been completed.

(*a*) Such frames are said to be *built in*. When the brickwork (or masonry) has been built to ground-floor level, the door is placed in position according to the plan, plumbed, and maintained temporarily in this position by an inclined strut (nailed to a joist and to the head). The brickwork is proceeded with, the jambs (sides) being constructed close to the posts of the frame. Creosoted wood slips or *pallets* (see H, Fig. 22, and Q, Fig. 24) are built in *dry* at the bed or horizontal joints of each jamb at about 600 mm intervals, with one near the foot and one near the head. The weight of the brickwork makes these pallets secure. Nails are driven through the posts into the pallets after the heads (which may have splayed horns) have been bonded in and there is no likelihood of disturbing the newly built walling. Wrought iron straps (see P, Fig. 24) are used occasionally instead of pallets; these straps are screwed to the posts in positions which will coincide with the bed joints of the brickwork when they are well bedded in mortar.

Building in is a common method of fixing frames. It is not adopted in first-class work, as the frames are liable to be damaged during building

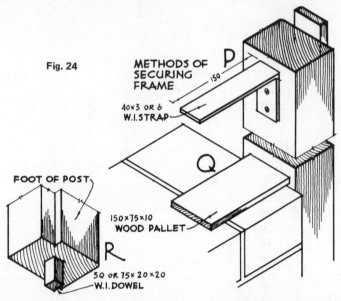

Fig. 24

METHODS OF SECURING FRAME

P

150

40×3 OR 6 W.I.STRAP

Q

FOOT OF POST

150×75×10 WOOD PALLET

R

50 OR 75× 20 ×20 W.I. DOWEL

operations, and lime, etc. is apt to stain it. The arrises of the frames may be protected by lightly nailing wood strips to them. Frames are bedded in mortar as the jambs are being constructed, and afterwards pointed in *mastic* (proprietary non-hardening compounds are used for this) to exclude rain and draughts (see H, Fig. 22).

External woodwork should be *primed* before being fixed. Priming is the first coat of paint which is applied to the timber.

(*b*) The second method of fixing frames, and one which is adopted in better-class work, is to nail them to the pallets after the whole of the brickwork has thoroughly set. Alternatively, *plugs* are used instead of pallets. Plugs should be of hardwood and shaped as shown at F, Fig. 49. A plugging chisel (4, Fig. 153, *Carpentry*) and hammer are used to form 75 or 100 mm deep holes in the bed joints and into which the plugs are driven; the latter have their projecting edges cut off to a vertical plane (a plumb-rule being used to ensure this) so that the clear distance between the plugs in the opposite jambs equals the overall width of the frame. The frame is then placed in position, and securely nailed to the plugs and lintel (if of wood) at the top of the opening. The fixing of the

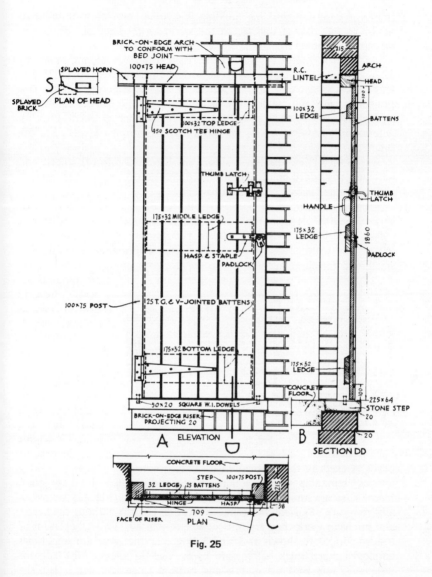

SPLAYED HORN

SPLAYED BRICK

PLAN OF HEAD

S

BRICK-ON-EDGE ARCH TO CONFORM WITH BED JOINT

100×75 HEAD

100×32 TOP LEDGE

450 SCOTCH TEE HINGE

THUMB LATCH

175×32 MIDDLE LEDGE

HASP & STAPLE
PADLOCK

100×75 POST

25 T.G. & V-JOINTED BATTENS

175×32 BOTTOM LEDGE

50×20 SQUARE W.I. DOWELS

BRICK-ON-EDGE RISER PROJECTING 20

A **ELEVATION**

R.C. LINTEL

100×32 LEDGE

HANDLE

175×32 LEDGE

175×32 LEDGE

CONCRETE FLOOR

B **SECTION DD**

215

ARCH

HEAD

BATTENS

THUMB LATCH

1860

PADLOCK

225×64 STONE STEP
20
20

CONCRETE FLOOR

STEP **100×75 POST**

32 LEDGE **25 BATTENS**

HINGE **HASP**

FACE OF RISER

709

PLAN C

215

38

Fig. 25

frames is deferred until the building is nearing completion in order to minimize the risk of damage to the woodwork. They are bedded in mortar and pointed in mastic.

Additional rigidity is given to the frame if a 19 or 25 mm square or 12 mm diameter round galvanized wrought iron dowel, 50 to 75 mm long, is partly driven into the bottom of each post before fixing. The projecting ends are inserted in mortices cut in the step and secured with lead mastic or grouted cement (see R, Fig. 24, and A and B, Fig. 25). Alternatively, hollow cast iron shoes may be adopted (see L, Fig. 33, and p. 58).

CLASSIFICATION.—Battened doors are classified into (*a*) ledged and battened, (*b*) ledged braced and battened, (*c*) framed ledged and battened, and (*d*) framed ledged braced and battened.

(*a*) LEDGED AND BATTENED DOOR (see Fig. 25).—This consists of vertical boards or *battens* which are secured to horizontal pieces called *ledges.* The boards vary from 100 to 175 mm by 19 to 32 mm. Those in "narrow widths" give a more satisfactory appearance if the door is small, and the shrinkage which occurs is correspondingly reduced. Four forms of joints between boards (known as *matchboarding*) which are adopted are shown in Fig. 26. The "vee-jointed" type is formed by chamfering one or both edges of each board, and the "beaded" joint shows the bead or

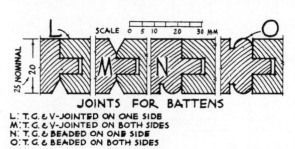

JOINTS FOR BATTENS

L: T.G. & V-JOINTED ON ONE SIDE
M: T.G. & V-JOINTED ON BOTH SIDES
N: T.G. & BEADED ON ONE SIDE
O: T.G. & BEADED ON BOTH SIDES

Fig. 26

beads worked on the tongued edge. These joints are effective in making less objectionable the appearance of the door when shrinkage takes place. They are sometimes only tongued and grooved (Fig. 11), occasionally they are ploughed and tongued (A, Fig. 16, but without the bead), and in cheap work they are butt or square jointed. Two other forms of beaded joints are shown at S and T. Fig. 32; the latter are sometimes employed when thick battens are used. The thickness of the ledges is usually 32 mm, and the middle and bottom ledges are wider than the top ledge, *i.e.,* 175 or 225 mm. When this type of door is employed externally, the top edges of the ledges should be bevelled as shown at B, Fig. 25, to prevent water lodging on them.

This is the simplest type of door, and is frequently used for narrow openings and in positions where the appearance is not material, as for temporary sheds, coal-houses, external water-closets, etc. It is relatively cheap, but is apt to sag, on account of its weight, towards the bottom of the free edge. This defect may not become so pronounced if the end and central battens are screwed, and not nailed, to the ledges. The door also has a tendency to twist, especially if the timber is not of good quality and thin ledges are used.

Preparation of Door.—The door is made in the following manner: The planing (on both sides), grooving, tonguing, chamfering, beading, thicknessing, etc. machine operations on the battens are performed in the planing and matching machine (p. 21). The battens, after having their edges painted to prevent water getting into the joints and setting up rot, are fitted together on the joiners' bench (Fig. 58), and pencil lines are drawn across them to indicate the position of the ledges. A cramp (Fig. 58) is applied near to one of the ledge positions to tighten the joints, and this ledge is lightly and temporarily nailed to the battens. The second ledge is then lightly nailed after the cramp has been applied near it. The door is turned over on the bench, two rough pieces of wood are placed under the ledges, and oval wire nails (A, Fig. 149, *Carpentry*) are driven through the battens and ledges. The nails are of sufficient length to project beyond the ledges when driven in, and as they pierce the rough pieces, the ledges are not damaged by splintering as the nails protrude. The door is reversed and the nails *clinched* or *clenched, i.e.,* the points are bent over, and by means of a punch (I, Fig. 156, *Carpentry*) and hammer are driven below the face of each ledge. The battens are cut off square and dressed off level at the top and bottom.

As stated above, the edges of the battens should be painted before being assembled. Besides preserving the timber, painting prevents an unsightly appearance resulting when shrinkage occurs and the joints open; otherwise, light unpainted margins would be exposed. The backs of the ledges should also be painted before fixing.

Hanging of Door.—The door is fitted between the rebates of the frame, a clearance of 2 mm being allowed between the edges of the door and the frame; this allows for the thickness of the paint, which is applied subsequently, and expansion of the timber. The width of the opening is measured (just below the head and also near the feet of the posts, as the frame may not be absolutely square) and transferred to the door. After allowing for the clearance, the door is placed lengthwise on edge on the floor, propped between the notch on the joiners' stool or trestle, and the uppermost edge is planed down (or "shot") to the "width" mark. The bottom is also planed to allow about 9 mm clearance between the door when hung and the step or floor; this edge should be well painted, as it is inaccessible for painting afterwards. The door is placed in position between the frame, a wedge is inserted between the floor and the door and forced in until the door is brought square with the frame. If the door does not fit correctly, any irregularities are noted, and the door is taken down and planed where necessary.

The door is now ready to receive the hinges. The form of fastening usually provided for this type of door is the *tee-hinge* or *cross garnet* (see A and C, Fig. 25, and A and B, Fig. 28). This is a wrought iron strap pivoted to a metal plate. The *knuckle* of the hinge is a pin round which two sections of the plate and the end of the strap are bent (see X, Fig. 35). The thickness of the strap varies from 2·5 to 6 mm, and its length increases in multiples of 50 mm from 250 to 600 mm, measured from the centre of the pin. Two straps are secured either against the face of the battens (see G, Fig. 22, and A, Fig. 25) or screwed direct to the ledges (H, Fig. 22). Those shown in the elevations in Figs. 25 and 28 are called *Scotch tee-hinges* and are of 3 mm thick galvanized wrought iron. Thicker hinges are only used for heavy doors. Other hinges are shown in Figs. 34 and 35.

HARDWARE OR IRONMONGERY include hinges and fittings such as bolts and locks. It also includes door knobs and handles (sometimes referred to as *door furniture*).

All that may be necessary for the ledged and braced door is a (1) *thumb latch*. If additional security is required, either a (2) *padlock* or one or two (3) *barrel bolts* may be used. The former is an external fitting (as for an external tool-house door), whereas the bolts would be used to secure the door from the inside. Alternatively, a (4) *rim dead lock* may be used instead of a padlock or barrel bolt, or a (5) *rim lock* may be adopted in lieu of a thumb latch and rim dead lock. The following is a brief description of this hardware:—

(1) *Thumb Latch* (see O, Fig. 27, and Figs, 25, 30 and 31).—It is sometimes called a *Norfolk* or *Suffolk latch,* and consists of: (*a*) a *back plate* with handle and pivoted *sneck*, (*b*) a *keeper* through which a (*c*) *beam* or *fall bar* passes to engage in a (*d*) *stop*. The usual length of beam is 175 or 200 mm and that of the back plate is about 225 mm. Another type of thumb latch with two handles, each having a sneck which passes under the beam, is shown at A and C, Fig. 30, and Fig. 31. A complete fitting is usually of malleable iron, although for first-class work it is of bronze.

In fixing a thumb latch, a hole is made in the door through which the sneck is passed and the back plate is screwed to one face of the door. The keeper M and plate to which the beam is pivoted are screwed to the opposite face of the door, the keeper (which limits the movement of the beam) being fixed near to the edge of the door. The plate to which the stop is attached is screwed to the inside face of the post. Two alternative forms of keepers are shown at O, Fig. 27, that at N being less conspicuous than that at M, as it is fixed to the edge of the door. A stop fitting somewhat similar to N may be fixed to the edge or jamb of the post.

(2) *Padlock with Hasp and Staple* (see Fig. 25, and P, Fig. 27).—The hasp and staple are usually of iron, and the padlock is of galvanized iron, brass or bronze. The staple is screwed to the door post, and the hasp is secured by two small bolts to the door. When the door is closed, the slotted hinged end of the hasp is passed over the staple, and the hinged ring of the padlock (after being passed through the eye of the staple) is "pressed home" to lock it. A key is used to free the ring.

(3) *Barrel Bolt* (see Q, Fig. 27, and A, Fig. 28).—It is made of iron,

brass or bronze. The length varies from 75 to 375 mm, a 150 mm bolt being sufficient for a ledged and battened door. The plate is screwed to the inside of the door, and the bolt engages or "shoots" in a metal *socket* or *staple* fixed on the door frame. Sometimes two bolts are fixed horizontally (as shown at A, Fig. 28), or they may be fixed vertically when one socket is let into the head of the frame and the other (similar to S′, Fig. 27) is let into the stone or concrete step.

(4) *Rim Dead Lock* (see R, Fig. 27, and Fig. 31).—This consists of a steel case (containing a brass bolt, spring, etc.) which is screwed to the face of

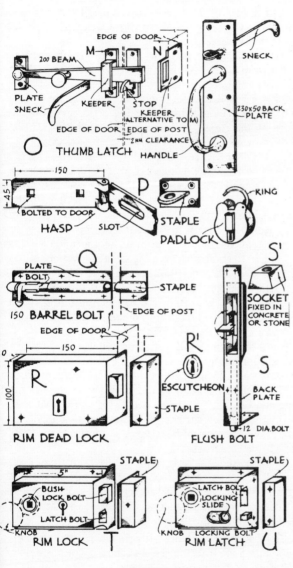

Fig. 27

the door, and a staple which is screwed to the frame to receive the bolt when the door is locked. The key required to operate the bolt is comparatively long, as it is needed to actuate the lock from both sides of the door. The lock may be obtained with one or two levers (see p. 81). An *escutcheon* (see R′, Fig. 27), or holed metal plate, is sometimes fixed on the face of the door opposite to that to which the lock is attached; this prevents the "keyhole" from being enlarged and damaged by continued action of the key. A *plate lock* or *stock lock* may be used for an external ledged and battened door; this is similar to the above lock, but the metal case is inserted in a wood block.

(5) *Rim Lock* (see T, Fig. 27, and Fig. 28).—This is obtained in standard sizes varying from 125 to 200 mm long by 75 to 100 mm deep. It is fixed to the face of the door. It has two bolts, *i.e.*, a "dead" bolt actuated by a key, and a bevelled or latch bolt operated by the handle and (when the door is being closed) by the action of the bevelled end sliding over the edge of the staple. The mechanism of this lock is described on pp. 81–85.

(*b*) LEDGED BRACED AND BATTENED DOOR (see Fig. 28).—This is a ledged and battened door to which inclined struts or *braces* have been added. These braces increase the rigidity of the door and prevent it dropping at the "nose" a defect which is common to the ledged and battened door. These braces must *incline upwards from the hanging edge*, otherwise they would be useless in counteracting the tendency for the door to droop out of square. The position of the middle ledge should be such as to allow the braces to have the same inclination, otherwise the appearance is not satisfactory; the appearance of the door when the braces are lined straight through (as at E, Fig. 29) is sometimes preferred. The width of the braces varies from 100 to 175 mm, and they are usually out of 32 mm stuff. The braces are housed (and not tenoned) into the ledges, as shown in the detail at G, Fig. 29.

An alternative ledged braced and battened door, suitable for a cottage where a simple type of door is required, is shown at E, Fig. 29. The alternate wide and narrow battens, 25 and 32 mm thick respectively, produce a pleasing effect. The detailed section at the jamb shows the battens tongued and grooved and vee-jointed; the tee-hinges (similar to that at X, Fig. 35) pass through the thicker batten. It is assumed that this is an internal door, as the frame is shown to be checked to receive the plaster; it can, of course, be adopted externally.

The ledged braced and battened door is employed for similar purposes, as described for the ledged and battened door (see p. 48), but on account of its greater strength it may be selected for larger openings. It is made as described on p. 49, the battens being nailed to the ledges, and the braces are then fitted to the ledges and clinch-nailed to the battens.

Hardware.—This door is generally hung with tee-hinges; those shown at A, Fig. 28, are 600 mm Scotch tee-hinges, and another form is shown at X, Fig. 35. The furniture may consist of a thumb latch (p. 50) and a rim dead lock (p. 51). Alternatively, a rim lock (p. 52) or a rim latch (see below) may be used instead of a thumb latch and a rim dead lock. In addition, barrel bolts (p. 50) may be used, as shown in Fig. 28.

A *rim latch*, such as that shown at U, Fig. 27, is a steel case, about 125 mm long, which contains a brass bolt and a spring which acts upon the bolt to maintain it in the staple when the door is closed. The mechanism is similar to that of the latch bolt of the mortice lock described on p. 81. The small locking bolt is used when required to prevent the door from being opened by the knob from the outside.

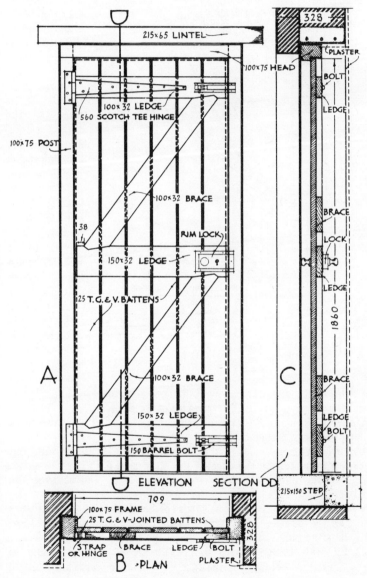

Fig. 28

There are many variations of latches and locks, by way of summary the broad difference between each being:—

A *rim latch* U, Fig. 27) is fixed to the face of a door, and consists of a casing which contains one *bevelled* bolt or latch (which is operated by a handle attached to a spindle) and a small locking bolt.

A *rim dead lock* (R, Fig. 27) has one bolt only which is actuated by a key.

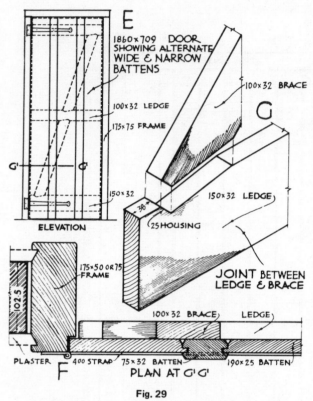

E
1860×709 DOOR SHOWING ALTERNATE WIDE & NARROW BATTENS
100×32 LEDGE
175×75 FRAME
150×32
G¹   G¹
ELEVATION

100×32 BRACE
G
150×32 LEDGE
38°
25 HOUSING
JOINT BETWEEN LEDGE & BRACE

175×50 OR 75 FRAME
102.5
PLASTER   F   400 STRAP   75×32 BATTEN
100×32 BRACE   LEDGE
190×25 BATTEN
PLAN AT G¹ G¹

Fig. 29

A *rim lock* (T, Fig. 21) has two bolts, one controlled by a handle and the other by a key. It is fixed to the face of the door.

A *plate lock* or *stock lock* is a rim dead lock, but with a wood block encasing the metal casing.

A *mortice lock* is similar to the rim lock in that it has two bolts, but the case is only seen on the edge of the door, as it is fixed in a mortice formed in the door. This lock is shown in Fig. 57 and described on pp. 81–85.

A *mortice latch* has only one latch (or bevelled bolt). The mortice latch, like the mortice lock, is fitted within the thickness of the door, and is therefore only visible on the edge of the door.

(*c*) FRAMED LEDGED AND BATTENED DOOR.—This is similar to type (*d*), described below, with the exception that the braces are omitted. The door tends to become distorted because of the absence of the braces, and it is in small demand for this reason.

(*d*) FRAMED LEDGED BRACED AND BATTENED DOOR (see Figs. 30 and 31).—This is superior to any of the foregoing types, and consists of a framing (which must not be confused with the door frame) strengthened

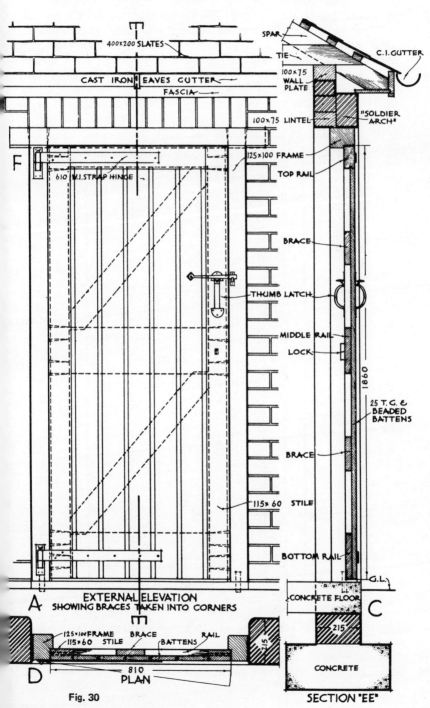

Fig. 30

by ledges, braces and battens. The framework consists of a *top rail* which is haunched morticed and tenoned into two vertical members called *stiles* or *styles*. The *middle* and *bottom rails* or ledges are morticed and tenoned into the stiles, and the braces are either housed into the rails at about 38 mm from the stiles (see Figs. 31 and 33), or are taken into the corners and tenoned into the stiles (see A, Fig. 30). The former is the stronger construction, although the arrangement at A,

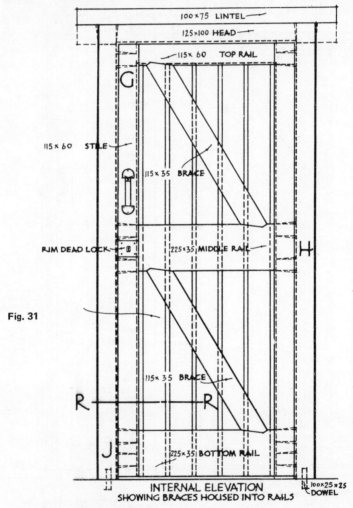

100×75 LINTEL

125×100 HEAD

115×60   TOP RAIL

G

115×60   STILE

115×35   BRACE

RIM DEAD LOCK

225×35 MIDDLE RAIL

H

Fig. 31

115×35   BRACE

R   R

J

225×35 BOTTOM RAIL

100×25×25 DOWEL

INTERNAL ELEVATION
SHOWING BRACES HOUSED INTO RAILS

Fig. 30, is often adopted because of its better appearance. *These braces must incline upwards from the hanging post* (see p. 52). The battens may be jointed as explained on p. 49, where reference is also made to the alternative joints shown at S and T, Fig. 32 (which are sections through

RR, Fig. 31). The upper ends of the battens are tongued into the top rail (see section VV at M, Fig. 33), the side battens are tongued into the stiles

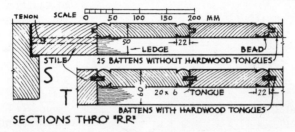

SECTIONS THRO' "RR"   Fig. 32

(see Fig. 32) and the lower ends of the battens *completely cover the bottom rail* (as shown at A and C, Fig. 30 and Fig. 31). The practice, sometimes adopted, of making the bottom rail the same thickness as the stiles and letting the battens into it is unsound if the door is to be fixed externally, as water will lodge on the rail and rot both it and the bottom of the battens.

Details of the various joints of the door illustrated in Figs. 30 and 31 are shown in Fig. 33. That at K shows the joint between the post and head of the large (125 by 100 mm) frame at F, Fig. 30. It is double-tenoned to ensure a tight fit at the shoulders (see p. 43).

The detail at M shows the haunched tenon joint between the top rail and the stile, and the housing of the brace as indicated at G, Fig. 31.

Detail N is that of the joint at H, Fig. 31. The middle rail has a *pair of single tenons*[1] and is notched to receive the lower end of the top brace and the top end of the lower brace. As the rail is comparatively thin, it is not advisable to form these tenons as previously described, but rather to make them flush with one face; such are called *barefaced tenons*.

The detail at O is that of the joint J, Fig. 31. This shows that the bottom rail has also a pair of single barefaced tenons. The lower tenon may be haunched like that shown at M.

The tenons are dowelled or pinned, in addition to being wedged. These dowels are of hardwood and are from 9 to 12 mm diameter (see M, N and O). One is inserted through each tenon at a distance from the shoulders of at least twice the diameter of the dowel to prevent the wood from splitting when the pin is driven in.

The framed ledged braced and battened door is a very satisfactory type for external use, and it is particularly suited for factories, warehouses, farm buildings and buildings in which the doors are subjected to rough treatment. The door shown in Figs. 30 and 31 is typical of the type used for farms; the former Figure also includes a portion of the roof details.

[1] These are sometimes called "double tenons", although this description is not quite correct. A double tenon joint (as shown at K, Fig. 33) has both tenons in the *thickness* of the member, whilst a member having a pair of single tenons has both tenons formed in its *width*.

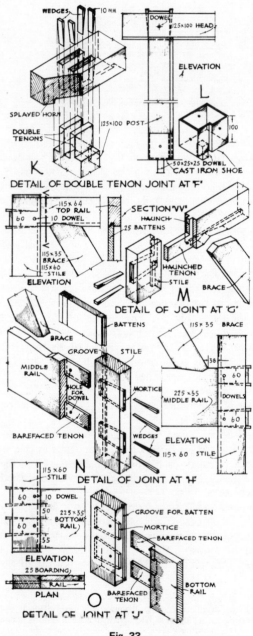

WEDGES | 10 MM

DOWEL
125×100 HEAD

ELEVATION

L

SPLAYED HORN

125×100 POST

DOUBLE TENONS

100

50×25×25 DOWEL
CAST IRON SHOE

K

DETAIL OF DOUBLE TENON JOINT AT 'F'

115×64 TOP RAIL
60 | 10 DOWEL

SECTION 'VV'
HAUNCH
25 BATTENS

115×35 BRACE
115×60 STILE

HAUNCHED TENON
STILE

ELEVATION

BRACE

M

DETAIL OF JOINT AT 'G'

BATTENS | 115×35 BRACE

BRACE

GROOVE | STILE

MIDDLE RAIL

HOLE FOR DOWEL

MORTICE

38

0 60

225×35 MIDDLE RAIL

DOWELS

0 60

BAREFACED TENON

WEDGES

ELEVATION

115×60 STILE

N

DETAIL OF JOINT AT 'H'

115×60 STILE

60 | 10 DOWEL
50

225×35 BOTTOM RAIL

60

55

GROOVE FOR BATTEN

MORTICE

BAREFACED TENON

ELEVATION

25 BOARDING
RAIL

PLAN

O

BAREFACED TENON

BOTTOM RAIL

DETAIL OF JOINT AT 'J'

Fig. 33

Preparation of Door.—The sequence of operations in framing this door are briefly: The rails are fitted loosely into the stiles, the braces are placed in position, the battens are accurately fitted and slipped into the grooves of the stiles and top rail, the tenons are wedged and pinned (a cramp being used as described on p. 90 to tighten up the joints), and the battens are nailed to the rails and braces. The setting out and construction of door framing is described in some detail on pp. 85–91.

The door frame should be securely fixed, as explained on pp. 45 and 46. The feet are shown secured by dowels. Alternatively, the door posts may be fitted with *cast-iron shoes* (see L, Fig. 33). These provide a sound method of fixing and also protect the lower ends of the posts from damage, such as may be caused in factories, farmsteads and similar buildings. The ends of the posts are shaped, painted and fitted tightly

FRAMED LEDGED BRACED AND BATTENED DOOR   59

into the shoes which are then screwed to the posts. The frame is now fixed with the dowels let into the mortices previously formed in the step and run in with lead.

Hanging of Door.—Heavy wrought iron Scotch tee-hinges are some-times used for hanging this type of door (see p. 49). Alternatively, 6 mm thick wrought iron *strap hinges* or *bands and gudgeon hooks* are used for this purpose, especially

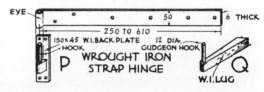

Fig. 34

for large and heavy doors (see Fig. 34). One end of the strap is bent to form an eye. Two straps are required and are secured by 9 or 12 mm diameter bolts which are passed through the rails and battens. The door is hung by passing the eyes of the straps over the pins or gudgeons which are welded to *back plates* bolted to the frame. Sometimes (as for certain farm buildings) doors are not provided with frames and are hung by engaging the eyes of the straps to gudgeon hooks smithed to wrought

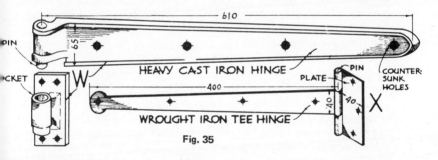

Fig. 35

iron *lugs* (see Q, Fig. 34). The lugs are secured to the stonework (or brick-work), mortices being cut to receive them. After insertion the lugs are

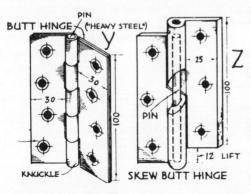

Fig. 36

well caulked with lead; the dovetail shape and the ragged surface give a good key for the lead and increase its holding power. The heavy *cast-iron hinge,* shown at W, Fig. 35, is another type of fastening employed for very large doors. A pair of these hinges is bolted to the door and their pins engage in sockets fixed to the frame.

Butt hinges (see Y, Fig. 36) are often used for hanging this type of door. The flanges or *wings* of the hinges are made of either cast iron, malleable iron or steel, and they are available in sizes from 25 to 150 mm. The *knuckle* consists of a central pin which passes through alternate eyes of each wing to form five segments. The wings have countersunk holes to receive the heads of the screws used to secure the wings to the door and frame.

The door is hung by butt hinges in the following manner: It is fitted into the frame and trimmed (p. 49) so as to leave a minimum clearance of 2 mm (see p. 49). The door is removed and one wing of each hinge is screwed to the edge of the hanging stile. This is done by forming slight housings in correct position on the stile to receive the wings of the hinges which are screwed to the door. The door is again placed into the opening, wedged temporarily (p. 49) and brought to the required position. The housings for the free wings are marked on the post, the door is removed and the housings are formed. The door is placed finally in position, and the wings of the hinges are screwed to the post (see Fig. 54). In order that the door shall swing freely, the centre of the pin of the top hinge should be 5 mm beyond the face of the door, and that of the bottom hinge should be 6 mm clear; whilst this has the disadvantage of leaving a space between the edge of the door and the frame when the door is slightly open, it does enable the door to be swung well back clear of any adjacent architrave (such as that shown in Fig. 54).

A description of the *skew butt hinge*, (or *rising hinge*), shown at Z, Fig. 36, and its application is given on p. 78.

Hardware for this door may be as previously described. If provision is required (for purposes of ventilation, etc.) to enable the door to be kept slightly open and yet secure from unauthorized entry from the outside, then a *door chain,* as shown in Fig. 37, may be fixed on the inside. This fitting may be either of malleable iron, brass or bronze. The plate to which the slotted shoot is attached is screwed in a horizontal position to the inside face of the door, and the staple to which the chain is fastened is screwed to the post. The free end of the chain is in the form of a stud which may be inserted in the slot at the end farthest from the staple only when the door is closed. The door may be opened to a maximum of 100 or 125 mm, when the stud is passed along the slot, and the stud cannot be removed from the outside.

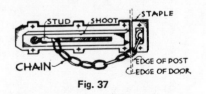

Fig. 37

CHAPTER FOUR

PANELLED DOORS

Types of panelled doors. Treatment of panels; alternative mouldings. Manufacture, including setting out. Frames and casings; methods of fixing. Hanging of doors; fixing architraves and locks. Hardware.

A PANELLED door consists of one or more wood[1] panels which are fitted into grooves formed on the inner edges of a framing. There are many designs, several of which are shown in Fig. 38; the British Standard sizes for panelled doors are the same as those given on p. 41. The number of panels varies from one to six; but this may be exceeded.

TYPES OF DOOR

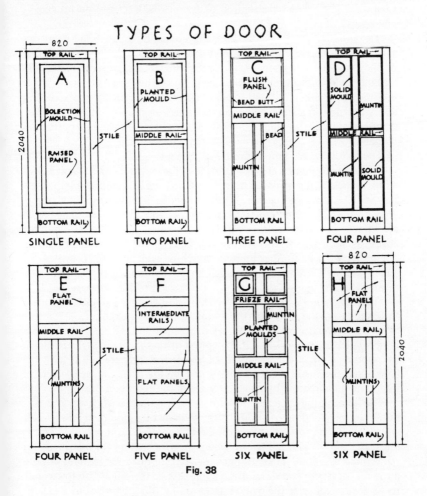

Fig. 38

---

[1] Glazed doors are described in Chapter Six.

The framing for a single panelled door comprises two stiles or styles (vertical members), a top rail and a bottom rail (horizontal members—see p. 56, A, Fig. 38 and Fig. 41). A two panelled door framing has an additional horizontal member or middle rail (p. 56, B, Fig. 38 and Fig. 51). Intermediate rails are required for the type of door shown at F, Fig. 38; in the six panelled door at G, Fig. 38, the upper intermediate rail is sometimes called a *frieze rail*. Other doors, such as those shown at C and E, Fig. 38, are provided with short vertical pieces, called *muntins,* fitted between the bottom and middle rails; additional muntins are required between the middle and top rails for the doors shown at D, G and H, Fig. 38 and Fig. 55. Semicircular headed doors are described in Chapter Eight. The construction of framing is described on pp. 69–70 and 85–91.

TREATMENT OF PANELS.—Finishings applied to panels are many and varied. The panels may be finished with simple or elaborate mouldings, or they may be left plain without mouldings. Intricate mouldings may harbour dust and are difficult to keep clean; they may be expensive to produce, especially if mitred by hand (see below and pp. 25 and 90). Most doors are now machine made, as described on pp. 85–91, and in their manufacture it is the aim to eliminate as far as possible labours performed by hand.

The following are the various panel finishes:—

Square.—Mouldings are not provided, the edges of the framing next to the panels being left square (see J and K, Fig. 39, and D—right side—Fig. 56); J shows the corner slightly rounded by sand-papering (see p. 25) and is called *pencil-rounded* (see also G and H, Fig. 78). The panels are known as *square sunk* or *flat* (see E, F and H, Fig. 38). *Chamfered* edges, as shown at L and M, Fig. 39, and M—left side—Fig. 60, are an alternative. These finishes are now much in evidence and, provided the panels are well proportioned, such simple treatment has much to commend it.

Solid or Stuck Mouldings.—The mouldings are "stuck" (meaning "worked") on the edges of the framing. Various examples are shown at L to Y (inclusive), Fig. 39, H—right side—Fig. 53, and M, Fig. 62. Observe that in each case (with exception of that in Fig. 62) the width of the mould is equal to the depth of the groove prepared to receive the panel (see the broken lines at R, S and Y, Fig. 39); the operations of moulding and framing by machinery are simplified when this is observed.

The joints at the angles of solid mouldings are *scribed* to give 45° mitres or intersections. Scribing is the shaping of a moulding on the ends which is required to fit against a similar but *continuous* moulding. This is illustrated at C, D and E, Fig. 40, which shows a bottom (or intermediate) rail scribed to a stile. The latter has an ovolo (or quadrant) mould worked on it for its *entire length,* and the shoulders of the rail are hollowed out to fit accurately over the ovolo mould on the stile. This is shown clearly on the plan at C, which indicates the shaped end of the rail separated from the stile; this results in a 45° mitre, as shown at D and E. This

PANEL MOULDINGS

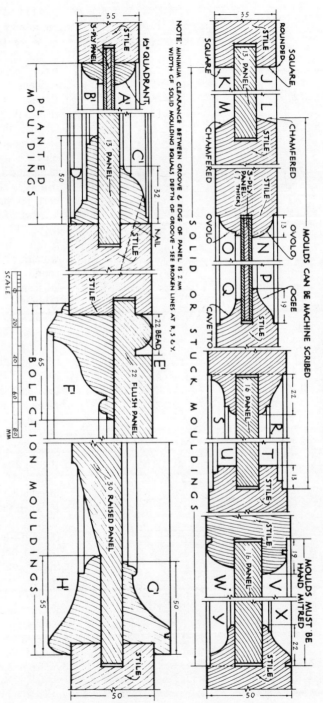

NOTE: MINIMUM CLEARANCE BETWEEN GROOVE & EDGE OF PANEL IS 2 MM
WIDTH OF SOLID MOULDING EQUALS DEPTH OF GROOVE - SEE BROKEN LINES AT R, S, & Y.

MOULDS CAN BE MACHINE SCRIBED

MOULDS MUST BE HAND MITRED

SOLID OR STUCK MOULDINGS

PLANTED MOULDINGS

BOLECTION MOULDINGS

SCALE

Fig. 39

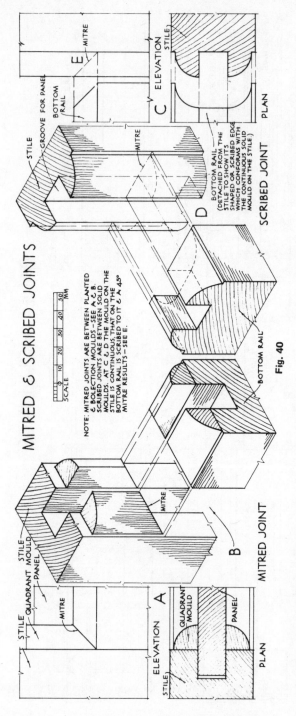

MITRED & SCRIBED JOINTS

NOTE: MITRED JOINTS ARE BETWEEN PLANTED
& BOLECTION MOULDS – SEE A & B.
SCRIBED JOINTS ARE BETWEEN SOLID
MOULDS. AT C & D THE MOULD ON THE
STILE IS CONTINUOUS, THAT ON THE
BOTTOM RAIL IS SCRIBED TO IT & A 45°
MITRE RESULTS – SEE E.

SCALE
0 10 20 30 40 50
MM

STILE
GROOVE FOR PANEL
MITRE
BOTTOM
RAIL
E
MITRE
ELEVATION
STILE
C
PLAN

STILE
MITRE
SCRIBED JOINT
BOTTOM RAIL
(DETACHED FROM THE
STILE TO SHOW ITS
SHAPED OR SCRIBED EDGE
WHICH CONFORMS WITH
THE CONTINUOUS SOLID
MOULD ON THE STILE)
D

Fig. 40

BOTTOM RAIL

STILE
QUADRANT MOULD
PANEL
MITRE
B
MITRED JOINT

STILE
QUADRANT MOULD
PANEL
MITRE
A
ELEVATION
STILE
QUADRANT
MOULD
PANEL
PLAN

mould and the solid mouldings shown at L to U (inclusive), Fig. 39, can be machine-scribed, and are therefore comparatively inexpensive; whereas those at V to Y (inclusive) can only be mitred by hand, and are accordingly relatively costly to produce.

Planted Mouldings.—These are separate mouldings which are "planted" round the panels adjacent to the framing. Examples of these are shown at A', B', C' and D', Fig. 39. The mouldings are nailed to the framing; care must be taken to ensure that the *nails do not pass through the panels,* otherwise the panels will crack owing to the internal stresses set up when the timber shrinks (see nail at C' indicated by a broken line). It is important to allow for the free movement (as when the wood shrinks or expands) of the panels, and there should be a space of from 2 to 3 mm between each edge

of a panel and the groove; the clearance in each of the examples shown in
Fig. 39 is 2 mm. Panel pins (F, Fig. 149, *Carpentry*) are used for fixing
these moulds, as the small heads are inconspicuous and cause the minimum
damage to the mouldings.

Planted mouldings are formed with *mitred joints* at the angles, each
adjacent end of the moulding being cut at an angle of 45°. A mitred
joint is shown at A and B, Fig. 40, and should be compared with the
scribed joint at C, D and E.

Planted moulds which finish level with the face of the framing are
called *flush mouldings* (see O, Fig. 62). Those which project beyond the
face of the framing are called *bolection mouldings* (see F', G' and H',
Fig. 39, P, Fig. 42, H, Fig. 53, Fig. 56, Fig. 60, T, Fig. 67 and Fig. 71;
these are usually rebated over the edges of the framing (to cover any
shrinkage which may take place), but occasionally they are non-rebated
(*i.e.* those in Fig. 60).

The panels may be made with one face flush with the framing; these
are termed *flush panels* (see C, Fig. 38). A bead, as shown at E', Fig. 39,
is usually formed on the vertical edges of the panel to render less conspicuous any openings which may occur if the panels shrink; these are
called *bead butt panels* (see C, Fig. 38). If, in addition, a similar bead is
worked on the horizontal edges of the panel, such are called *bead flush
panels*.

Raised Panels.—The central portion of such a panel is thicker than the
edges or *margin*. That at H', Fig. 39, shows the panel chamfered from
the edge of the moulding to leave a flat or *fielded* central portion; such
is called a *raised, sunk and fielded panel* (see also Fig. 71). Sometimes
the edges of the sinking next to the central flat portion is moulded, when
the panel is said to be *raised, sunk and moulded*. A *raised and chamfered
panel*, when square, is chamfered from a central point down to each edge
of the panel moulding; when the panel is oblong, the chamfered margins
meet to form a ridge.

Sunk Mouldings.—Such a moulding is formed *below* the surface; the
sinking is usually continued to form a *sunk panel*, and the portion
enclosed by the moulding may be below or flush with the outer margin.
The panel is thus formed out of the solid. The transome (see p. 97)
shown at O, Fig. 62, is sunk moulded.

Examples of panels and mouldings are shown in the elevations in
Fig. 39 and in several of the drawings which follow.

Students are recommended to cultivate the habit of drawing details
involving mouldings to full size scale rather than make sketch details only,
which are very frequently far too small. They should appreciate that it is
not always necessary to show mouldings consisting of many small
members and *fillets* (small straight portions separating others which may
be moulded), for very often the simpler the mouldings the better. In
this connection it should be noted that whilst mouldings of hardwoods
may have small members, those of softwoods should not, for they are

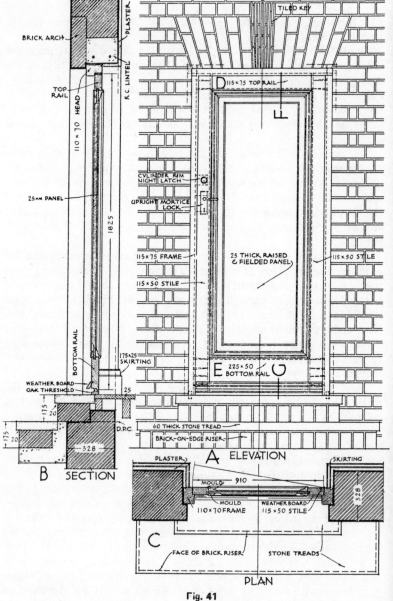

BRICK ARCH

PLASTER

TOP RAIL

110 × 70 HEAD

R.C. LINTEL

25MM PANEL

1825

TILED KEY

D 115 × 75 TOP RAIL

F

CYLINDER RIM NIGHT LATCH

UPRIGHT MORTICE LOCK

115 × 75 FRAME

115 × 50 STILE

25 THICK RAISED & FIELDED PANEL

115 × 50 STILE

BOTTOM RAIL

175 × 25 SKIRTING

25

WEATHER BOARD
OAK THRESHOLD

175

20

175

20

D.P.C.

328

B   SECTION

E 225 × 50 BOTTOM RAIL G

60 THICK STONE TREAD

BRICK-ON-EDGE RISER

A   ELEVATION

PLASTER

SKIRTING

MOULD 910

328

MOULD
110 × 70 FRAME

WEATHER BOARD
115 × 50 STILE

C

FACE OF BRICK RISER

STONE TREADS

PLAN

Fig. 41

66

difficult and expensive to make and disappear when two or three coats of paint are applied.

Details of several panelled doors will now be considered.

SINGLE PANELLED DOOR.—An example of this type, suitable for the main entrance to a house, is shown in Fig. 41. The construction of the joints of the frame has been described on pp. 41–43. The outside edges of this frame may be pencil-rounded (as indicated at P, Fig. 60) or otherwise moulded (such as the ovolo shown at O, Fig. 39, or the cyma indicated in Fig. 71) and thus rendered less liable to damage than if left square.

External doors, such as this, are usually prepared with 50 mm (nominal)[1] thick framing, especially if they are fitted with mortice locks (p. 81), although cheap doors of average size can be 40 mm in thickness if they are fitted with rim locks (p. 54). In this example the door is 50 mm thick on account of the thick (25 mm) panel which is necessary because of its large size (see below). Full size details must be drawn to the *finished sizes*. In accordance with the footnote to this page, the usual total allowance for painted work is equivalent to 5 mm when both faces are planed and sand-papered. If great care is exercised in dressing expensive hardwoods, the total loss when dressing both sides may be reduced to 4 mm, and this allowance has been made in the details shown, for example, in Figs. 53 and 56.

This door is detailed in Fig. 42. The detail at P shows the top rail "broken"; this saves space, and it is unnecessary to give the complete rail when the size is specified, as shown. The 22 mm (finished) thick raised, sunk and fielded panel has bolection mouldings on both sides; alternative mouldings may be selected from Fig. 39 and some of the subsequent drawings. Whilst certain timbers, such as mahogany, can be obtained of sufficient width to enable this wide panel to be formed in one piece, it may be formed in two or three pieces carefully jointed together. This jointing is done by shooting the edges of each piece to a true plane so that the adjacent edges will make a good fit throughout the length of each piece; the edges are glued (as this is an external door, waterproof glue—see p. 247—would be used), fitted together, securely cramped until the glue has set (see p. 90), when the panel is planed to a smooth finish; this is called *jointing*. The machine used for this purpose is the planing and jointing machine (p. 17). If shot and squared by hand, the jack plane (I, Fig. 154, *Carpentry*) is first applied to each edge, followed by the trying plane (6, Fig. 154, *Carpentry*) until it is perfectly straight, when tested with a straight-edge (for long panels), and square (tested with the try square—2, Fig. 151, *Carpentry*). An alternative panel, not raised, could consist of a multi-ply board, such as 5-ply shown at D,

---

[1] As mentioned on p. 41, an allowance from the nominal sizes for dressed (wrought or finished) work must be made. The usual allowance for work which is given a smooth finish (as for painted work) is 1·7 mm for *each* dressed surface, plus 0·8 mm for sand-papering each surface.

Fig. 15 in *Carpentry* and which is 19 mm thick; such plywood should be resin-bonded as waterproof glue is necessary for external work.

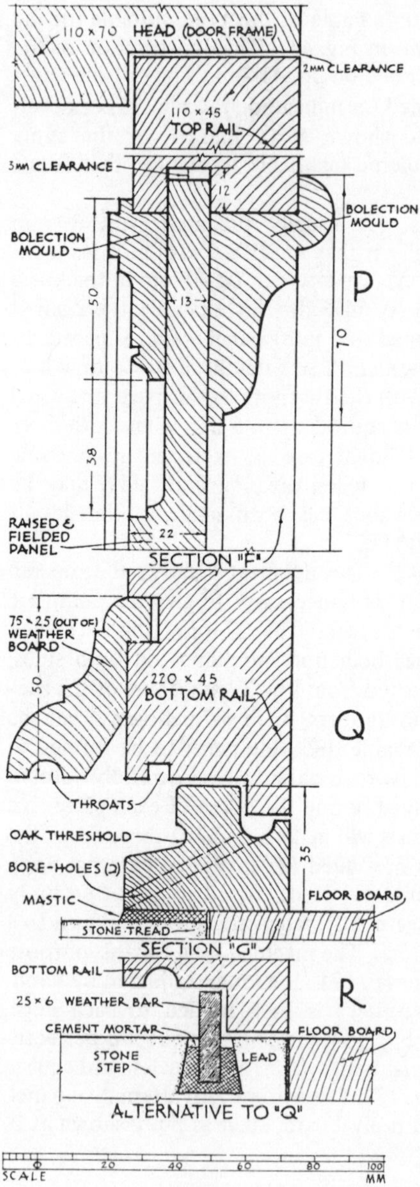

Any panel, not of plywood, exceeding 280 mm width for an average good quality internal door should be jointed in this manner.

Attention is drawn to the construction at the bottom of door to prevent the entrance of water and shown at Q, Fig. 42. An oak (or similar hard-wearing timber) sill or *threshold* extends the full width of the door opening, well screwed to the floor and bedded on mastic. The larger groove on the inside serves to catch any water which may have penetrated and which escapes down the two bore-holes. The top of this threshold is approximately on a level with that of a door mat (assuming that a "mat well"—which is not recommended as it is difficult to keep clean—has not been provided). There is therefore little danger of tripping over the threshold. Incidentally, small sills or projecting weather bars (see below) are more dangerous in this respect than are deeper and wider sills. A wider, but otherwise similar, threshold is shown at R, Fig. 63. A cheaper detail is shown at M, Fig. 62.

An alternative method of weather exclusion is shown at R, Fig. 42, the wrought iron *weather bar* or *water bar* being let into the dovetailed sinking and secured with molten lead, run in hot and afterwards well caulked (consolidated with a blunt chisel);

Fig. 42

this lead is covered with cement mortar flush with the top of the step so as to exclude rain-water which may otherwise cause discoloration.

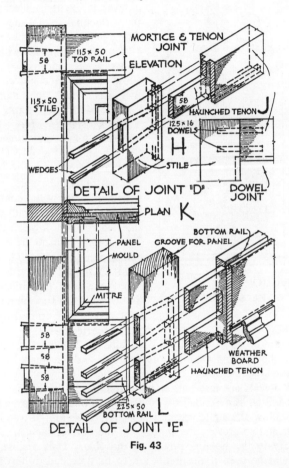

Fig. 43

The moulded weather board shown at Q, Fig. 42, is tongued into the bottom rail of the door and should fit as tight as practicable between the door posts; this throws rain clear of the threshold; its end at the *striking* (or *free*) *edge* (as distinct from its *hinged edge, i.e.,* that at which the hinges are fixed) is slightly splayed (see C, Fig. 41) in order that the weather board will clear the post of the frame when the door is opened. Plain weather boards are detailed at M, Fig. 62, and J, Fig. 64, and a moulded weather board is shown at R, Fig. 63.

JOINTS OF DOOR FRAMING.—The joints of the framing may be either (*a*) morticed and tenoned or (*b*) dowelled.

(*a*) *Morticed and Tenoned Joints.*—These are similar to the joints of the framed ledged braced and battened door shown in Fig. 33, and are illustrated at H and L, Fig. 44. The width of each tenon is 57 mm. The

grooves formed along the inner edges of the framing to receive the panel
are shown. The depth of the grooves is usually made equal to the thickness of the panel, although it should not be less than 12 mm (see P, Fig. 42—which also shows a clearance of 3 mm to allow for the free movement of the panel—and the details in Fig. 53, 54, 56, 60, 62 and 78).

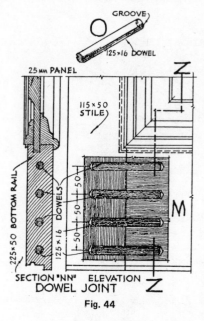

SECTION "NN"   ELEVATION
DOWEL JOINT

Fig. 44

(b) *Dowelled Joints.*—Typical dowelled joints are shown at J, Fig. 43, and M, Fig. 44. That at J shows two dowels used to connect the top rail to the stile, and the details at M show the connection between the bottom rail and the stile where four dowels are used. The dowels, which are machine made, are of hardwood. Their diameter should not be less than about one-third the thickness of the framing, and a common size is 125 mm by 16 mm (see O,
Fig. 44); they are placed at about 50 mm centres (see M). The ends of the rails are bored (by the boring machine—p. 23), glue is applied to the edges of the rails and the inside of the holes, and the glued dowels are inserted; the stiles are bored, the holes are glued, the projecting portions of the rail dowels are inserted, and the framing is finally cramped to tighten the joints, as described on p. 90. The dowels are grooved (see O, Fig. 44) to allow the air to escape when the dowels are "driven home" in the holes and so prevent the splitting of the timber; incidentally, the grooves increase the holding power of the glue. Only well-seasoned timber should be used if the joints are to be dowelled, otherwise the shrinking and warping of unseasoned timber may cause the dowels to snap, followed by the destruction of the joints.

Dowelled jointing is almost universally adopted for doors made by machinery, as it is a cheaper form than the mortice and tenon joint on account of the saving of timber which results. Most imported doors, and the immense number of doors made daily by mass production methods of this country, have dowelled and not morticed and tenoned joints (see p. 86).

HARDWARE.—The door shown in Fig. 41 would be hung with three 100 mm butt hinges as described on p. 60. It would be fitted with a 75 mm four-lever *upright mortice lock* with *striking plate* (see Fig. 45). This type of lock is necessary, for owing to the absence of a middle rail, the usual type of mortice lock (see p. 81) would be too long, and the two handles should be of the *lever*[1] type, as shown in Figs. 41 and 45; if knobs (as illustrated at X′, Fig. 57) were used, injury to the hand may be caused owing to their close proximity to the door post. The striking plate serves a similar purpose for a mortice lock as does a staple for a rim lock (p. 51), and is housed and screwed to the rebate of the post after two small mortices to receive the ends of the bolts have been cut in the post. The projecting lug on the plate is slightly bent so that, when the bevelled latch bolt strikes it as the

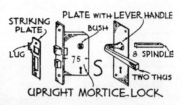

Fig. 45

door is being closed, the bolt will be gradually pressed in. This furniture may be obtained in bronze, chromium plated or oxidized silver metal, plastic, etc.

A cylinder rim night latch (see M, Fig. 46) would be required in addition to the above lock. This is one of many patent latches which

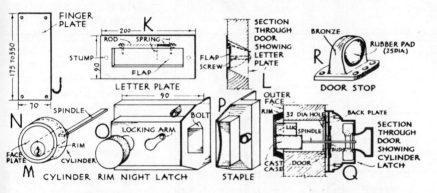

Fig. 46

are on the market and consists of a bronze *cylinder* fitting N, the latch O and the staple P. A section through the latch attached to the door is shown at Q, Fig. 46. The fitting N comprises a separate circular rim with its inner edge rebated to receive the circular *face plate* which is cast on the *case* (see N and Q); the case contains the cylinder to which the spindle is attached, and this cylinder is caused to rotate within the case by the action of a key. The latch bolt may be operated from the outside by the key (which is inserted in the cylinder to rotate both it and the spindle for the latter to cause the bolt mechanism to function), or the bolt may be shot back from the staple by turning the knob of the latch from the inside. The *locking arm* (see O) is used when required to permanently fix the bolt and prevent it from being operated by either

[1]This and following terms will be better understood if reference is made to the description of the mortice lock on pp. 81–85.

the key or the knob; thus, the bolt may be fixed in the staple to afford greater security, or it may be fixed when it is clear of the staple.

The directions for fixing this cylinder latch are as follows: A 32 mm diameter hole is bored through the door, the centre of the hole being 60 mm from the edge of the door. The cylinder fitting N is passed through the hole from the outside. The *back plate* (see Q) is screwed to the back of the door. Two long screws are then passed through holes in the back plate to secure the *lug* attached to the *case*. The end of the spindle is passed through the *bush* of the latch O, and the latter is screwed to the back of the door. The staple is screwed to the edge of the door.

A pair of antique bronze *flush bolts* may also be provided (see S, Fig. 27). These are not so conspicuous at the barrel bolt type (Q, Fig. 27), as the back plate is screwed through the stile in a housing formed to bring the plate flush with the face of the stile. The end of the bottom bolt slides into a metal socket (S') let into the floor or step, and the upper bolt engages in a socket fitted into the head of the frame.

Sometimes a *letter plate*, preferably of antique bronze, is required (see K and L, Fig. 46). The flap opens inwards and is suspended on a horizontal rod round one end of which is coiled a spring which forces the flap tightly against the back of the plate. A mortice, approximately 150 mm

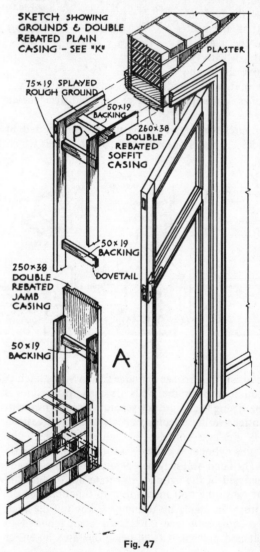

SKETCH SHOWING GROUNDS & DOUBLE REBATED PLAIN CASING - SEE "K"

PLASTER

75×19 SPLAYED ROUGH GROUND

50×19 BACKING

P

260×38 DOUBLE REBATED SOFFIT CASING

50×19 BACKING

250×38 DOUBLE REBATED JAMB CASING

DOVETAIL

50×19 BACKING

A

Fig. 47

long and 50 mm deep, is made in the door with the horizontal edges splayed downwards (see L), and the fitting, which entirely covers the hole, is secured to the door by means of two screws which are threaded to stumps.

A door chain (see p. 60) may be fixed.

DOOR CASINGS OR LININGS.—Whilst external doors are hung to solid frames, it is customary to fix internal doors to casings or linings which provide a suitable finish to the openings. Casings are fixed to either (*a*) pallets, (*b*) plugs or (*c*) grounds.

(a) *Pallet pieces* or slips, 9 mm thick, are built into the bed joints at the jambs of the openings as shown at Q, Fig. 24 and D, Fig. 48 and at intervals as described on p. 45. This method of fixing is very general.

(b) A cheaper and less satisfactory method is to plug the jambs. *Wood plugs* (which should be of hardwood but are often made from pieces of floor boards), shaped as shown at F, Fig. 49, are driven into holes formed in the mortar joints by means of the plugging chisel (4, Fig. 153, *Carpentry*) and hammer. The plugs are driven tightly up to their shoulders and would take the place of the pallets shown at D, Fig. 48; those indicated at D would be used for the fixing of architraves (see p. 228).

(c) *Grounds.*—As implied, the purpose of these is to provide a ground-work for the casings and architraves. This method of fixing is only adopted in the best practice. The simplest form consists of 19 mm thick (or thickness of plaster) pieces of undressed timber, called *rough grounds* (as distinct from *wrought grounds*—see p. 75), and are usually 75 mm wide, although this depends upon the thickness of the architraves. They provide a continuous means of fixing for the casings such as is not afforded by plugs or pallets. One edge is sometimes splayed to afford a key for the plaster (see Fig. 47, E, Fig. 49, J, K, L and N, Fig. 50, and Figs. 53 and 54). The jamb grounds are fixed in true alignment on each face of the walls to plugs at intervals, and the head or soffit grounds are nailed to the lintel (see Fig. 47). They project about 19 mm beyond the jambs, depending upon the size of the brick (or stone) opening and that of the door. In good work the head grounds are haunched tenoned and wedged to the jamb grounds (see P, Fig. 47, and E, Fig. 49). The above preparation is all that is necessary for ½-brick thick walls.

For thicker walls, however, 50 mm wide by 19 mm or 25 mm thick short horizontal *backing pieces* are fixed to the edges of the grounds, as shown at Fig. 47, C, Fig. 48, E, Fig. 49, and K, L and N, Fig. 50). These cross pieces provide extra means of fixing the wider casings and, if the ends are dovetailed and fitted into the notches formed in the grounds (see Figs. 47 and 49), they are effective in preventing the grounds from expanding and twisting when they absorb moisture from the plaster which is applied subsequently to the walls. The backings are fixed near to the top and bottom of the jambs, and at about 300 mm intervals; they are also nailed to wood lintels (see Fig. 56).

DOOR CASINGS

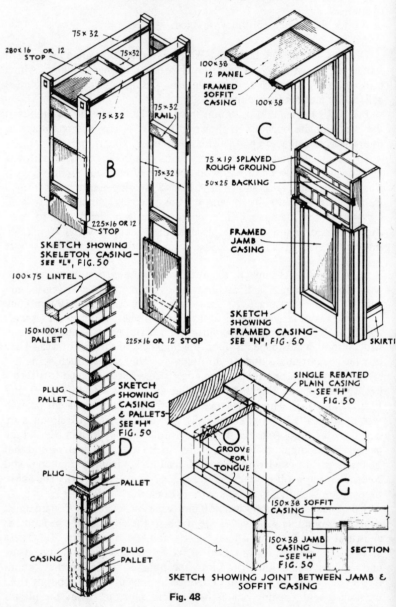

75 × 32

280×16 OR 12
STOP

75×32

75×32

75×32
RAIL

75×32

B

225×16 OR 12
STOP

SKETCH SHOWING
SKELETON CASING—
SEE "L", FIG. 50

100×75 LINTEL

150×100×10
PALLET

PLUG
PALLET

SKETCH
SHOWING
CASING
& PALLETS
SEE "H"
FIG. 50

D

225×16 OR 12 STOP

PLUG

PLUG — PALLET

CASING

PLUG
PALLET

100×38
12 PANEL

FRAMED
SOFFIT
CASING

100×38

C

75 ×19 SPLAYED
ROUGH GROUND

50×25 BACKING

FRAMED
JAMB
CASING

SKETCH
SHOWING
FRAMED CASING—
SEE "N", FIG. 50

SKIRTI

SINGLE REBATED
PLAIN CASING
—SEE "H"
FIG. 50

GROOVE
FOR
TONGUE

O

G

150×38 SOFFIT
CASING

150×38 JAMB
CASING
—SEE "H"
FIG. 50

SECTION

SKETCH SHOWING JOINT BETWEEN JAMB &
SOFFIT CASING

Fig. 48

There are three types of casings, *i.c.* (1) plain, (2) skeleton and (3) framed.

74

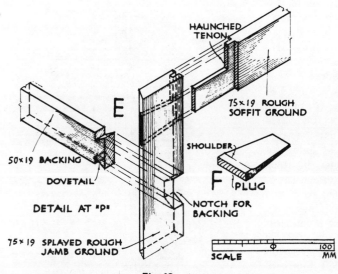

HAUNCHED TENON

75×19 ROUGH SOFFIT GROUND

E

SHOULDER

F PLUG

50×19 BACKING

DOVETAIL

DETAIL AT "P"

NOTCH FOR BACKING

75×19 SPLAYED ROUGH JAMB GROUND

SCALE 100 MM

Fig. 49

(1) *Plain Casings.*—These are usually prepared from 32 mm thick boards, and are suitable for openings in walls which do not exceed 1-brick thick. They may be either single rebated (see D and G, Fig. 48, H, Fig. 50, and H, Fig. 53) or double rebated (see Fig. 47, K, Fig. 50, and D, Fig. 56). Alternatively, in cheap work, a 12 or 16 mm thick stop is nailed to the casing, when the thickness of the latter may be reduced to 25 mm (see J, Fig. 50, and L, Fig. 65). Double rebating a wide casing gives it a balanced appearance which is noticeable when the door is open. The soffit casing is grooved or *trenched* to receive the tongues formed on the jamb linings (see G, Fig. 48). This groove extends to the outer edge when softwood is to be used and which would be painted; but if the linings are of hardwood and subsequently polished, the groove in the soffit does not extend right across but is stopped to house the abbreviated tongue, as shown by thick broken lines at O, Fig. 48.

(2) *Skeleton Casings* (see B, Fig. 48, and L, Fig. 50).—This type consists of a skeleton jamb and soffit framing comprising 75 mm by 32 mm stuff to which 12 or 16 mm thick boards or stops are nailed to give the appearance of a double rebated lining. The short rails of the framing are tenoned to the long members, and the latter of the soffit framing are tenoned to the jamb framing (see B). The short rails should coincide with the backings and be nailed to them after the long members have been secured to the rough grounds; the stops are then nailed to the framing. An alternative detail is shown at M, Fig. 50, to introduce a dressed or wrought ground which requires only a small architrave. Skeleton linings for thick walls are cheap and effective, although there is a danger of the

wide stops splitting if they shrink excessively, as movement is restricted when they are securely fixed at their edges.

(3) *Framed Casings* (C, Fig. 48, and N, Fig. 50).— This is the best form of lining for openings in thick walls. It consists of panelled jamb and soffit frames, and the construction conforms to the principles of panelled door construction. The treatment of the panels should be in keeping with the design of the door. This casing is fixed to the grounds and backings, as described for a skeleton lining.

Casings secured to grounds are less liable to damage during the subsequent building operations than those fixed to plugs or pallets, as they are not fixed to the grounds until after the plastering has been completed.

Although internal doors are generally fixed to casings, there are certain exceptions.

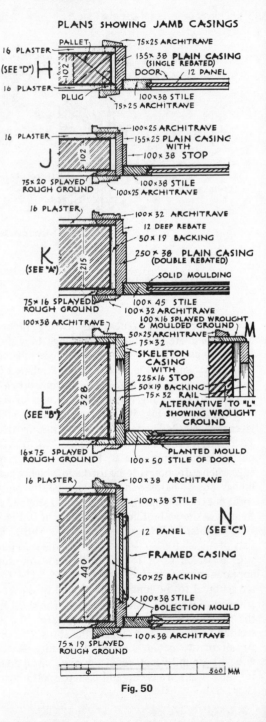

PLANS SHOWING JAMB CASINGS

Fig. 50

Thus, heavy internal doors (such as the framed ledged braced and battened type), as used for warehouses, etc., are sometimes hung with straps and gudgeon hooks fixed in jamb stones (see p. 59), and the casings are then dispensed with. Another exception is shown at F, Fig. 29, where a frame and not a casing is used. Internal coal-house, etc. doors are often fixed to frames instead of casings.

The fixing of casings is described on pp. 92–94.

Two Panelled Door (see B, Fig. 38, Fig. 51 and Fig. 59).—The construction of the framing is similar to that described for the single panelled door with the exception that provision has to be made for the *middle* or *lock rail* (so called as the lock is usually secured to it). The height of this rail varies, and whilst it was the invariable practice to make it at a convenient height for the door handle (which is approximately 840 mm to the centre of the rail), this height is now often departed from. Thus, the position of the middle rail in each of the doors at B, Fig. 38 and Fig. 59 is such as to give two panels of equal height, whilst the centre of the lock rail of the "high-waisted" door in Fig. 51 is 1400 mm from the floor. It will be observed that, whilst the appearance of the latter door is satisfactory, the position of the lock is not convenient for small children. If this door is to be fitted with a rim lock, the middle rail will be formed with a single tenon at each end when the rail is only 100 mm deep, as shown at A, Fig. 51, and with a pair of single tenons (p. 57) at each end when the rail is 175 mm or wider. If, however, a mortice lock (p. 81) is to be used, the door is often 50 mm thick, and the ends of the lock rail will be prepared as follows: If it is a narrow rail, the end to be fitted into the hanging stile will be prepared with a single tenon, and the opposite or striking end will have two tenons (to form what is called a *twin tenon*) which are equal in width to that of the rail, less the depth of the panel grooves, and with a space between them equal to the thickness of the lock; for a wider rail, the end secured to the hanging stile will have a pair of single tenons (as shown at A, Fig. 55) whilst the striking end may have four tenons, usually called a *pair of twin tenons* (see Fig. 52), in order that the preparation for the lock will not weaken the joint.[1] A mortice lock, illustrated in Fig. 57, is shown in position in the elevation and section, Fig. 52. Note that the combined thickness of the twin tenons equals one-third that of the rail (see p. 42).

The detail at the head is given at H, Fig. 53. The clearance between the lintel and casing varies, depending upon the height of the door opening and that of the door. Note the clearance between the top rail and casing (see p.49).

The detail at the bottom of the door is shown at J, Fig. 53. It is necessary to keep the bottom of the door at least 12 mm clear of the floor to enable it to pass a carpet with underfelt. It is advisable to screw

[1] See reference on p. 85 to thin mortice locks for which twin tenons are not required.

TWO PANELLED DOOR

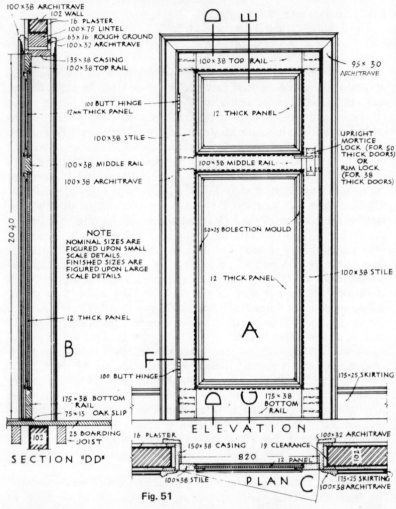

100×38 ARCHITRAVE
102 WALL
16 PLASTER
100×75 LINTEL
65×16 ROUGH GROUND
100×32 ARCHITRAVE

135×38 CASING
100×38 TOP RAIL

100 BUTT HINGE
12mm THICK PANEL

100×38 STILE

100×38 MIDDLE RAIL

100×38 ARCHITRAVE

2040

NOTE.
NOMINAL SIZES ARE
FIGURED UPON SMALL
SCALE DETAILS.
FINISHED SIZES ARE
FIGURED UPON LARGE
SCALE DETAILS.

12 THICK PANEL

B

100 BUTT HINGE

175×38 BOTTOM
RAIL
75×13 OAK SLIP

25 BOARDING
JOIST

102

SECTION "DD"

100×38 TOP RAIL

95×30
ARCHITRAVE

12 THICK PANEL

UPRIGHT
MORTICE
LOCK (FOR 50
THICK DOORS)
OR
RJM LOCK
(FOR 38
THICK DOORS)

100×38 MIDDLE RAIL

50×25 BOLECTION MOULD

12 THICK PANEL

100×38 STILE

A

F

175×38
BOTTOM
RAIL

175×25 SKIRTING

ELEVATION

16 PLASTER
150×38 CASING
820
100×38 STILE

19 CLEARANCE
12 PANEL

PLAN

100×32 ARCHITRAVE

C

175×25 SKIRTING
100×38 ARCHITRAVE

Fig. 51

to the floor a 9 or 12 mm thick hardwood *slip* in order to minimize draughts; that shown at J has rounded edges, whilst a slip shown at N, Fig. 65 has splayed edges. Alternatively, a slip is not required if the door is hung with a pair of 100 mm polished brass *skew butt hinges* (sometimes called *lifting* or *rising butt hinges*) instead of the ordinary butt hinges; a skew butt hinge is illustrated at Z, Fig. 36. These lifting hinges cause the door to rise 12 mm (and thus clear a mat or carpet) on being opened on account of the helical knuckle joint. The top edge of the door and the rebate on the soffit of the casing must be splayed to permit of this vertical movement. These hinges are very conspicuous and are objected to for this reason, although their appearance is somewhat improved if the knuckles are provided with moulded ends.

Fig. 54 is a detail at the hanging stile of the door, the butt hinge being shown.

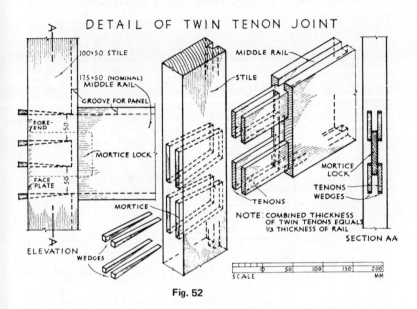

DETAIL OF TWIN TENON JOINT

100×50 STILE
175×50 (NOMINAL) MIDDLE RAIL
GROOVE FOR PANEL
FORE-END
MORTICE LOCK
FACE PLATE
MORTICE
ELEVATION
WEDGES

MIDDLE RAIL
STILE
MORTICE LOCK
TENONS
WEDGES
TENONS
NOTE: COMBINED THICKNESS OF TWIN TENONS EQUALS ⅓ THICKNESS OF RAIL

SECTION AA

SCALE

Fig. 52

A *door stop* is often used to prevent a door handle or projecting key from damaging the plaster or a piece of furniture situated near a door. This stop may be entirely of rubber or a rubber pad in a bronze fitting (see R, Fig. 46), and it is screwed to the floor in such a position as to restrict the swing of the door.

FOUR PANELLED DOOR (see D, Fig. 38, and Fig. 55).—This introduces two central members of the framing called *muntins.* Note that the stiles are continuous for the full height of the door, the rails are tenoned into the stiles, and the muntins are stub-tenoned into the rails for about 50 mm (see A, Fig. 55, and F, Fig. 56). Two details of the door are shown in Fig. 56. That at D shows a cross-section through the head; the ground on the left, to which the double rebated casing and the architrave are fixed is splayed; that on the right is not splayed. The detail at F includes a stub-tenon of the muntin, grooves for panels, mitred bolection mouldings, etc. The general construction follows very closely that already described. One special advantage of this door is the narrow panels which are employed. These can be obtained in one width, and therefore jointing (described on p. 67) is eliminated.

Finger plates were often fixed to both sides of the stile of a panelled door just above (and sometimes below) the lock, but these are not now in much demand unless there is a likelihood of damage being caused to the paint or varnish by finger marks. These can be obtained in various sizes in bronze, oxidized silver, plastic, etc. (see J, Fig. 46).

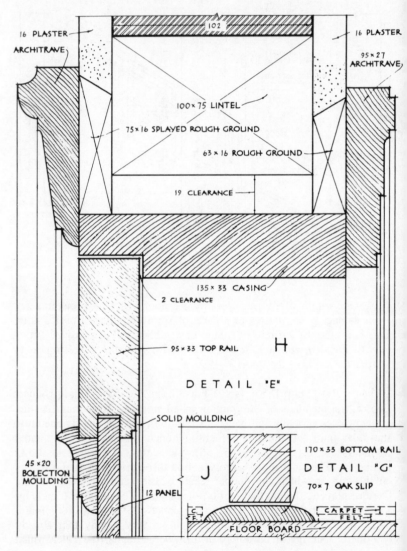

Fig. 53

Mortice Locks.—Whilst a rim lock is shown at A and B, Fig. 55, the less conspicuous mortice lock with knob or lever handle furniture may be preferred. A classification of locks and latches is given on pp. 52—54. As there stated, a mortice lock resembles a rim lock in that it has two bolts, but unlike a rim lock (which is secured to the face of a door), a mortice lock is fitted into the door thickness (see Fig. 52).

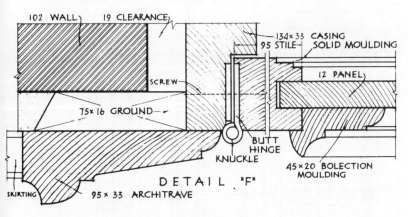

Fig. 54

A mortice lock and striking plate (which is let in flush with the rebate of the casing or frame and screwed) are shown at H, Fig. 57.

The internal construction of a rim lock is similar to that of a mortice lock.

The interior of a mortice lock of good quality is shown at J, Fig. 57, and the following description is that of (1) the lock bolt mechanism and (2) the latch bolt mechanism.

(1) The lock bolt is of brass (or phosphor-bronze or gunmetal) and has a pin or *bolt stump* attached to it to form a pivot for the three thin brass *levers* (hence this would be called a "three lever lock") which are slipped over it. Each lever has two recesses, K and L, with a narrow connecting slot through which a small *lever stump* (connected to the bolt) passes when the bolt is operated. Attached to each lever is a fine metal *spring*. When the door is unlocked, the lever stump occupies the upper portion of recess K. To lock the door, the key is inserted in the keyhole formed in the phosphor-bronze *bush* which has three thin raised rings called *wards,* the key (see sketch) being shaped to fit these wards. When the key is turned, it causes the bolt to move outwards and the pivoted levers to swing upwards until the slot between the recesses is opposite to the lever stump. After the key (indicated by broken lines) has been rotated until it is free of the lower edge of the bolt, the lever springs shoot the bolt through the hole in the striking plate (or into the staple if a rim lock), and the lever stump now occupies the upper portion of the recess L when the lever has rotated downwards. To unlock the door the

operations are reversed, the key forces the levers upwards and the bolt into the lock in the direction of the arrow "1," whilst the lever stump passes from recess L to the upper portion of recess K after the levers have dropped.

FOUR PANELLED DOOR

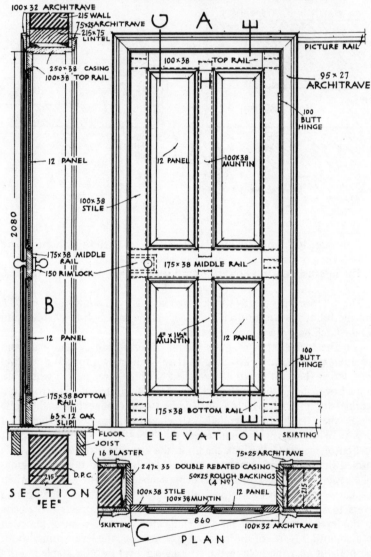

Fig. 66

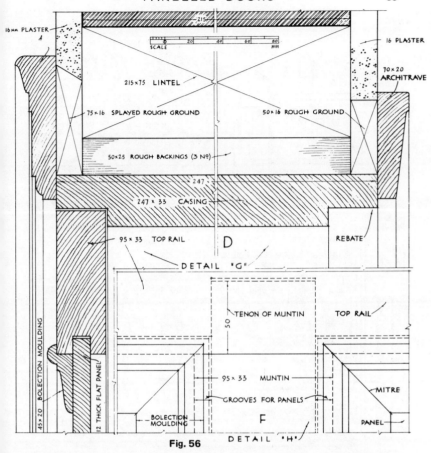

Fig. 56

(2) The latch bolt is operated either by the handle or by the action of the bevelled end of the bolt upon the *lug* of the striking plate (see H, Fig. 57) or the staple (if a rim lock) when the door is being closed. The handles usually consist of two knobs, one of which is permanently fixed to one end of a steel *slotted spindle,* and the other is loose. The spindle is passed through a *rose plate* (which is screwed to the face of the door) and through the bush and *follower* of the lock (see X′, Fig. 57). There are various devices for securing the opposite or "loose" knob, an effective one being shown at J′ and X′, and consists of a small metal *key* which is pivoted on a countersunk screw let into the end of the loose knob; the second rose plate is passed over the projecting end of the spindle, followed by the loose knob which is pressed against the rose plate until the latter is brought tightly against the face of the door, when the key is then dropped into one of the slots in the spindle; each rose is now screwed to the door to make the knobs secure. Note at J that one of the *feather springs* acts upon one end of the latch bolt, and this causes the opposite end to protrude. The follower acts upon the *crank roller;* the latter is

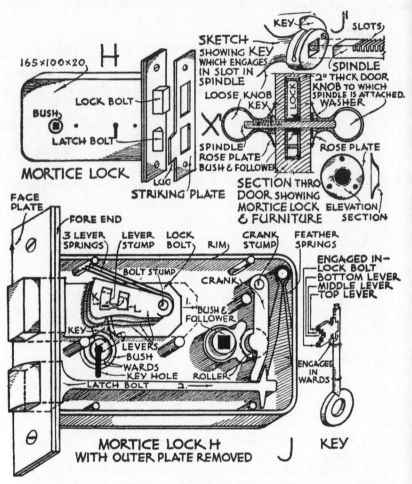

Fig. 57

fitted to the *crank* which is pivoted at the *crank stump* at one end, and the other end bears upon a projection on the end of the latch bolt. To open the door when the lock bolt is disengaged, the handle is turned to cause the follower to bear upon the crank roller, which is turn causes the crank to rotate and operate upon the latch bolt and move it horizontally in the direction of arrow "2" until it is clear of the striking plate (or staple). When the knob is released, the feather spring forces the crank and bolt to assume their original positions.

As shown at J, Fig. 57, the steel case is fixed to a steel *fore-end* to which is secured a brass *face plate* by two set screws. As indicated by broken lines in the elevation in Fig. 52, the face plate is flush with the edge of the door when the lock is fixed. The method of fixing a mortice lock is described on p. 95.

Mortice locks are now available which are only 11 mm thick, and they obviate the necessity for adopting twin tenons (p. 85) unless, for some special reason, a large lock is required. Another type of mortice lock is triangular or wedge-shaped and requires for its accommodation the removal of only a small portion of the tenon.

Architraves are shown in the details given in Figs. 50, 53, 54, 56, 154–158. A description of architraves is given on pp. 226–231.

MANUFACTURE OF PANELLED DOORS.—Doors are usually (*a*) manufactured by machinery or (*b*) very occasionally prepared principally by hand.

(a) *Machine-made Doors.*—As implied on p. 62, most doors are made by machinery. Mass-production methods have been responsible for a large reduction in the cost of such doors, and this is the chief reason for the large demand for them. Alterations are constantly being made to the machines with a view to reducing still further the machine operations and a corresponding reduction in cost.

The following brief description refers to the manufacture of typical panelled doors. A *cutting list* (see p. 91), in duplicate, is prepared by the "setter-out" (the joiner who does the setting out—see p. 86). If, for example, two doors (as numbered on the setting out rod at A, Fig. 58) are to be made of the type illustrated in Fig. 55, the sizes and the amount of timber, etc. will be as stated in the specimen cutting list (or *material sheet*) on p. 91. A copy of this list is sent to the machine shop.

The timber required for this job is sent into the shop and deposited near the circular sawing machine (see Fig. 1). The operator or *sawyer* who will do the *cutting out* will then examine the timber and cut out the members to the sizes shown on the sheet in columns "L" "W" and "T" (third, fourth and fifth columns—p. 91), taking care to select the pieces so that they will be used to the best advantage. After being sawn to length on the cross-cut saw (see p. 11) and sawn to width and thickness on the ordinary circular saw, the pieces are faced and edged on the hand-feed planing machine (see Fig. 6) in order to ensure that they are not in twist or winding. Next, the pieces are planed to the required width and thickness on a thicknessing machine (p. 18). They are then marked out for further machine operations consisting of morticing on the mortising machine (Fig. 8), tenoning on the tenoning machine (p. 24), and grooving on the vertical spindle moulding machine (Fig. 7). The tenons are cut to form the haunches either on the bandsawing machine (Fig. 4) or a small type circular sawing machine. The panels, after being dealt with on the panel planing and thicknessing machine (p. 19) and cut accurately to the finished sizes (with at least 2 mm clearance all-round) may be finished on the sand-papering machine (p. 25). The material is then ready to be sent, along with the cutting list, to the joiners' shop for assembly (p. 90).

To facilitate operations, especially in repetitive work (such as the morticing of members), improvised aids, called *jigs*, are used on certain machines. A jig is shaped to suit the work in hand, and is designed to give a machine operator a measure of safety in carrying out his work on the machine, and to assist in accurately guiding and controlling machine tool operations. An application of a jig is given on p. 134. In some cases, jigs are used in hand tool operations.

In the manufacture of what is termed a "standard" door the whole of the operations of planing the timber, reducing it to the correct widths and thicknesses for the various members, forming the joints, gluing and finally cramping the members together to form both the frame and the door are done by machinery. Machinery is also employed to trim the door to the size of the frame, form the mortices for the locks (including the keyhole and hole for the spindle) and screwing the hinges to the door and frame. Most of these mass-produced doors are dowel jointed (see p. 70) and, briefly, the operations involved in their manufacture are: The timber is sawn to suitable scantlings and machine-planed; rails are bored, glued and dowelled by a machine in one operation; stiles are bored; glue is squirted into the dowel holes in the stiles; rails with their projecting dowels are fitted into the holes in the stiles after the panels have been slipped into the grooves and, finally, the assembled members are cramped together to complete the door. See also p. 91.

(b) *Hand-made Doors.*—Whilst machinery has eliminated most of the operations which were formerly performed by hand, there is still a demand for doors and similar framework which require a certain amount of hand preparation. This applies particularly to the highest quality framed and panelled doors and those which are not of standard size (p. 41). The operations involved are: (1) Setting out, (2) forming mortices and tenons, (3) assembling, gluing and wedging up, and (4) cleaning off.

(1) *Setting Out.*—This is the reproduction on a board (called a *setting out rod*) of the full size detials of the door, such as may have been prepared by the architect. This rod is usually of plywood and is from 2·5 to 3 mm long, 175 to 280 mm wide and 6 to 19 mm thick. Both edges are planed straight and parallel, and both sides, after being planed and smooth finished with fine glass paper, are either chalked or brushed over with a mixture of whiting and thin glue.

For a framed piece, such as a door, the rod would be set out as shown at A, Fig. 58, which indicates full size vertical and horizontal sections of the four panelled door, casing, etc. illustrated in Fig. 55. Alternatively, the vertical section, called the *height rod*, is set out on one face of the board, and the horizontal section, called the *width rod,* is detailed on the reverse. The reference number of the contract, number of doors required, etc. are indicated on the rod.

The pieces of timber used for the various members should be carefully selected to obviate waste during conversion. *If machinery is not available,* each piece is cut down by means of a rip saw and across the grain by a

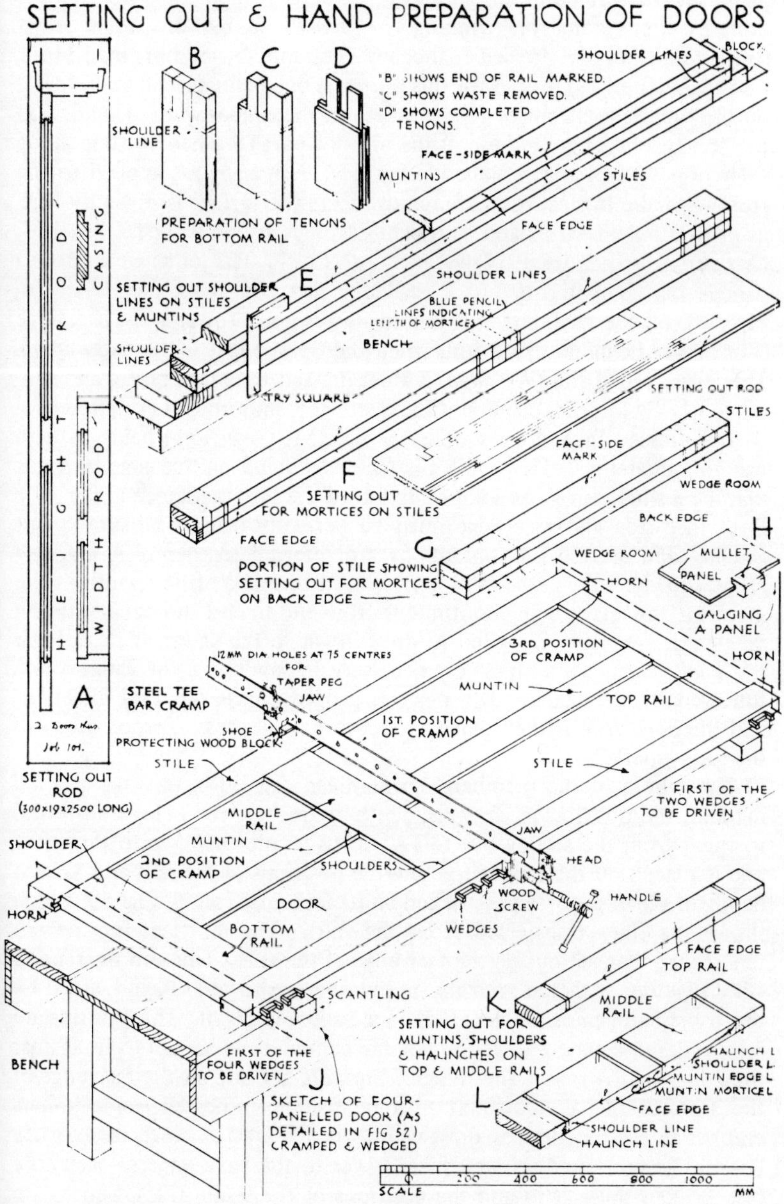

SETTING OUT & HAND PREPARATION OF DOORS

B "B" SHOWS END OF RAIL MARKED.
C "C" SHOWS WASTE REMOVED.
D "D" SHOWS COMPLETED TENONS.

SHOULDER LINES
BLOCK

SHOULDER LINE

FACE-SIDE MARK

MUNTINS   STILES

FACE EDGE

PREPARATION OF TENONS FOR BOTTOM RAIL

SETTING OUT SHOULDER LINES ON STILES & MUNTINS

E

SHOULDER LINES

BLUE PENCIL LINES INDICATING LENGTH OF MORTICES

BENCH

SHOULDER LINES

TRY SQUARE

SETTING OUT ROD

STILES

FACE-SIDE MARK

F
SETTING OUT FOR MORTICES ON STILES

FACE EDGE

WEDGE ROOM

BACK EDGE

H

WEDGE ROOM   MULLET
PANEL
HORN

G
PORTION OF STILE SHOWING SETTING OUT FOR MORTICES ON BACK EDGE

GAUGING A PANEL

HORN

HEIGHT ROD
WIDTH ROD   WOOD   CASING

3RD POSITION OF CRAMP

12MM DIA HOLES AT 75 CENTRES FOR TAPER PEG

STEEL TEE BAR CRAMP

JAW

SHOE PROTECTING WOOD BLOCK

STILE

1ST. POSITION OF CRAMP

MUNTIN   TOP RAIL

STILE

FIRST OF THE TWO WEDGES TO BE DRIVEN

MIDDLE RAIL

MUNTIN

2ND POSITION OF CRAMP

SHOULDER

SHOULDERS

JAW   HEAD

DOOR

WOOD SCREW   HANDLE

HORN

BOTTOM RAIL.

WEDGES

FACE EDGE
TOP RAIL

2 DOORS HIGH
Job 104.

A

SETTING OUT ROD
(300x19x2500 LONG)

BENCH

FIRST OF THE FOUR WEDGES TO BE DRIVEN

SCANTLING

J
SKETCH OF FOUR-PANELLED DOOR (AS DETAILED IN FIG 52) CRAMPED & WEDGED

K

SETTING OUT FOR MUNTINS, SHOULDERS & HAUNCHES ON TOP & MIDDLE RAILS

MIDDLE RAIL

HAUNCH L
SHOULDER L
MUNTIN EDGE L
MUNTIN MORTICE L

FACE EDGE

L

SHOULDER LINE
HAUNCH LINE

SCALE   0   200   400   600   800   1000   MM

Fig. 58

87

panel saw (described in *Carpentry*). The stuff is then *trued up*. This is done by first testing for "winding" or "twist". A pair of *winding strips* (pieces of carefully dressed mahogany, 350 mm by 50 mm by 12 mm, with parallel edges) is used for this purpose, one being placed at each end on top and at right angles to the length of the timber when lying flat on the joiners' bench. If these strips are not parallel when sighting along their upper edge, a jack plane (1, Fig. 154, *Carpentry*) is applied to the stuff until the highest parts are removed and the surface is perfectly true, as proved by the strips and a straight-edge. A trying plane (6, Fig. 154, *Carpentry*) is then used to give a smooth finish. The joiner or setter-out pencils his characteristic mark, called a *face side mark* (see E and G, Fig. 58), on the face, and this should always point towards the best edge (door stiles being an exception, when the "best edge" is the outer edge). This edge, called the *face edge,* is then dressed by a jack plane, and subsequently by a trying plane, until it is straight, smooth and at right angles to the dressed face, a try square (2, Fig. 151, *Carpentry*) being used to test for squareness. He pencils his *face edge mark* on this edge, and this may be a single stroke as a continuation of the face mark (see F, Fig. 58). Both face side and face edge must be perfectly true, as all subsequent gauging and setting out operations are referred to them. A marking gauge (4, Fig. 151, *Carpentry*) is now used to mark off the width of the member, this mark being continuous from end to end and parallel to the face edge. A plane is applied to dress down to the gauge mark to form the *back edge;* sometimes it is necessary to saw down the gauge mark, followed by the plane. The piece is gauged to the required thickness, and the *back face* is then planed to remove any excess of wood down to the gauge mark.

The whole of the members, having been dressed in this manner, are marked, the position of the rails, depth of grooves, etc. being transferred to them from the setting out rod A. Thus, commencing with the stiles, one is placed on the height rod and the positions of the rails and 12 mm depth of panel grooves are pricked on its face edge (see F, Fig. 58, which shows the lines transferred from the rod). The mortices for the rail tenons are then set out on the face edge of the stile. This and the second stile, together with the muntins, are placed as shown at E, and, aided by the try square, the shoulders (see J) are squared down. The muntins are removed and squared all round for the shoulders which are to fit against the edges of the rails. The mortice lines are set out on the face edge of the second stile as shown at F, and as there indicated, some joiners emphasize the mortices by drawing blue pencil lines between the mortice lines. The mortice lines are squared over to the back edge of each stile (see broken lines at F) and the positions of the 9 mm thick wedges are marked on the back edge (see G). Note that the length of the stiles exceeds slightly that shown on the rod.

The setting out of the rails from the width rod (see A) is similar to that described for stiles. The setting out for muntins, shoulders and haunches (or haunchings) on the top rail is shown at K, and the middle rail is shown set out at L, the latter indicating the names applied to the various lines.

(2) *Forming Mortices and Tenons.*—The stiles are now morticed. If a mortising machine (see Fig. 8) is not available, the mortices are made with a mortise chisel (see *Carpentry*) and mallet (4, Fig. 156, *Carpentry*). A mortise gauge (6, Fig. 151, *Carpentry*) is used to scribe or mark the mortices on each edge of the stile, the points of the gauge being set to the width of the chisel which should equal one-third the thickness of the stuff (p. 42). These mortices are always gauged from the face side of each stile. Each mortice is cut half-way through, commencing at the centre of the back edge and removing the core by small cuts, and the mortice is completed from the face edge in a similar manner. A core-driver (a piece of hardwood the size of the mortice) is punched through from the face edge of the back edge to "clean" each mortice, and a paring chisel (1, Fig. 153, *Carpentry*) is used to finish off. The 50 mm deep stub mortices are formed on the rails to receive the tenons at the ends of the muntins.

To form the tenons, the ends of the rails are gauged from the face side as shown at B, Fig. 58. The "mortice lines" are rip sawn down to the "haunch lines", the "waste" is removed, and the "gauge lines" are sawn down to the "shoulder lines" (see C). Both ends of each rail are treated in this manner. The panel groove is then formed, by means of a plough plane (2, Fig. 154, *Carpentry*), on the face edge from end to end of each stile, the top or face edge of the bottom rail, both edges of the middle rail, the bottom or face edge of the top rail, and both edges of each muntin; the plough iron must be of the proper size, be set at the correct depth (12 mm in this case), and the plough must always be worked from the face side of each member. The tenon cheeks (outer portions) are now removed by using the tenon saw (7, Fig. 152, *Carpentry*) to carefully cut down the outside of the shoulder lines (leaving the lines in) to complete the end, as shown at D, Fig. 58. The tenons on the muntins are formed in a similar manner.

After the corners of the tenons have been chiselled off so that they may readily engage in the mortices, the whole of the members is assembled temporarily to see if the joints fit accurately, any necessary adjustments are made, and the framing is put aside pending the preparation of the panels.

The panels are then made. The dimensions are taken from the rod or framing, one face and edge are planed with the trying plane, and the face and edge marks are put on these. A panel gauge (see *Carpentry*) is used to mark the required width, the panel is cut along this line, and the ends are squared and cut off to the exact size. The panel is now *mulleted* or gauged; the mullet—a piece of wood grooved to the required size (see H, Fig. 58)—is slipped along the edges of the panel to indicate any excessively thick places which are eased by planing. The four panels are made in this manner, the sides are smoothed by a smoothing plane (7, Fig. 154, *Carpentry*), glass paper is rubbed across the grain, and the panels are inserted temporarily in the framing by removing one stile at a time.

(3) *Assembling, Gluing and Wedging.*—Two pieces of scantling or *skids* are placed on the bench as shown at J, Fig. 58, these must be of equal thickness and level. A cramp is necessary to ensure that the shoulders of the various members fit tightly. One form of cramp, called a T-cramp, is shown at J and is described in Chapter X, *Carpentry*.

A joiner and an apprentice generally work together when gluing up a door. The door is taken to pieces and both sides of the tenons and the insides of the mortices are glued; it is at once assembled; the cramp is then used. Commencing at the middle rail, the cramp is fixed in the position as shown at J; the shoe is slid along to the required position, the peg is inserted in the appropriate hole, small protecting blocks of wood are placed between the stiles and the shoe and screw cheeks, and the cramp is then screwed up tightly to bring the shoulders right up. The wedges are dipped in glue and tightly driven in at each end. The cramp is moved to the bottom rail (shown by broken lines at J), tightened up and wedged as described above, the bottom wedge at each end being driven first so as to bring the shoulders of the bottom muntin tight up against the rails. The cramp is finally moved to the third position along the top rail, glued, wedges are inserted and driven home, the top wedge at each end being fixed first so as to move the top rail to close the joints between the top muntin and rails. The cramp is removed and the projecting ends of the rails are sawn off.

(4) *Cleaning Off.*—Any superfluous glue is removed by a chisel from the joints, commencing on the face side of the door. The trying plane is applied on the muntins to bring them level with the rails, and the latter are levelled to the face of the stiles, any inequalities at the shoulders being removed. A smoothing plane is then used, and, if necessary, the surfaces are scraped before being glass papered. The other side is treated similarly. The outer edges of the door are not planed, nor are the horns removed, until the door is being hung in position.

If the door is moulded, the hand operations vary with the type of mould. Thus, if the panels are to have solid mouldings (p. 62), the face edges of the stiles, rails and muntins will be moulded to the required shape by means of the appropriate moulding plane (see Chap. X, *Carpentry*) before they are assembled. The moulded edges of the stiles will be continuous, those on the rails will be scribed to them (see Fig. 40) and those on the muntins will be scribed to the rail mouldings. If planted mouldings (p. 64) are required, they are formed by moulding planes to the required section on the rod. Mouldings are planted in the following manner: The ends of each piece are cut to a $45°$ mitre—a mitre block (4, Fig. 158, *Carpentry*) being used for this purpose; the two short lengths for each panel are placed in position on the door and the two longer pieces are "sprung" into place; the mouldings are nailed to the framing and the nail heads are punched. Each panel is treated in this manner.

As mentioned on pp. 62 and 85, the extensive use of woodworking machinery has eliminated most of the labours formerly done by hand, and even if standard machine-made doors as described on p. 85 are not required, many of the operations detailed on pp. 85 and 86 would be performed by machines. Thus, the stiles, rails and muntins would be cut into lengths and widths by the circular saw (Fig. 1); they would be faced and edged on a surface planer (p. 17); the tenons would be formed by a tenoning machine and the mortices by a mortising machine (Fig. 8); if required, they would be solid moulded on the spindle moulder (Fig. 7). Many of these operations can be done by a general joiner (p. 26). The panels would be finished by a panel planer (p. 19). Planted mouldings could be prepared on the spindle moulder. After being assembled and cramped, the door would be given a smooth finish by a sand-papering machine (p. 25).

Whilst some of these large and more expensive machines may not be available in the smaller shops there are comparatively few firms who have not a circular saw and mortising and tenoning machines, and are thereby enabled to reduce some of the relatively costly hand labours.

The operations involved in framing casings will be understood from the foregoing description. The manufacture of windows is described on pp. 134–139 and 154–160.

CUTTING LISTS OF MATERIAL SHEETS.—A cutting list of materials required for each job gives (1) the reference number of the job, (2) the number, lengths and nominal and finished sizes of the various members, (3) the kind of timber to be employed and (4) any special instructions. The various dimensions are taken from the height and width rods. The list is prepared, in duplicate, by the foreman or setter out, one copy being filed and the other used by the workmen engaged in preparing the work (see p. 85).

A typical cutting list or material sheet is given below. It includes the particulars as they would be filled in for the *two* doors (the number indicated on the bottom of the setting out rod at A, Fig. 58), the preparation of which has just been described; the setting out rods (height and width) would be prepared from the door shown in Fig. 55. The letters "L", "W" and "T" stand for length, width and thickness respectively.

NAME AND ADDRESS OF FIRM:

Description of Work: 2 Doors for painting.

Name or Number of Job: 101.   *Date:* 15/12/73.

No. of Pieces.	Description.	L.	W.	T.	Finished Sizes. W.	T.	Timber.	Remarks.
		mm	mm	mm	mm	mm		
4	Stiles	2100	100	38	35	35	Redwood	To be put in
2	Top rails	840	100	38	35	35	Redwood	hand imme-
4	M. & B. rails	840	175	38	172	35	Redwood	diately.
2	Muntins	1120	100	38	97	35	Redwood	
2	Muntins	770	100	38	97	35	Redwood	
4	Panels	1020	280	12	–	9	Yellow pine	
4	Panels	670	280	12	–	9	Yellow pine	

FIXING CASINGS.—The following description applies to casings fixed to (a) pallets, (b) plugs and (c) grounds.

(a) If a casing is to be secured to pallets (see p. 73), such as at the jambs of an opening in a ½-brick thick wall (see H, Fig. 50), the following work is carried out: The pallets, having been built in the bed joints at each jamb as the work proceeds (at about 600 mm vertical intervals, with the top and bottom pallets about 150 mm from the head and floor respectively, and with their outer edges projecting into the opening), are cut.

The distance between the cut edges of the pallets in opposite jambs should equal that between the outside face of the two vertical or jamb members of the casing. This measurement is taken direct from the casing which will be on the job ready for fixing, it having been prepared at the shop (with the jamb linings tongued to the soffit lining—see p. 75). A straight length of timber, called a *rod,* is used on which the casing measurement is marked; the rod is applied to the bottom pair of pallets (in opposite jambs), and the width is transferred to the edges of the pallets which are marked, leaving an approximate equal margin (distance from the side of the opening to the mark) at each pallet. The plumb-rule (1, Fig. 158, *Carpentry*) is now applied at one side of the opening; with its edge against the mark on the bottom pallet and with its cord coinciding with the gauge line (marked on the rule—Chap. X, *Carpentry*), lines are marked down the edges of the rest of the pallets at the jamb coinciding with the edge of the rule; these lines will therefore be vertical. The pallet edges at the opposite jamb are "lined up" in a similar manner. This preliminary work is tested by placing the casing against the edge marks, and, if the setting out is accurate, the backs of the jamb linings should coincide with the pallet edge marks. At the same time, the casing is tested to see if it is square by applying the rod diagonally, when the distance between each pair of opposite corners should be the same. Before removing the casing, the clearance between the soffit lining and the lintel is measured and three backings of thickness equal to the clearance are nailed across the lintel, one being in the middle and one near each end; if the clearance is not uniform, three marks are made on the edge of the lintel at the backing positions, and backings are cut to the required thickness (equal to the clearance at the marks) and fixed in correct position. After the casing has been removed, the try square (2, Fig. 151, *Carpentry*) is applied on top of each pallet at the edge mark and a "square line" is marked on it. The ends of the pallets are sawn off to the lines.

It is assumed that the architraves are to be secured to plugs (and not grounds—see p. 73) as shown at H, Fig. 50. These plugs are driven in at each jamb on both sides of the wall; there are thus four sets of plugs, and these should have been fixed before the pallets are lined out and sawn, as described above. The plugs project 19 mm (or the thickness of the plaster) from the wall, although if the wall is not plumb this projection will vary. The edges of the plugs must be cut square and each set must be plumb. To ensure this, a straight-edge (7, Fig. 151, *Carpentry*) is laid on the bottom pair (one at each side of the opening) of plugs at 19 mm from the face of the wall, and a line is drawn on each along the straight-edge. The two plugs are sawn off to these lines. The plumb-rule is held in line with the cut edge of one of the plugs and, when vertical (see p. 92), lines are drawn along the edges of the rule on the edges of the plugs above. This is repeated on the plugs at the opposite side of the opening. With the straight-edge resting on each opposite pair of plugs (*i.e.,* one at each side of the opening) in turn, and in line with the edge marks, lines are drawn along the plugs, and the ends are sawn off. The plugs on the opposite face of the wall are dealt with in a similar manner. This work should be done with care. As a check for accuracy, the distance between the cut edges of each pair of plugs at each jamb should equal the width of the casing (*i.e.,* 150 mm—nominal—for the casing shown at H, Fig. 50). The casing is placed in the opening, with the rebated edges of the jambs in alignment with the cut edges of the plugs. If the plugs have been properly trimmed, those on the other side of the wall should be in line with the unrebated edges of the casing, as tested with a straight-edge. Adjustments are made when necessary. Thus, if the width of the casing is slightly in excess of the width between the cut edges of the plugs, a straight-edge is held against the plugs at one side and a mark is made in line at the top and bottom of the back of the jamb lining; this is repeated on the other side; the casing is removed, lines are drawn joining the marks on each jamb, and the top of the soffit lining is lined between the jamb lines; the unrebated edges of the casing are now planed down to these lines. If the width between the cut edges of the plugs exceeds that of the casing, the ends of the plugs projecting beyond the unrebated edges of the casing are removed after applying the straight-edge across the opening against the casing and marking each pair of plugs in turn. A length of ground is now nailed to each face of the lintel (see H, Fig. 53). The casing is again placed accurately in position and nailed to the pallets, soffit backings and soffit grounds.

(*b*) If a casing is to be fixed to jamb plugs in lieu of pallets (see p. 73), the plugs are trimmed in correct alignment, as described for pallets.

(*c*) If grounds (see p. 73) have to be provided as a fixing for a casing (and architraves), the plugs to which the grounds are to be fixed are trimmed in a similar manner to those required for fixing architraves and described above, the only difference being that these plugs have only a very slight projection. A *set* of grounds consists of two vertical or jamb grounds and a soffit ground; as stated on p. 73, the latter or head ground is tenoned to the jamb grounds. It is usual for a set to be framed together at the shop, the necessary measurements having been taken on the job; the dovetailed notches to receive the ends of the backings (p. 73) are also cut. As two sets are required per opening, it is also usual to send them on to the job in pairs, lightly nailed together (so that they can be readily separated on the job) with the head of one next the feet of the other. One set of grounds is fixed to the plugs, care being taken to ensure that the jambs are plumb (by applying the plumb-rule) and the set is square (when tested diagonally with the rod—see p. 93). The second set is then fixed, plumb and square, and also square with the first set as tested with the try square. The grounds are twice nailed at each plug, care being taken not to overdrive the plugs by pricking holes in the grounds to receive the nails and not unduly hammering the grounds when driving the nails home. The casing is now fixed to the grounds after the prepared backings have been secured to the edges of the grounds (see Fig. 49). If the grounds have been correctly framed together to the required size and fixed plumb and square, little if any adjustment to the casing (such as planing the edges) will be necessary to ensure a good fit.

FIXING ARCHITRAVES.—These are described on pp. 226–229 and are fixed after the plastering has been completed. The two vertical members are fixed first. One is placed vertically against the casing with its inner edge parallel to and 3 to 6 mm from that of the casing; the height up this edge is marked, it being equal to the distance from the floor to a point which will coincide with the head piece of the architrave. As the floor may not be quite level, the second "leg" is placed against the opposite jamb of the casing and marked in a similar manner. The top ends of these pieces are then tenon-sawn "full to length" in a mitre block (4, Fig. 158, *Carpentry*) and the mitre cuts made. A block plane or smoothing plane (10 and 7 respectively, Fig. 154, *Carpentry*) is applied to the cut edges to shoot a true finish. Each vertical length of architrave is now nailed along both edges to the casing and plugs (or ground), care being taken to ensure that the *margin* (distance between the edge of the casing and architrave) is uniform and equal. The head architrave is fixed; the piece is placed on the points (top of the mitres) of the vertical members, marked, and each end is cut to a 45° mitre in the mitre block, sufficient allowance being made for planing the edges; it is fitted against the mitred ends of the vertical members, any adjustment being made by planing; it is now fixed after ensuring that the margin all round the casing is equal. The architrave on the other side of the wall is fixed in a similar manner.

For best work, and especially if the architraves are to be provided with plinth blocks (p. 228), it is usual to frame up each set (consisting of the two vertical pieces, fixed to the blocks, and the head) at the shop after the necessary measurements have been taken off the fixed casing. So that the margin at the soffit lining is uniform with those at the jambs, it is necessary to scribe (p. 230) the blocks to the floor. This is done in the following manner: The set is placed in position against the casing and plugs (or grounds), and a wedge is placed under each block until the lower edge of the head architrave is parallel to the edge of the soffit casing; the compasses (5, Fig. 151, *Carpentry*) are adjusted to the distance between these two edges, less the amount of the margin; the compasses are then drawn along with one point on the floor and the other across the block faces. The blocks are sawn to the scribed lines, the edges are planed and the complete architrave is fixed to the casing, etc.

HANGING OF DOOR.—The hanging of a ledged and battened door and a framed, ledged, braced and battened door is described on pp. 49 and 59. The method of hanging a panelled door is similar. When fitting and trimming the door, care should be taken to remove, by sawing (when necessary) and planing, an equal amount from each stile and so avoid an unequal margin. The jamb casings should be tested with a straight-edge, any irregularities being marked on the door when temporarily wedged (p. 60) and allowed for when planing the stiles.

FIXING MORTICE LOCK.—In a large shop a special mortising machine (p. 22) forms mortices in doors to receive mortice locks (see Fig. 57); the holes for the key and handle spindle are also formed by the boring machine (p. 23).

If a mortice for the lock is to be prepared by hand, the following is the usual procedure: Before the door has been hung, the case of the lock is carefully marked round in the centre of the striking stile (*i.e.,* that which receives the end of the middle rail which has been prepared with twin tenons—or pair of twin tenons, see p. 77) and central with the rail. The brace (45, Fig. 155, *Carpentry*), fitted with a bit of size equal to the thickness of the casing, is then used to bore several holes within the marked rectangle, to the required depth and close to each other. Boring is facilitated if a wood dowel (of diameter equal to that of the holes and 25 to 50 mm longer than their depth) is lightly driven into the last formed hole before the next is bored; the dowel prevents the bit from entering the adjacent hole. The hole is then neatly pared out to the lines, a *swan's neck chisel*[1] being sometimes used to clean out the bottom of the mortice.

The case of the lock is then inserted in the mortice, and the outline of the fore-end (Fig. 57) is accurately marked on the edge of the stile, the top being squared (with the try square). A sinking is formed with the chisel (and mallet—4, Fig. 156, *Carpentry*) to a depth equal to the combined thickness of the fore-end and face plate (Fig. 57). The lock is withdrawn, removal being facilitated by pulling on a couple of screws which have been placed through holes in the fore-end, from the back, before inserting the lock. The lock is placed on the outside of the door, immediately over the mortice and with the face plate (secured to the fore-end by means of two set screws—see p. 84) flush with the edge of the door. The holes for the spindle (p. 83) and key are marked on the door with the point of the marking knife (8, Fig. 151, *Carpentry*), and the centres of these holes are squared (by means of the try square) round to the opposite side of the door. The holes are partly bored with the brace and suitable sized bits, and then completed by boring from the other side. The keyhole is cut to shape by means of the pad saw (5, Fig. 152, *Carpentry*).

With the face plate removed, the lock is placed in the mortice and the fore-end is screwed to the stile. The face plate is re-fixed, and, if the

[1] This chisel has a curved end which acts as a fulcrum when pressing and levering the handle backwards.

sinking has been properly formed, the plate should be flush with the edge of the door. The spindle (with knob) is placed in its hole, and the rose plates and "loose knob" are fixed (as described on p. 83), together with the escutcheon (R', Fig. 27).

The mortices for the lock and latch bolts are now formed in the casing. The position of these is readily found if, after smearing the ends of the bolts with black oil wiped off the oilstone, the bolts are "shot" out by applying the handle and key. The bolt mortices are cut at the oiled patches on the rebate, and, after a sinking has been accurately formed, the striking plate (Fig. 57) is sunk and screwed flush with the face of the rebate.

CHAPTER FIVE

TRANSOMED DOORS

Doors with fanlights of the fixed and open type.

IN order to provide lighting to an outer lobby, hall, etc., it is sometimes necessary to provide one or more glass panels in an external door, and/or glaze a portion of the frame above the door. This glazed portion above the door is called a *fanlight* or *transome light*. Fanlights are also provided above internal doors to light corridors, etc.; such are known as *borrowed lights*.

Fanlights are of the (*a*) fixed and (*b*) open type. The latter serves as a means of ventilation.

(*a*) DOOR WITH FIXED FANLIGHT.—An external door, suitable for a house with stone outer walls, is shown in Fig. 59. The door has two equal panels and a fixed fanlight is provided. The horizontal member of the frame which separates the door and fanlight is called a *transome*. The fixed fanlight is glazed with seven pieces of glass.[1] The glass is secured between small hardwood outer beads, inner beads and two curved glazing bars.

Details of this door are given in Fig. 60. The panels are 20 mm thick, bolection moulded on the external side and chamfered stuck moulded on the other; alternative finishes to panels may be selected from details supplied in Chapters Four and Six. In order to prevent the access of water at the floor level, a hardwood threshold (see N) is securely screwed to the floor; any water blown in is caught by the groove and escapes through two bore-holes (one near each end), indicated by broken lines. The weather board throws water, streaming down the door, clear of the threshold. Alternative details are shown at Q and R, Fig. 42, M, Fig. 62, and R, Fig. 63.

The transome is weathered, grooved, throated and rebated (see M, Fig. 60). Alternative details of transomes are given at L and O, Fig. 62, and Q, Fig. 63. The outer beads of the fanlight are tongued and grooved to the head, transome and posts of the frame (see K and M, Fig. 60). The small inner beads are screwed to the frame after the glass has been fixed. As shown at L, Fig. 60, the two narrow curved *glazing bars* are rebated to receive the glass, and the two curved inner *glazing beads* are screwed to the bars after the glazing has been completed. The glass is bedded in putty before the inner beads are fixed in order to exclude water (see p. 126).

Briefly, the curved glazing bars and beads are bent in the following

---

[1] Consideration of this type of door may be deferred until Chapter Nine, dealing with windows, has been studied.

DOOR WITH FANLIGHT

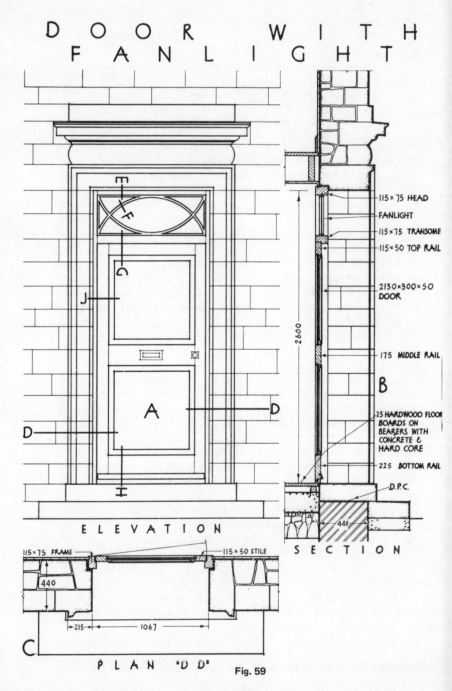

ELEVATION

- 115 × 75 HEAD
- FANLIGHT
- 115 × 75 TRANSOME
- 115 × 50 TOP RAIL
- 2130 × 300 × 50 DOOR
- 175 MIDDLE RAIL
- 25 HARDWOOD FLOOR BOARDS ON BEARERS WITH CONCRETE & HARD CORE
- 225 BOTTOM RAIL
- D.P.C.
- 2600
- 440

SECTION

- 115 × 75 FRAME
- 115 × 50 STILE
- 440
- 215
- 1067

PLAN "D D"

Fig. 59

manner: The pieces to be bent are first placed in a steam chest or oven where the wood is softened and rendered pliable by the action of steam. This softening process takes approximately three-quarters of an hour per 25 mm thickness of wood. Immediately each piece is removed from the chest, it is curved over a stout wood templet, shaped as required, and a second shaped templet or *caul* is placed over it. All three are tightly clamped together and left until the piece has dried out. As the pieces are apt to spring back slightly after being bent, it is advisable to allow for this and use lengths of timber a little thicker than the finished thickness. The pieces, after being bent, are then worked to the required section.

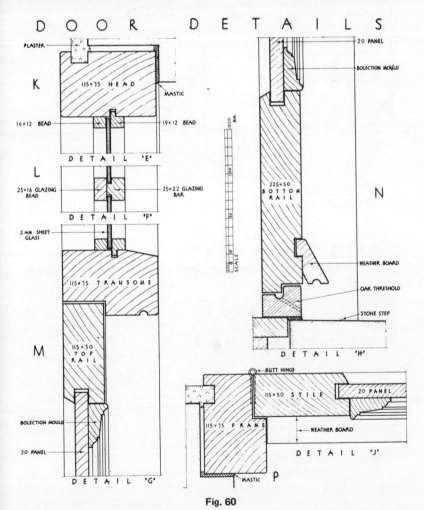

Fig. 60

As shown at B and C, Fig. 59, and K, Fig. 60, the frame projects slightly beyond the face of the plaster. A wood architrave is not therefore required. The frame must, however, be grooved to receive the plaster (see K), otherwise shrinkage gaps may occur, *i.e.* a space will be formed if the frame shrinks and leaves the plaster (see also p. 103). Two further examples are given at K, Fig. 62, and P, Fig. 63.

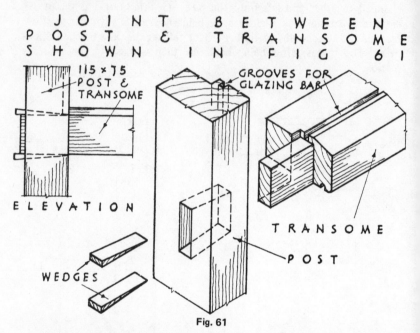

J O I N T　　B E T W E E N
P O S T　　&　　T R A N S O M E
S H O W N　　I N　　F I G　　6 1

115 × 75
POST &
TRANSOME

GROOVES FOR
GLAZING BAR

ELEVATION

TRANSOME

POST

WEDGES

Fig. 61

The joints between the posts and head of the frame are as described on pp. 42–43. The joint between a post and the transome is illustrated in Fig. 61. As shown, the top of the single tenon is cut level with the bottom of the glazing bar groove. The ends of the wedges and tenon are trimmed off before the frame is fixed. The thickness of the tenon is 25 mm (being the distance between the rebate and the top line of the weathering); this is adequate for this intermediate member, although it is less than one-third the thickness of the member (see p. 42). If the frame exceeds 115 mm in width it is advisable to provide double tenons (see p. 43) to ensure the maintenance of a tight fit at the transome shoulders. If the outer edge of the frame and the underside of the transome are moulded (and not pencil-rounded—as shown—by removing the arrises with sand-paper), the transome moulding would be scribed to the continuous moulding on each post (see p. 62).

Another fixed fanlight is shown in the small scaled section at A, Fig. 62, and detailed at K and L. The glass is received in a sash (see Chapter Nine), placed in rebates formed on the head and posts and fixed with top, side and bottom inner beads. The front edge of the transome has a narrow raised panel flush with the posts of the frame. The frame, like that shown in Figs. 59 and 60, projects beyond the face of the plaster and, as shown at K, is sunk-chamfered. The door framing is stuck moulded both sides (see M). The underside of the bottom rail is rebated over a small hardwood threshold; this is a less effective, but cheaper, detail than that shown at N, Fig. 60. Small triangular blocks are fixed at intervals between the door and the underside of the weather board.

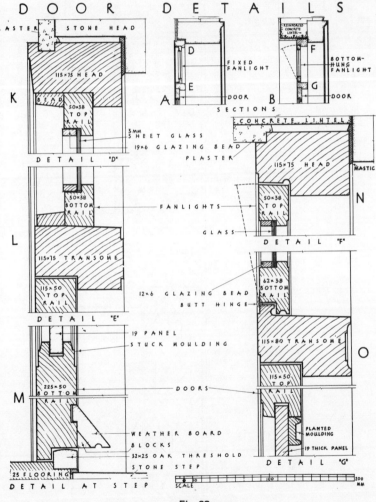

Fig. 62

(b) DOOR WITH FANLIGHT MADE TO OPEN.—It is seldom that a fanlight is required to open, but if it is, the sash may be either (i) bottom-hung, or (ii) top-hung or (iii) pivoted.

TRANSOMED DOORS

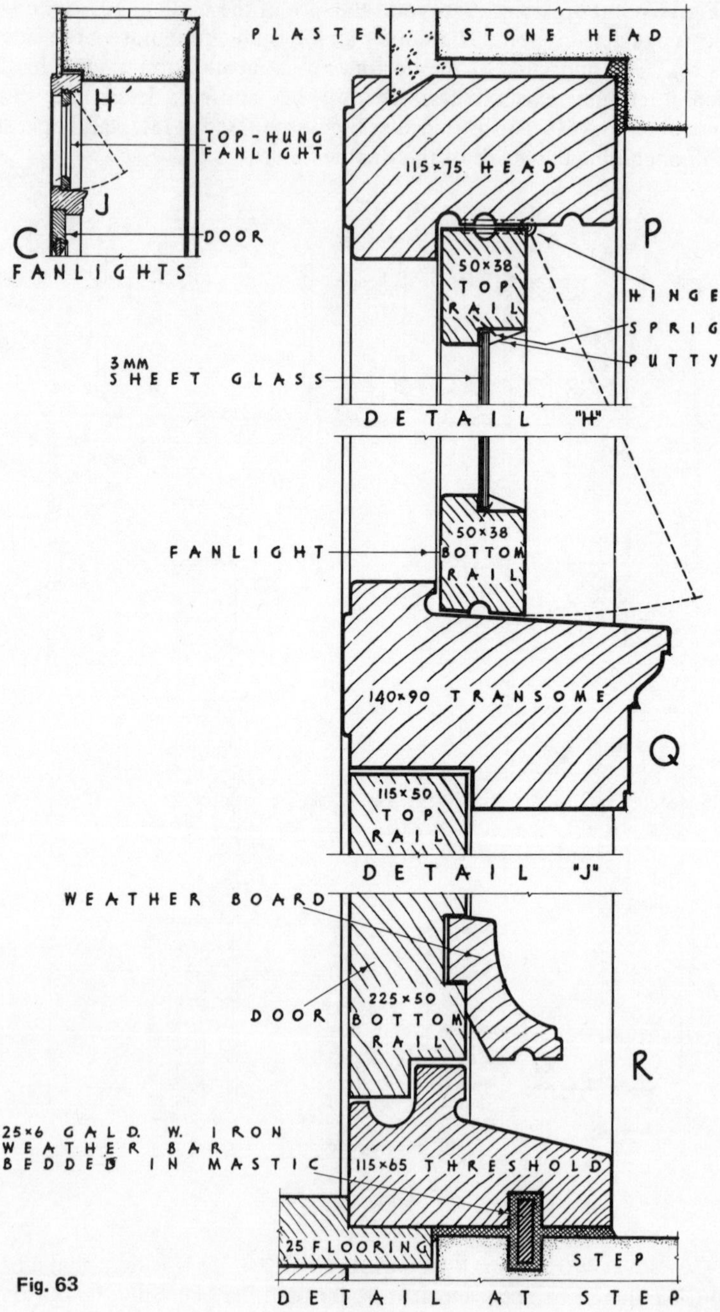

H´

TOP-HUNG
FANLIGHT

J

DOOR

C

FANLIGHTS

PLASTER   STONE HEAD

115×75 HEAD

P

50×38
TOP
RAIL

HINGE

SPRIG

PUTTY

3MM
SHEET GLASS

DETAIL "H"

FANLIGHT

50×38
BOTTOM
RAIL

140×90 TRANSOME

Q

115×50
TOP
RAIL

DETAIL "J"

WEATHER BOARD

225×50
BOTTOM
RAIL

DOOR

R

25×6 GALD. W. IRON
WEATHER BAR
BEDDED IN MASTIC

115×65 THRESHOLD

25 FLOORING

STEP

Fig. 63

DETAIL AT STEP

(i) A bottom-hung fanlight is shown in the small section at B, Fig. 62, and detailed at N and O. The bottom rail of the sash is fixed to the transome by a pair of hinges (see O). The head of the frame and the top rail of the sash must be slightly splayed, as shown, to permit of the necessary clearance required when the sash is opened. One of several types of gear available for opening and closing the fanlight consists of a small ratchet wheel and bar arrangement, the small wheel fitting and the bar being fixed at one side (preferably the hanging side of the door) at the top of the sash and to the frame respectively, and operated by a cord. The details show the usual rebates and capillary grooves (described on p. 129) necessary to exclude water and draughts between the sash and frame. The transome has a sunk panel formed on its front edge as an alternative to that at L. The head and posts are rebated to receive the plaster; alternatively, a cover mould, such as that shown at N, Fig. 84 or B, Fig. 85, may be fixed.

(ii) A key section of a top-hung transome light is shown at C and detailed at P and Q, Fig. 63. The sash is fixed at the head of the frame by a pair of hinges and opens outwards. A casement peg stay (see Fig. 87) will serve to maintain the sash in an open position; alternatively, a patent opener similar to that described above may be preferred. The transome is moulded, as shown at Q, as a further alternative to those at L and Q, Fig. 62; its treatment on the inside face conforms with that on the head and posts of the frame.

The check for the plaster, shown at P, is an alternative to the rectangular groove shown at K, Fig. 60.

The hardwood threshold shown at R, Fig. 63, extends the full width of the frame. It is an alternative to those already described, including the detail at Q, Fig. 42, and somewhat resembles a window sill detail (see M, Fig. 83). It is most effective but costly. A simple alternative detail of a wrought iron weather bar is shown at R, Fig. 42, and J, Fig. 64.

(iii) The construction of a pivoted fanlight is similar to the pivoted sash window shown in Figs. 115, 116 and 117 and described on pp. 174–175.

The glass in fanlights may be secured by either putty, as shown in Fig. 63, or beads (bedded in putty and secured with small brass screws with cups, as shown in Fig. 62)—see pp. 126 and 127.

CHAPTER SIX

GLAZED DOORS

Doors, wholly or partially glazed, with alternative details.

GLAZED or *sash doors*[1] are adopted to light lobbies, halls, corridors, staircase landings, etc., occasionally to supplement the lighting provided by windows, or to make the interior of one room visible from another.

The joints between the stiles and rails of the door framing are either morticed and tenoned or dowelled (see pp. 69 and 70). The joints between the glazing bars are usually tenoned and scribed (see p. 126).

Several designs of glazed doors appear in this chapter. *The details show architraves, panel moulds, etc. of various shapes and sizes. The reason for this is to provide for reference a wide range of sections, and it must not be assumed, therefore, that any particular moulding is the most appropriate for the detail concerned. Further, whilst for the above reason two different architraves are shown in each of the details K, Fig. 65, T, Fig. 67, and P, Fig. 69, it is customary in practice to adopt a common section throughout a building or for similar rooms on the same floor.*

Glass shown fixed with glazing beads may, alternatively, be secured with sprigs and putty, and vice versa.

Fig. 64 shows at A an elevation of an external five-panelled door, all of the panels being of glass. The detail at J shows the glass bedded in putty and beaded. The weather board is alternative to those in Figs. 60, 62 and 63, and the wrought iron bar,

[1] A study of this type of door may, with advantage, be deferred until Chapter Nine, dealing with windows, has been read.

Fig. 64

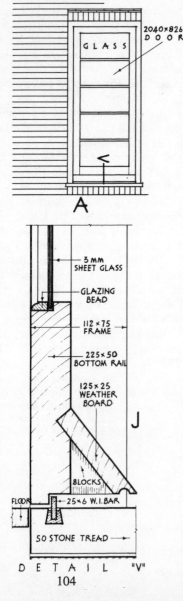

caulked with lead and covered with cement (see p. 69), is alternative to a hardwood threshold. It is again noted that persons are more apt to trip over a bar which has only a small projection than over the more conspicuous thick wood threshold (p. 68).

The elevation of a fifteen glass-panelled door is shown at B and detailed at K, Fig. 65. The small half-round architrave is shown with a

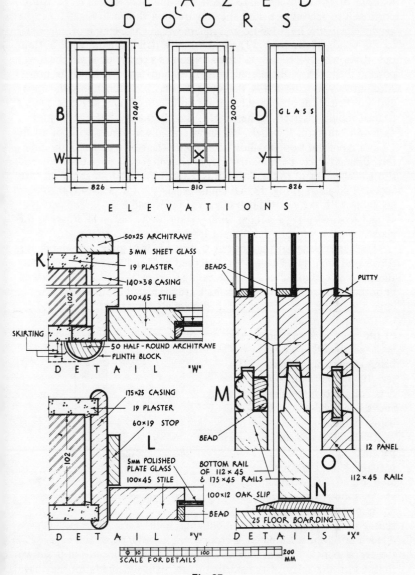

Fig. 65

106

plinth block (see p. 228) to provide a suitable finish for the skirting. Alternatively, if a thicker skirting is used, as shown by the broken line at K, the blocks can be dispensed with and the skirting finished with a curved end against the casing; the feet of the architrave would then be mitred to the upper splayed edge of the skirting. The ovolo moulded glazing bead conforms with the stuck moulding on the opposite side of the door.

Each of the eighteen glazed panels of the door at C, Fig. 65 is proportioned in accordance with the construction shown in Fig. 91, *i.e.* the height equals the hypotenuse of a square which has a length of side equal to the width of the pane. Three alternative details of the wide bottom rail are shown at M, N and O. That at N shows a compound rail, the lower portion being sunk-chamfered both sides and tenoned into the upper Alternatively, as shown at M, the lower rail may be tenoned into the upper and finished flush on one side with a double bead, and having a similar beaded mould inserted in the other. The alternative finish at O shows a narrow 12 mm thick panel. As an internal door should be kept about 12 mm from the floor to allow it to swing clear of a carpet with underfelt, draughts may be minimized if, as shown at N, a splayed hardwood slip is well screwed to the floor; this is an alternative to that shown with rounded edges at J, Fig. 53. Of course, such is not necessary if the doors are hung with skew butt hinges (see Z, Fig. 36 and p. 78). The details at M and N show the glass fixed with glazing beads; as an alternative, the glass at O is shown sprigged and puttied.

The single panel of the door at D, Fig. 65, is of glass. The detail at L shows that architraves have been dispensed with and the projecting casing finished with rounded edges. The casing is grooved to receive the plaster at both sides, and a 12 or 19 mm thick stop is nailed to it. Because of the large size of the sheet, 5 mm polished plate glass has been specified.

The upper panel only of the door at E, Fig. 66, is glazed, the other panels being of plywood (Chapter II, *Carpentry*). A detail at S shows the glass above and the 3-ply panel below the rail.

An elevation of a single panelled door which is partially glazed is shown at F, Fig. 67. The detail at T shows the thick (25 mm nominal) panel

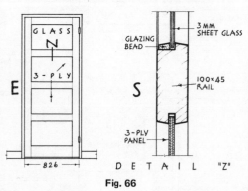

Fig. 66

finished with large bolection mouldings both sides. The glazed sash, divided into four small panes, is grooved on its outer edges and engaged in the wood panel. The architrave at the bottom of the detail is shown finished on the splay of the skirting. Alternatively, the latter may have the same projection and a similar moulding as the architrave, to provide a mitred joint.

Fig. 67

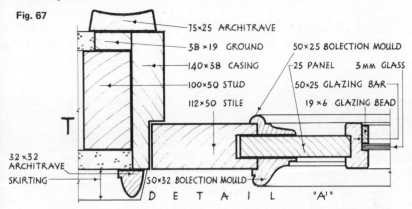

75×25 ARCHITRAVE
38×19 GROUND
140×38 CASING
100×50 STUD
112×50 STILE
50×25 BOLECTION MOULD
25 PANEL   3 MM GLASS
50×25 GLAZING BAR
19×6 GLAZING BEAD
T
32×32 ARCHITRAVE
SKIRTING
50×32 BOLECTION MOULD
D E T A I L "A"

An elevation of the old-fashioned *diminished stile door,* still occasionally used, is shown in Fig. 68 and detailed in Fig. 69. It has either one or two wood panels at the bottom, and the upper portion is glazed. In order to provide the maximum area of glass, the width of the upper portions of the stiles which receive it is decreased; hence the terms *diminishing stiles* and *gun-stock* stiles which are applied to these vertical members. The joint between the middle rail and stile is shown at R, Fig. 69, the stile

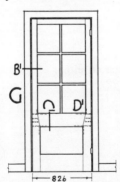

B¹
G
D¹
826

Fig. 68

being diminished from 115 to 75 mm nominal. The development in this sketch presents a somewhat peculiar appearance due to the opposite shoulders not being parallel. If required, a stuck moulding, of width equal to the depth of the glazing rebate, could be worked on the rails and stiles, and parallel shoulders would result. A vertical section through the middle rail is shown at Q. A detail at one of the jambs above this rail is illustrated at P; this shows a moulded architrave and splayed[1] ground at one side, and a simple splayed architrave with square-edged ground at the other.

An external entrance is shown in Fig. 70. The door has an octagonal-shaped glazed panel divided by glazing bars. A detail of this door and frame is given in Fig. 71. The construction is somewhat similar to that at T, Fig. 67, except that it is bolection moulded on one side only and the thick panel is raised and fielded. Being an external door, the glass is tinted or otherwise obscured. In this detail it is assumed that the frame is set back slightly from the inner face of the wall. If, as shown in the part plan in Fig. 70, the door is set

[1]*Preferably, the splayed edge of the ground should be reversed, as shown in Fig. 54.*

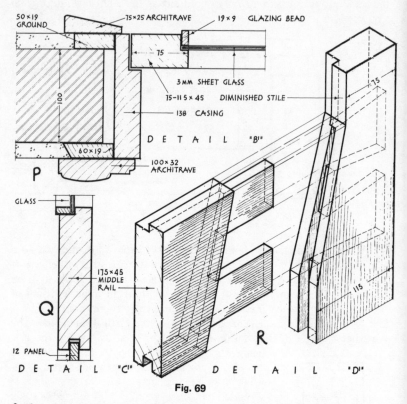

50×19 GROUND

75×25 ARCHITRAVE

19×9 GLAZING BEAD

75

3 MM SHEET GLASS

75-115×45 DIMINISHED STILE

138 CASING

DETAIL "B"

100

60×19

P

100×32 ARCHITRAVE

GLASS

175×45 MIDDLE RAIL

Q

12 PANEL

DETAIL "C"

R

DETAIL "D"

75

115

Fig. 69

farther back, the detail at the frame will be similar to either of those shown at P, Fig. 60, K, Fig. 62, P, Fig. 63 or G, Fig. 78.

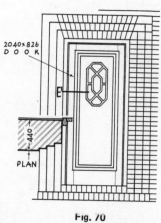

2040×826 DOOR

E

440

PLAN

Fig. 70

The door illustrated in Fig. 75 (detailed in Figs. 76, 77 and 78) is partially glazed, as is also the flush door in Fig. 79 (detailed in Fig. 80).

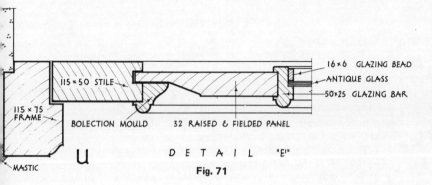

16×6 GLAZING BEAD
ANTIQUE GLASS
50×25 GLAZING BAR

115 × 50 STILE

115 × 75 FRAME

BOLECTION MOULD   32 RAISED & FIELDED PANEL

MASTIC

DETAIL "E"

Fig. 71

FLUSH DOORS

THESE doors were in large demand during the years immediately before the war, and one type especially (that shown at B, Fig. 73) has been employed extensively during the war because of the economy in material used in its manufacture.

A flush door is so called, as it is of uniform thickness throughout, both faces being therefore even and not panelled.

Flush doors do not twist, but keep true to shape.

There are two classes of flush doors, *i.e.,* (1) framed or hollow core and (2) solid or laminated core.

Most flush doors are mass produced by specialist firms who are generally manufacturers of plywood and allied products, although the hollow core class can be readily made in most joiners' shops (see p. 115). The British Standard sizes are the same as those given on p. 41.

1. FRAMED OR HOLLOW CORE FLUSH DOORS.—This type consists of a softwood frame comprising stiles, top and bottom rails, and narrow intermediate rails, and this frame is covered on each side with a sheet of plywood (described in Chapter II, *Carpentry*). It is also called a *skeleton* or *hollow frame flush door*. With exception of the door shown at B, Fig. 73, the stiles and top and bottom rails are 75 to 100 mm wide; these rails are either tenoned or dowelled (see pp. 69 and 70) to the stiles, and the intermediate rails are sub-tenoned to the stiles. The joints of the framing are glued and cramped, and the 3-ply sheets are glued to the framing under pressure. A lock *block* is provided (sometimes one at each side—see p. 113) to widen the stile(s) for the insertion of a mortice lock.

A typical example of this class of door is shown at B, Fig. 72. A hardwood edging slip is fixed to one or both stiles to prevent damage to the plywood edges; one form is shown at E and another at F, Fig. 72 (see also Figs. 73 and 74). Small holes are drilled through the rails, as shown in Figs. 72, 73, 79 and 80, to provide ventilation to the interior of the door.

These doors are light and economical to produce. Most mass-produced doors are of this type. Softwoods are invariably used for the frames and these are also employed for the coverings of the cheaper doors; they include western red cedar (much favoured because of its light weight), Canadian red pine, Douglas fir, redwood, western hemlock and parana pine. A wide range of hardwoods is used for plywood facings of the better class doors, and those for superior facings are specially selected for their attractive figure; they include ash, beech, black bean, birch, canary whitewood, mahogany, oak, rock maple, sycamore and walnut. These timbers are described in Chapter I, *Carpentry*.

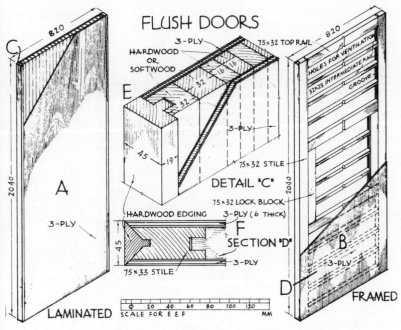

Fig. 72

A hollow core flush door is shown at A and detailed at F, Fig. 73. The frame consists of 100 mm by 38 mm (nominal) stiles, top and bottom rails, and 50 mm by 38 mm intermediate rails at 150 to 225 mm centres; alternatively, 75 mm wide intermediate rails at approximately 300 mm centres may be employed. The top and bottom rails are tenoned and glued to the stiles, the tenons preferably extending the full width of the stiles, as shown at Q, and wedged. The intermediate rails are glued, tenoned and cramped into the continuous grooves formed in the stiles (see F, Fig. 72, F and R, Fig. 73, and Fig. 80). One hole (see B, Fig. 72) or preferably two holes (as shown in the elevation at A, Fig. 73) are bored through each of the rails to ensure a thorough circulation of air within the framing. One or two additional "loose" vertical members are also sometimes glued in position (see p. 115) between each pair of rails, each vertical strip being 25 mm shorter than the distance between the rails and placed alternately with one end against a rail to leave the 25 mm clearance at the other; whilst these strips do not impede a free circulation of air, they do prevent drumming or hollow sound which would be otherwise caused when the door is knocked. Care should be taken to see that the "vent holes" in the top rail are not subsequently "stopped" with putty by the painter. For good class doors the plywood facings should be 5 mm thick.

Edging slips, especially on the striking stiles, are necessary; they are often fixed on all edges of good class doors. Several forms of these are shown in Fig. 72, F, Fig. 73, and Fig. 74. The square tongued and

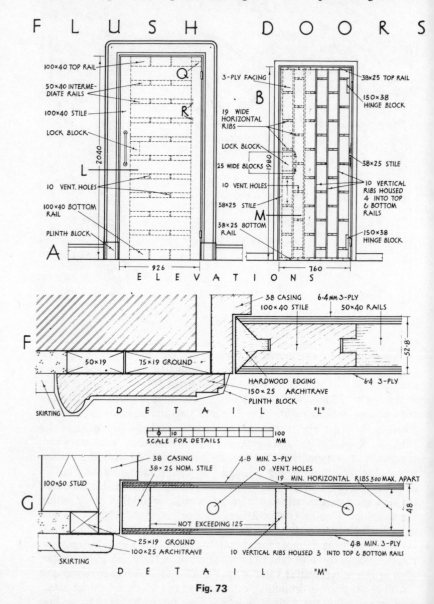

Fig. 73

grooved edging piece (*i.e.,* types H and J, Fig. 74) is preferred to the mitred one (F, Figs. 72 and 73), as any trimming of the latter when fitting the door throws the mitres away from the arrise and exposes the edges of the plywood to damage; for this reason it is advisable to do all the fitting of a mitred edged door on the hanging stile. If, as shown at G, Fig. 73, an edging slip is not provided at the striking stile and the plywood is continued to the edge of the door, the plywood is readily damaged by splintering, especially if the door swells on account of the absorption of moisture, and a tight fit between it and the casing results.

A lock block should be provided, as indicated at A, Fig. 73, to allow for the fitting of a mortice lock; they should be stub-tenoned to the intermediate rails. The position of this block should be indicated on the outside. Many mass-produced doors are provided with a lock block at each stile so that a mortice lock can be fixed to either stile of a door when fitted in position; the lock pieces to these doors should be of sufficient length in order that the position of the lock may not be unduly restricted.

The wide architrave (which should be in at least two pieces, if it exceeds 150 mm, to avoid splitting if shrinkage occurs) detailed at F, Fig. 73, is shown at A with rounded corners. To prevent opening at the mitres, the joints should be either cross-tongued (mitred and slip feathered) or handrail bolted, or the horizontal member should be tenoned into the verticals and screwed from the back (see p. 226 and Fig. 150).

Another type of a hollow core flush door is shown at E and J, Fig. 74. This is a good sound-insulating and fire-resisting door, as compressed granulated cork is filled between the members of the framing. Each stile and edging slip are double tongued and grooved together, and, as a lock block is provided at each side, either stile may be hung.

2. SOLID OR LAMINATED CORE FLUSH DOORS.—This type is shown at A and E, Fig. 72, and D and H, Fig. 74. As implied, the core is solid throughout and consists of narrow strips (laminæ) of wood glued together under great pressure; this is faced on each side with a 3-ply board which is glued under pressure to the core. As indicated at E, both softwoods and hardwoods are used for the core, the former producing lighter doors than the hardwoods. The strips should be arranged with the grain alternating as shown; this reduces shrinkage and distortion. Hardwood laminæ are usually narrower than those of softwood. Laminboards are often used for cores, the strips (or slats) not exceeding 8 mm in width. Blockboards are also used for cheaper cores; these are built up with strips which are 25 mm wide or less. Laminboards and blockboards are described in Chapter II, *Carpentry*. A hardwood edging such as is shown at E and F, Fig. 72, is used at each edge to cover the core and the edges of the plywood. Solid cored flush doors require much more timber than the hollow core type, and are therefore relatively heavy and more costly.

The solid core flush door shown at D, Fig. 74, is detailed at H in Fig. 74. The laminæ are only 8 mm wide, and this detail, therefore, shows an application of laminboard (Chapter II, *Carpentry*). As stated above, blockboards are also used as cores. The tongued edging slips (as is that shown at J) are also dovetailed to receive the edges of the plywood facings which, after being glued, are sprung into position and pressed. In order to provide a contrast in colour, these slips may be of a different wood to the plywood facings. An effective appearance results if the

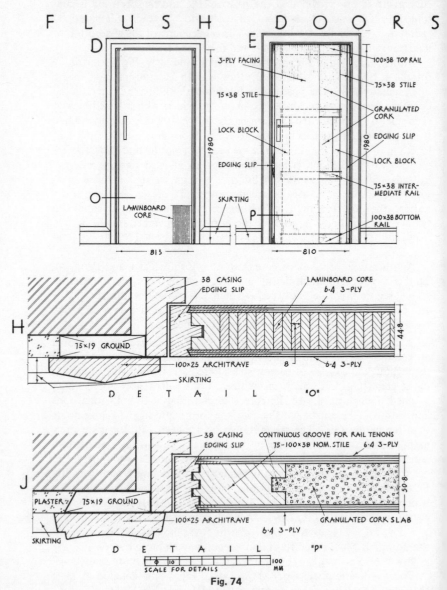

F L U S H   D O O R S

D

3-PLY FACING

75×38 STILE

LOCK BLOCK

EDGING SLIP

1980

O

LAMINBOARD CORE

SKIRTING

815

E

100×38 TOP RAIL

75×38 STILE

GRANULATED CORK

EDGING SLIP

LOCK BLOCK

1980

75×38 INTER-MEDIATE RAIL

100×38 BOTTOM RAIL

P

810

H

38 CASING
EDGING SLIP

75×19 GROUND

100×25 ARCHITRAVE

SKIRTING

LAMINBOARD CORE
6·4 3-PLY

44·8

8

6·4 3-PLY

D E T A I L   "O"

J

38 CASING
EDGING SLIP

CONTINUOUS GROOVE FOR RAIL TENONS
75-100×38 NOM. STILE   6·4 3-PLY

PLASTER   75×19 GROUND

100×25 ARCHITRAVE

6·4 3-PLY

50·8

GRANULATED CORK SLAB

SKIRTING

D E T A I L   "P"

SCALE FOR DETAILS   0   10   100 MM

Fig. 74

section of the skirting is similar to the outer splay of the simple architrave; the resulting mitres are shown in the elevation at D. This is a good type of door, although heavy, and is more fire-resisting and sound-insulating (although not so economical) than the skeleton-framed variety shown in Fig. 73.

Flush doors (such as those required for hospitals) are often prepared for glass, the glazed panel being square, circular, elliptical, octagonal, etc. A glazed flush door (with semicircular head) is shown in Fig. 79 and detailed in Fig. 80.

Preparation of Flush Doors.—In the manufacture of mass-produced flush doors, modifications and refinements are constantly being introduced and new machinery or apparatus employed, with a view to reducing labour and machine operations and cost. The following is a brief description of the preparation of a framed flush door which may be carried out in the average shop: The stiles, rails and blocks are cut to size and planed, and mortices, tenons, grooves and vent holes are formed. The framing is then assembled, glued, cramped and wedged on the bench; to ensure that the frame when taken off the bench is true and "out of twist", these operations should be done with the frame supported on two *skids* placed across the bench and lying out of twist or winding. The wedges at the top and bottom joints are sawn off, and the framing is either passed through a sander machine (see p. 25) to plane the surfaces, or planed by hand and toothed by the application of the toothing plane (Chapter X, *Carpentry*) to provide a key for the glue. One face of the frame and a face of the plywood sheet are then glued; it is advisable to cut the sheets of plywood 12 mm larger in length and width to allow for any slipping that may take place during the pressing operation (see below). This first sheet of plywood is panel pinned to the frame and the door is turned over on the skids. Any "loose" vertical strips (p. 111) are rubbed glue jointed to the plywood and rails (with 25 mm clearance at one end of each strip). The second face of the frame and one side of the second plywood sheet is glued, and after the latter has been placed in position on the frame, the door is taken to the press (if available) and subjected to the necessary pressure, or weighted on the bench, to effect close joints between the plywood sheets and the frame. The plywood edges along the stiles and top and bottom rails are trimmed, and the vertical edges of the door are machined to receive the edging slips (see pp. 112 and 113), which are tongued, glued and cramped to the grooved stiles.

If the door is of the solid core flush type, the laminboard or block-board core is formed, as described in Chapter II, *Carpentry,* trimmed to size, and both sheets of plywood and the hardwood edge slips are fixed, as described above. These doors are generally produced by specialist firms.

If the door requires a glass panel, the solid core and the plywood sheets will have been cut to roughly the size of the opening before the sheets are fixed. The latter are then trimmed off after the glue has set and the necessary glazing beads fitted.

METAL-FACED FLUSH DOORS.—Some flush doors, such as those required for laboratories, lavatories and wash-houses, are constructed of metal-faced plywood, *i.e.,* plywood boards which are covered both sides with sheets of thin gauged metal, such as aluminium, bronze and nickel alloys, and galvanized and stainless steel. The metal is bonded to the plywood by special waterproof cement. The edges of the plywood are also covered with the metal; at least some—and preferably all—edges should be sealed (by soldering or welding) to exclude moisture, and so prevent corrosion of the inner surfaces of certain facings and swelling of the core. A sample of metal-faced plywood is shown in Fig. 19, *Carpentry;* this indicates one form of sealed edge.

FIRE RESISTING DOORS.—Various Acts of Parliament and Building Regulations give rules for the amount of fire protection to be provided for buildings. This amount depends upon the purpose of the building, e.g. domestic, shop, hall or factory etc.

Part of this protection is obtained by ensuring that the elements of a building (wall, floor, roof, beam, door etc.) withstand damage by fire for an adequate period. Thus fire-resistance periods are stipulated varying from ½-hour to 4-hour.

A ½-hour fire resisting timber door has 95 mm by 38 mm top, middle and bottom rails forming the core of the door. This is clad with 9·5 mm plasterboard set into rebates of the core members; to the faces of the door 3·2 mm plywood is then glued (metal fastenings are not permitted). The rebate depth of the door frame is twice the normal amount and is 25 mm.

A 1-hour fire-resisting timber door has the core members impregnated with a fire retardant like mono-ammonium phosphate in water to a depth of 12 mm.

The construction is the same as for the ½-hour door plus a 5 mm sheet of asbestos-cement wallboard glued between the plasterboard (and core) and plywood faces of the door. The door frame is the same as for the less resistant door but 1½ pairs of hinges are used for hanging the door.

Doors requiring fire-resistance of 2 hours and longer are of steel.

SEMI - CIRCULAR
HEADED DOOR

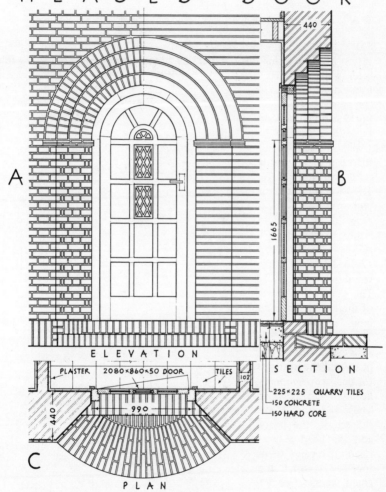

ELEVATION

SECTION

PLASTER   2080×860×50 DOOR   TILES

225×225 QUARRY TILES
150 CONCRETE
150 HARD CORE

PLAN

Fig. 75

CHAPTER EIGHT

SEMICIRCULAR HEADED DOORS

Panelled and flush doors with semicircular heads. Details of joints.

SEMICIRCULAR HEADED PANELLED DOOR.—The plan, section and elevation of an external door and frame suitable for a splayed opening in a brick wall which has a four-ringed semicircular arch is shown in Fig. 75 and detailed in Figs. 76, 77 and 78.

The construction of the head of the frame is shown in Fig. 76. The head is built-up of two ribs or "thicknesses", glued, and either screwed together or secured by 12 or 16 mm hardwood pins or dowels. The outer rib consists of three pieces and the inner of two pieces. The joints at the springing between the posts and the head are formed of *hammer-headed key tenons*. These tenons are shaped on the posts, and the head is morticed to receive them together with the glued wedges (see F). When the two wedges are tightly driven in at each joint, the shoulders are brought close together and exceptionally strong joints result. The

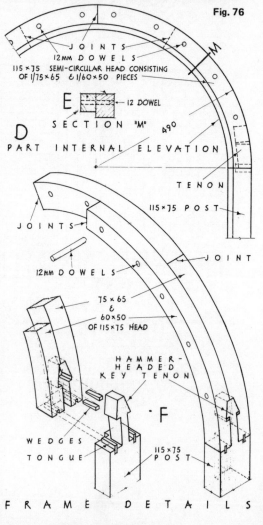

Fig. 76

JOINTS
12mm DOWELS
115×75 SEMI-CIRCULAR HEAD CONSISTING
OF 1/75×65 & 1/60×50 PIECES

E — 12 DOWEL

SECTION "M"

D

PART INTERNAL ELEVATION 49°

TENON

115×75 POST

JOINTS

JOINT

12mm DOWELS

75×65
&
60×50
OF 115×75 HEAD

HAMMER-HEADED
KEY TENON

·F

WEDGES

TONGUE

115×75
POST

FRAME DETAILS

118

maintenance of a tight fit is further assured if two small glued shoulder or *cross tongues,* as shown, are employed, but these are often dispensed with. Cross tongues are about 4 mm thick and are so called because they are cut across the grain of the squared end of the board from which they are made; they are stronger than *feather tongues* (used for similar purposes), as the latter are cut diagonally across the grain. These springing joints may be formed of loose hammer-headed keys similar to that used at the crown of the door (see Fig. 77) or by handrail screw bolts (see Q, Fig. 109) and hardwood dowels, but these are less effective than the tenon shown at F.

The construction of the head of the door is shown in Fig. 77. The head consists of two pieces which are jointed at the crown. The joints between the stiles and the head are similar to those of the frame,

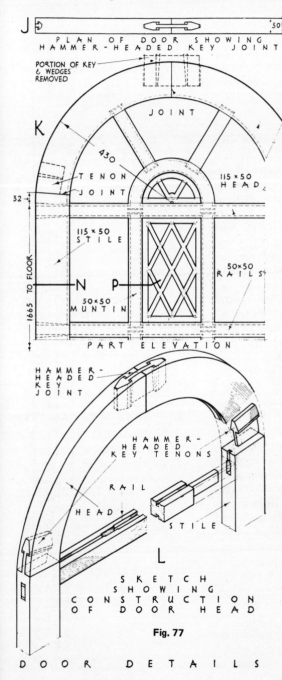

PLAN OF DOOR SHOWING
HAMMER-HEADED KEY JOINT

PORTION OF KEY
& WEDGES
REMOVED

JOINT

K

430

TENON
JOINT

32

115×50
HEAD

115×50
STILE

50×50
RAILS

N   P

50×50
MUNTIN

1665   TO FLOOR

PART ELEVATION

HAMMER-
HEADED
KEY
JOINT

HAMMER-
HEADED
KEY TENONS

RAIL

HEAD

STILE

L

SKETCH
SHOWING
CONSTRUCTION
OF DOOR HEAD

Fig. 77

DOOR   DETAILS

the hammer-headed tenons being formed on the stiles; the upper tapered portion of the tenon (and mortice) is commonly cut square (and not radial as shown) to facilitate the entry of the tenon. It will be noted, however, that these radial joints are slightly (32 mm) above the springing. This is necessary because of the presence of the top rail which is, of course, tenoned into the stiles. Very weak joints would result if they coincided with the springing. Shoulder tongues are not necessary because of the reduced thickness of the framing. A hammer-headed key joint is shown at the crown. This is tightened up by means of the four glued wedges. A handrail screw bolt and dowels or pins may be used in lieu of the key (see Q, Fig. 109).

One or more of the central panels of the door may be glazed, as shown in Fig. 75, antique glass (tinted glass) being specified (Fig. 78). The small glazing bars are stub-tenoned (see K, Fig. 77). Enlarged details of the door are shown in Fig. 78. These indicate an entire absence of mouldings, the arrises of the rails, muntins, stiles, frame, etc. being pencil-rounded, i.e., rounded off by sandpapering. The simple architrave conforms; alternatively the architrave can be omitted if, as shown at K, Fig. 60, the frame is allowed to project beyond the face of the wall and is grooved to receive the plaster. As a weather board is not considered to improve the appearance of a door, it has been omitted here, as it assumed that the door opens into an outer lobby. A weather board and threshold, as illustrated in Figs. 42, 60, 62, 63 and 64, are, however, necessary to

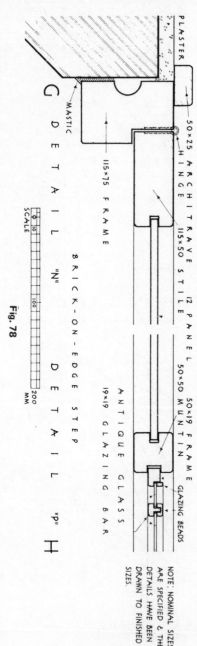

Fig. 78

exclude water if the entrance is in an exposed position and if the door opens directly into a living-room or hall.

SEMICIRCULAR HEADED FLUSH DOOR.—The elevation of a framed flush door, having a glazed panel, is shown in

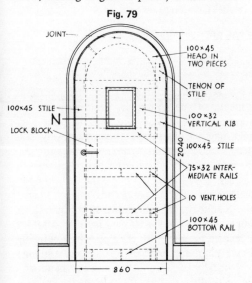

Fig. 79

JOINT

100×45 STILE

LOCK BLOCK

N

100×45 HEAD IN TWO PIECES

TENON OF STILE

100×32 VERTICAL RIB

100×45 STILE

2040

75×32 INTER-MEDIATE RAILS

10 VENT. HOLES

100×45 BOTTOM RAIL

860

Fig. 79 and detailed in Fig. 80. A description of the general construction of this type of door is given in the previous chapter. The head of the door framing may be in two pieces only, with the central joints cross tongued; or alternatively, it may be built-up in two thicknesses like the frame shown in Fig. 76. The joints between the head and the stiles are tenoned as shown; hammer-headed key joints (see Fig. 76) are not necessary, as the joints are not exposed to view and because of the stiffening effect of the plywood facings.

The treatment at the stiles of the door shown at K, Fig. 80, is an alternative to the details shown in Figs. 73 and 74. The outer veneer only of the 3-ply facing covers the framing. This veneer may be highly decorative and costly. Its edges are vulnerable to damage, especially at the striking stile (see p. 113), and, as shown, they are bevelled to minimize this tendency. The detail of the glazed panel is somewhat similar to those shown in Figs. 67 and 71. The top of the skirting is assumed to be moulded with a fillet and curve similar to the architrave. This results in a mitre and a satisfactory finish (see Fig. 79).

K

DETAIL "N"

Fig. 80

50×19 GROUND

SKIRTING

OAK OUTER PLY OF 6·4 3-PLY SHEET

50×19 ARCHITRAVE

CONTINUOUS GROOVE TO RECEIVE TENONS OF RAILS

10 VENT. HOLES

57×25 GLAZING SASH FRAME

3MM SHEET GLASS

38 CASING

100×45 NOM. STILE

MAHOGANY OUTER PLY OF 6·4 3-PLY SHEET

75×32 RAILS

100×32 VERTICAL RIB

45

19×6 GLAZING BEAD

CHAPTER NINE

CASEMENT WINDOWS

Windows with fixed lights and sashes opening outwards. Mullioned casement
windows. Ironmongery. Manufacture, including setting out.

THE chief object of a window is, of course, to light a room, hall, corridor,
etc. It may also serve as a means of ventilation. A window includes a
frame and, usually, one or more *sashes* which are glazed. The frame may
have solid wood members, or it may be constructed of comparatively thin
pieces to form what is called a *cased* or *boxed frame* (see Chapter X).
The sashes may be fixed or made to open. The latter, when associated
with a solid frame, may be attached by hinges to enable the sash to open
either outwards (which is usual) or inwards like a door, or it may be hinged
at the lower edge to open inwards (like the fanlight shown at B, Fig. 62), or
it may be hung at the top edge to open outwards (see Fig. 63). Another
type of sash is pivoted at the centre to open with the upper half swinging
inwards (see Figs. 115, 116 and 117), and another form consists of one
or more sashes which slide horizontally (see Fig. 119). Sashes when made
to open in a cased frame slide vertically (see Figs. 92 to 96 inclusive).

The size of windows should be adequate and depends upon the use
of the room. The Building Regulations stipulate that, in habitable rooms,
the area of the window which opens to the external air shall be not less
than one-twentieth of the floor area. Actually, the window area is frequently at least equal to one-quarter the floor area and most of the sashes
are made to open.

The type of window which is to be described in full in this chapter
is that which has a solid frame with one or more sashes which open
outwards.

WINDOWS WITH SOLID FRAMES AND VERTICALLY HUNG SASHES
OPENING OUTWARDS.—Sashes which are made to open like a door are
called *casements*, and the window is usually specified as a *casement window*. It is adopted extensively and is illustrated in Figs. 81 to 90
(inclusive).

Frame.—If the window has only one sash (as shown at A and D, Fig. 81),
the frame consists of two vertical posts, stiles or *jambs,* a head and a wood
sill. If it has two sashes (see B and E, Fig. 81), the additional vertical
member is called a *mullion.* Sometimes a window has a horizontal dividing
member, called a *transome* (see Figs. 59 to 63, inclusive), with or without
mullions.

Typical joints of a window frame are shown at A, B and C, Fig. 82.
Note that the jamb is haunched tenoned (see p. 42) at each end, and the
head and sill are morticed to receive the tenons and wedges. The outer

123

shoulder of the lower end of the jamb is scribed (pp. 62 and 230) to the sill (see B and section EE at C). These joints are sometimes pinned, as

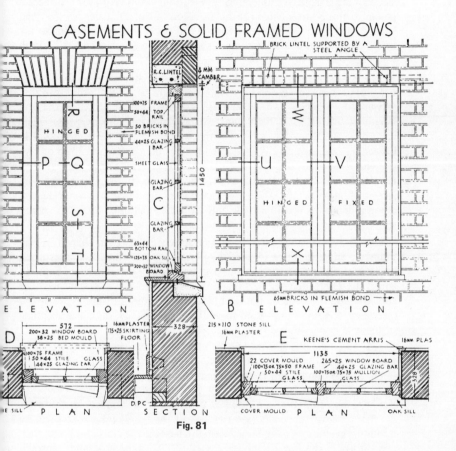

Fig. 81

described (pp. 57 and 139). The frames may be fixed as described on pp. 45 and 46, the horns being removed if the frames are fixed after the walling has been completed. The bedding and pointing of the frames must receive special attention if, as shown in Fig. 81, they are not to be built in recesses. The head and jambs are rebated, 12 to 16 mm deep, to receive the sash. The inside edge of the frame may be square, pencil-rounded, chamfered, ovolo-moulded, etc. as shown. The capillary grooves are referred to on p. 129.

The sill is double *sunk-weathered* (a slope or bevel which begins with a vertical sinking) to cast off rain-water. Each vertical sinking is grooved or throated (see M, Fig. 83 and O, Fig. 84) to prevent the water from being driven by the wind from the lower to the higher surface. Special attention must be paid to the bed joint between the wood sill and the brick or stone sill, as it is particularly vulnerable. Precautions taken to prevent the access of rain at this point include (*a*) the provision of a metal *water bar*, (*b*) lead tucked into a groove formed in the sill and continued as a covering to the brick sill, and (*c*) a mortar tongue formed in the groove of the sill. With reference to:

(*a*) A groove is formed in the brick sill (see A, Fig. 86 and Q, Fig. 94) or stone sill (see M, Figs. 83, 93 and 112) and the 25 mm by 6 mm galvanized wrought iron water (or "weather") bar, which is the full length of the sill, is partially inserted and bedded in cement mortar. The groove in the wood sill is filled with a mixture of white lead ground in linseed oil, and the frame is firmly bedded on the mortar, spread to receive it, with the projecting bar engaging in the groove. This groove, with bar, should be as near as possible to the outside (preferably nearer than the position shown at Q, Fig. 94—see Fig. 112) so that any water passing along a defective bed joint will only affect a small portion of the wood sill.

(*b*) The brick sill is covered with lead which has been shaped by the plumber, and the frame is carefully placed in position with the upturned portion of the lead fitting into the groove of the wood sill (see Figs. 85 and 87). The efficiency of this joint is increased if white lead mastic is spread along the edge of the lead before the frame is fitted. A water bar (see above) is sometimes used in addition to the lead, the upturned edge of the lead being dressed over the top edge of the bar.

(*c*) A rectangular groove (see O, Fig. 84) or half-round groove is filled with mortar as the frame is pressed down on the bedding. This is adopted in cheap work and is not a reliable method.

In a mullion frame, as shown at B, Fig. 81, the mullion is tenoned into the head and sill. If the window is provided with a transome, the latter is tenoned into the posts (see Fig. 61); if the window has one or more mullions, in addition to the transome, the latter is the continuous member, and the upper and lower mullions are tenoned into the head and transome and the sill and transome respectively.

Scantings of Frame.—Heads, jambs, mullions and transomes are generally either 100 mm by 62 mm, 100 mm by 75 mm or 115 mm by 75 mm; sills vary from 100 mm by 62 mm, 100 mm by 75 mm, 115 mm by 75 mm, 115 mm by 90 mm and 125 to 175 mm by 75 to 90 mm. These sizes may be exceeded for large frames.

For ordinary good-class work it is usual to specify redwood or Douglas fir for the head, jambs, mullions and transomes, and either oak, teak or pitch pine for the sill; for first-class work the whole of the frame may be specified to be in oak or teak.

Sashes.—The members of a sash or casement are similar to those of a door *i.e.,* two vertical stiles, a top rail and a bottom rail. In addition,

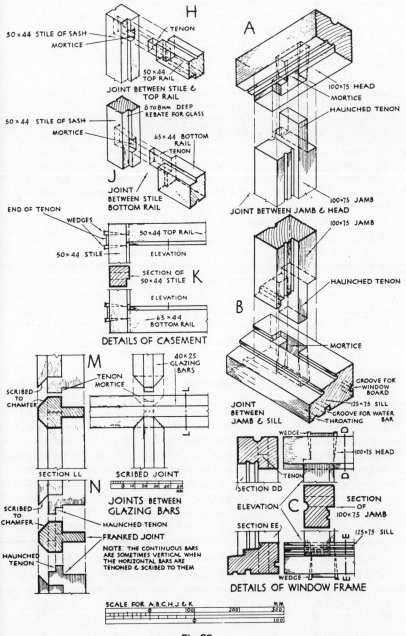

50 × 44 STILE OF SASH
MORTICE
TENON
50 × 44 TOP RAIL
H
JOINT BETWEEN STILE & TOP RAIL

50 × 44 STILE OF SASH
MORTICE
6 to 8MM DEEP REBATE FOR GLASS
63 × 44 BOTTOM RAIL
TENON
J
JOINT BETWEEN STILE BOTTOM RAIL

END OF TENON
WEDGES
50 × 44 STILE
50 × 44 TOP RAIL
ELEVATION
SECTION OF 50 × 44 STILE
K
ELEVATION
63 × 44 BOTTOM RAIL

DETAILS OF CASEMENT

M
40 × 25 GLAZING BARS
TENON
MORTICE
SCRIBED TO CHAMFER
SECTION LL
SCRIBED JOINT

N
SCRIBED TO CHAMFER
HAUNCHED TENON
FRANKED JOINT
HAUNCHED TENON
NOTE: THE CONTINUOUS BARS ARE SOMETIMES VERTICAL WHEN THE HORIZONTAL BARS ARE TENONED & SCRIBED TO THEM

JOINTS BETWEEN GLAZING BARS

A
100×75 HEAD
MORTICE
HAUNCHED TENON
100×75 JAMB
JOINT BETWEEN JAMB & HEAD

100×75 JAMB
HAUNCHED TENON
B
MORTICE
GROOVE FOR WINDOW BOARD
125×75 SILL
GROOVE FOR WATER BAR
THROATING
JOINT BETWEEN JAMB & SILL

WEDGE
100×75 HEAD
TENON
SECTION DD
ELEVATION
SECTION OF 100×75 JAMB
C
SECTION EE
125×75 SILL
WEDGE

DETAILS OF WINDOW FRAME

SCALE FOR A.B.C.H.J & K
100   200   300   MM
100

Fig. 82

125

a sash may be divided by both horizontal and vertical bars or horizontal bars only. These are called *glazing bars* or *sash bars* or *astragals*.

The construction of the sashes is illustrated at H, J and K, Fig. 82, which show the top and bottom rails tenoned and wedged to the stiles. If, as shown in Fig. 82, the members are not moulded, the tenons should be haunched (see R, Fig. 96), otherwise the sash would tend to twist; provision for the haunching is made in the setting out at J and K, Fig. 90. In addition, the joints are preferably pinned (p. 123). The projecting ends of the tenons and wedges are, of course, removed before the sash is fixed.

The joints between the glazing bars are shown at M and N, Fig. 82. The *scribed joint* at M shows the horizontal bar to be continuous and morticed to receive the tenons formed on the ends of the vertical bars. The chamfered mould on the latter is scribed to the moulding on the horizontal bar (see p. 62). This is the commonest form of joint. The *franked joint* at N shows the continuous horizontal bar morticed to receive the halved and haunched tenons worked on the vertical bars. Another satisfactory method of jointing glazing bars is halving, and this is shown at M, Fig. 96. All these joints are glued immediately before assembly.

In both the scribed and franked joints the continuous bars may be either horizontal or vertical, depending upon circumstances. For casements, greater stiffness of the sash is obtained if the short horizontal bars are made continuous and the lengths of vertical members tenoned into them. For vertical sliding sashes (see Fig. 92) it is customary to make the vertical bars continuous. In the halved joint both horizontal and vertical bars are, of course, continuous.

The ends of the bars are tenoned and scribed to the sash stiles or rails.

The sash is rebated for glazing. These rebates are from 16 to 19 mm wide by approximately 6 or 9 mm deep. The glass[1] is secured by either putty (made of whiting ground in raw linseed oil), as indicated in Figs. 83, 84 and D and F, Fig. 85, or small fillets called *glazing beads* (see D and F, Fig. 85). Note that the rebates for the glass are on the outside when putty is used, and are on the inside when beads are adopted.[2] The glass is usually *sheet glass* (produced by fusing a mixture of sand, silicates of soda and lime, etc., the sheet of uniform thickness is withdrawn from a tank containing this molten glass and cut into lengths), but *plate glass* (made by the "float" process which involves casting the molten material on to a bed of molten tin) is sometimes used for glazing first class work. Glass is specified by its thickness, i.e., 2, 3, 4, 5, 5·5 and 6 mm; for small panes 2 and 3 mm thickness is used, large sheets are 6 mm thick. Obscure glass, of which there is a wide range, is used to glaze windows of lavatories, water-closets, cloak-rooms, etc. Small metal sprigs (which are without heads) are driven in, as shown in the various details, to temporarily retain the glass in position until the putty is set. Glazing beads should be secured by small screws ("cups and screws"—see Figs. 93 and

[1] Glass is fixed by either the painter or plumber, depending upon local custom.
[2] Except for special double glazing panes (Fig. 85).

94—as shown at O and N, Fig. 149, *Carpentry*) rather than nails, to allow for ready removal when broken panes have to be replaced. The glass should be well bedded in putty, before the beads are fixed, to prevent the entrance of water.

Scantlings of Sashes.—These vary with the size of sash. Small sashes may be 38 mm (nominal) thick, average-sized sashes may be 45 mm thick, and large sashes may be 50 mm thick. The stiles and top rails are generally 50 mm wide with deeper (62 to 90 mm) bottom rails to give added strength and an improved appearance. The glazing bars are equal in width to the thickness of the frame and are out of 25 or 45 mm thick stuff, the latter being reduced to 25 mm finished thickness unless the sheets of glass are large.

As shown at M, Fig. 83, O, Fig. 84, D and E, Fig. 85 and Fig. 87, the bottom of the inside of openings are finished with 25 or 32 mm (nominal) thick *window boards*. These are tongued into the wood sills (to prevent open joints when the boards shrink); they are secured to plugs driven into the vertical joints of the walls or nailed to 38 mm thick bearers plugged to the top of the walls. Some window boards are finished with *bed moulds* which have returned ends (see Figs. 83 and 112); these moulds are usually nailed to plugs and to the window boards after the latter have been secured; large moulds are fixed to grounds which are plugged to the wall (see R, Fig. 94 and Fig. 112). Tiles may be used instead of a wood window board to form an internal sill; these may be white or coloured glazed tiles (about 9 mm thick) or they may be square quarry tiles (about 19 mm thick on the average) bedded on cement. An example of the latter finish is shown at A, Fig. 86.

In the elevations A and B, Fig. 81 the panes of glass are small, this was the traditional size for comparatively small buildings, such as houses. A satisfactory proportion of such a pane is obtained if its height approximates to the length of the hypotenuse of a right-angled triangle having both sides equal to its width, as shown in Fig. 91. A reasonable size is 280 mm high by 95 to 220 mm wide. The vertical bars may be omitted to emphasize the effect of horizontality.

These two windows are not built into recesses such as that at B, Fig. 86. This is not sound construction (although often adopted) for, unless great care is taken in the bedding and pointing of the frame, water may gain entrance between it and the wall; the appearance of windows placed between square brick jambs (like those in Fig. 81) or stone jambs is very satisfactory, as the full width of the frames is exposed to view. Sounder construction is shown in Fig. 86 (see p. 132).

The details shown in Figs. 85 and 86 are alternative to those shown in Fig. 83, which latter are those of the window at A, Fig. 81; Fig. 84 gives details of the window at B, Fig. 81. Students should study carefully these details and observe the several variations.

It is important to note that small grooves are shown in the rebate of each frame and along the edges of each sash; thus, round grooves are indicated in Figs. 83, 85 (C and F) and 86 (C), whilst rectangular grooves

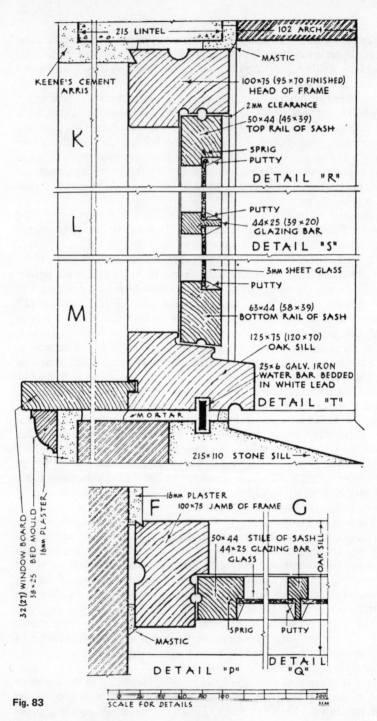

215 LINTEL

102 ARCH

MASTIC

KEENE'S CEMENT
ARRIS

100×75 (95×70 FINISHED)
HEAD OF FRAME

2MM CLEARANCE

50×44 (45×39)
TOP RAIL OF SASH

SPRIG
PUTTY

K

DETAIL "R"

PUTTY

44×25 (39×20)
GLAZING BAR

L

DETAIL "S"

3MM SHEET GLASS

PUTTY

63×44 (58×39)
BOTTOM RAIL OF SASH

125×75 (120×70)
OAK SILL

25×6 GALV. IRON
WATER BAR BEDDED
IN WHITE LEAD

M

DETAIL "T"

MORTAR

215×110 STONE SILL

32(21) WINDOW BOARD
38×25 BED MOULD
16MM PLASTER

16MM PLASTER
100×75 JAMB OF FRAME

F

G

50×44 STILE OF SASH

44×25 GLAZING BAR
GLASS

OAK SILL

SPRIG

PUTTY

MASTIC

DETAIL "P"

DETAIL "Q"

Fig. 83

SCALE FOR DETAILS

MM

128

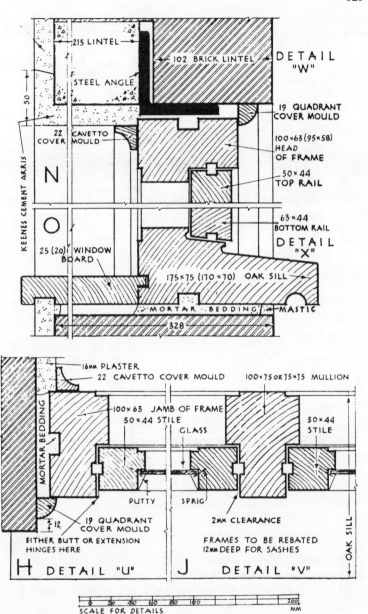

Fig. 84

are shown in Figs. 84 and 86 (A). These are called *capillary grooves*, as they are capable of arresting water which could pass by capillarity round the sash to the inside. The brick lintel at B, Fig. 81, is supported on a

130

mild steel angle, such support is needed for spans over 900 mm; for lesser spans the brick head can be built on the head of the frame.

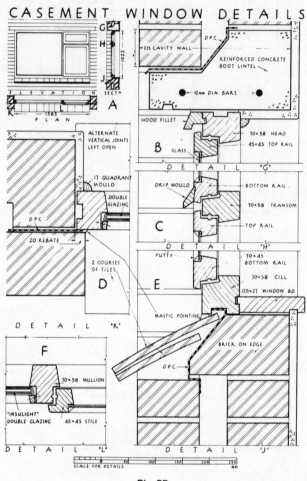

Fig. 85

The alternative details shown from B to F, Fig. 85, show sound construction; this type of window is very effective in excluding rain and wind. One of the disadvantages of the normal type of casement window is the "binding" of the sash which results when the timber expands due to the absorption of moisture. When this occurs the sashes are "eased" (the edges being planed to remove the excess wood), and there is a likelihood of rain and wind entering the enlarged clearance when the timber subsequently shrinks. The details in Fig. 85 obviate these defects; the lips

CASEMENT WINDOW DETAILS

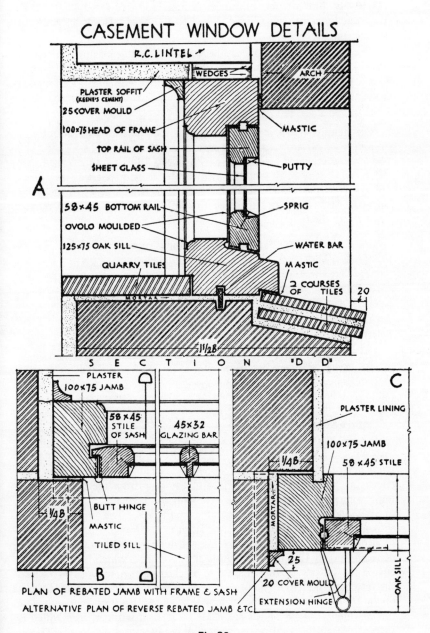

A

R.C. LINTEL

WEDGES

ARCH

PLASTER SOFFIT
(KEENE'S CEMENT)

25 COVER MOULD

100×75 HEAD OF FRAME

TOP RAIL OF SASH

SHEET GLASS

MASTIC

PUTTY

58×45 BOTTOM RAIL

OVOLO MOULDED

125×75 OAK SILL

QUARRY TILES

SPRIG

WATER BAR

MASTIC

2 COURSES
OF TILES

20

MORTAR

1½B

S E C T I O N "D D"

B

PLASTER

100×75 JAMB

58×45
STILE
OF SASH

45×32
GLAZING BAR

BUTT HINGE

MASTIC

TILED SILL

¼B

PLAN OF REBATED JAMB WITH FRAME & SASH

ALTERNATIVE PLAN OF REVERSE REBATED JAMB ETC

C

PLASTER LINING

100×75 JAMB

58×45 STILE

¼B

MORTAR

25

20 COVER MOULD

EXTENSION HINGE

OAK SILL

Fig. 86

effectively prevent the entrance of rain and reduce draughts. The throated *hood* or *drip fillet,* tongued to the head, affords an additional protection.

The window in Fig. 85 has a large pane of double glazing ("Insulight" by Pilkington Bros.) comprising two sheets of glass separated by an air space; the edges of the sheets are fused together with glass. This requires a glazing rebate depth of 11 mm minimum, external glazing beads are used.

The details shown in Fig. 86 are also recommended for adoption in buildings which are exposed to severe weather conditions. Those at A and B show a rebated brick jamb which gives a 38 mm cover to the frame; the *hanging* stile (only) of the sash is rebated and tongued, the tongue being splayed, as shown, to enable it to clear the frame when the sash is opened. If it is desired to show the full frame and retain the rebated brick jamb, the latter may be reversed, as shown at C.

Internal soffits and jambs of the openings .in the various details to be plastered. These are called *plastered linings,* and, as plaster is easily damaged at the edges, a good finish is provided when a comparatively hard material, such as Keene's cement, is used to form the arrises. A Keene's cement arris is at least 50 mm wide in each direction, and narrow linings may be entirely covered with this cement instead of plaster.

The height of windows above floor level should be given some consideration. That shown in the section at C, Fig. 81, is satisfactory for a house. Upper floor windows of houses should be as near to the eaves as possible.

HARDWARE.—This comprises hinges, fasteners and stays, see Fig. 87.

Hinges.—Ordinary butt hinges (see p. 60) may be used, one pair per sash. These are not, however, entirely satisfactory, as they are apt to be wrenched off and, when fixed to upper floor windows, difficulty is experienced in cleaning the external face of the glass from the inside. A big improvement upon the butt hinge for hanging casements is the *extension* or *cleaning hinge* which is illustrated in Fig. 87. The upper fitting is shown at A and the lower at B; the latter is also shown at C, Fig. 87. As indicated on the plan in Fig. 87, the sash can be opened to give a clearance of from 100 to 125 mm between it and the frame, which is sufficient to enable the outside of the window to be cleaned from the inside (see also the isometric sketch). The vertical edge of the free stile and the adjacent rebate on the jamb should be slightly splayed to permit of the opening of the casement. These hinges are made of steel or wrought iron which is *sherardized,* a process of rendering the metal rust-proof by the application of powdered zinc. Metal windows are also provided with extension hinges (see p. 171).

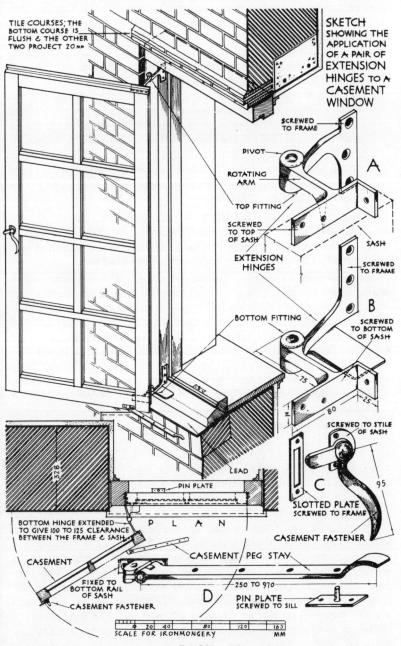

TILE COURSES; THE BOTTOM COURSE IS FLUSH & THE OTHER TWO PROJECT 20 MM

SKETCH SHOWING THE APPLICATION OF A PAIR OF EXTENSION HINGES TO A CASEMENT WINDOW

SCREWED TO FRAME

PIVOT

ROTATING ARM

TOP FITTING

SCREWED TO TOP OF SASH

EXTENSION HINGES

A

SASH

SCREWED TO FRAME

B

BOTTOM FITTING

SCREWED TO BOTTOM OF SASH

75

25

80

SCREWED TO STILE OF SASH

C

SLOTTED PLATE SCREWED TO FRAME

CASEMENT FASTENER

95

528

LEAD

PIN PLATE

PLAN

BOTTOM HINGE EXTENDED TO GIVE 100 TO 125 CLEARANCE BETWEEN THE FRAME & SASH

CASEMENT

CASEMENT PEG STAY

FIXED TO BOTTOM RAIL OF SASH

CASEMENT FASTENER

250 TO 970

D

PIN PLATE SCREWED TO SILL

0 20 40   80   120   160
SCALE FOR IRONMONGERY   MM

Fig. 87

Casement Fastener (see C and sketch, Fig. 87). The plate to which the pivoted handle is attached is screwed to the inside face of the free stile and the projecting point of the handle (when the sash is closed) engages in a slotted plate which is screwed to the frame near to the rebate. This type is also known as a *cockspur fastener* and is of sherardized iron or bronze (see also the type of handle used for metal windows, p. 173).

Casement Stay (see D, plan and sketch, Fig. 87). This form is called the *peg stay* and consists of a bar, holed at about 50 mm centres, which is pivoted to a small plate that is screwed to the inside face of the bottom rail; there is in addition a *peg* or *pin plate* which is screwed to the top of the wood sill. As is implied, the object of the stay is to maintain the sash when in the open position, and this it does when the peg is engaged in one of the holes. This fitting is made of sherardized iron, bronze, gunmetal, etc. Another form of stay, the sliding type, is referred to on p. 173 in connection with metal windows.

MANUFACTURE OF CASEMENT WINDOWS.—These, like doors, are machine manufactured on a large scale. Relatively few windows, especially of the ordinary type, are made by hand. Cutting lists of materials (see pp. 85 and 91) are prepared for both machine and hand production.

Machine-made Casement Windows.—Much of the description on the manufacture of doors (see pp. 85—91) applies to window manufacture. Extensive use of wood jigs (p. 86) is made, as for example, in the mortising of sash stiles to receive the tenons of the top and bottom rails and the glazing bars; such a jig is notched at the correct distance apart (obtained from the setting out rod) and the notches are equal in width to that of the tenons; the jig is fixed above the table of the mortising machine (Fig. 8), and the table on which each stile is placed is stopped in its longitudinal travel at each notch, in succession, before the chisel is caused to descend to form the mortice in the stile.

Hand-made Casement Windows.—The following brief description will be better understood if reference is made to pp. 86—89 regarding setting out, etc. It is assumed that the window shown at A, Fig. 81 and detailed in Figs. 82 and 83 is to be made entirely by hand. The window will be set out on the height and width rods (see B and E, Fig. 89, and C and G, Fig. 90), a cutting list will be made, and the stuff will be selected and prepared as described on pp. 86—89.

In preparing the frame, a start is usually made with the sill. The various stages of preparation are shown in Fig. 88. The bottom face EF is trued up (out of winding), the edge ED is squared, and each end is marked to the section taken off the rod (see E, Fig. 89). A stock of standard sill templets (thin shaped pieces of wood) is usually kept in the shop, and if the required section is standard, the templet is applied at each end, as shown at A, Fig. 88, and the sill marked. The top face DG is dressed square to the face edge, the triangular portion above the weathering is removed by sawing along GH, and two 6 mm wide grooves (see B, Fig. 88) are formed with the plough plane (2, Fig. 154, *Carpentry*) to the

135

required depth. The weathered surfaces are planed down to the marks
by a badger plane; this, like the jack plane (1, Fig. 154, *Carpentry*), is

FIRST, SECOND & FINAL STAGES

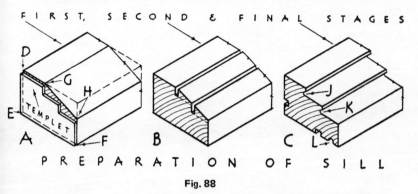

PREPARATION OF SILL

Fig. 88

430 mm long and its cutting iron is 60 mm wide; the iron, however,
extends to the far side of the stock and the plane is, therefore, useful in
dressing well into the corners; in this respect it resembles the small rebate
plane (5, Fig. 154, *Carpentry*). The grooves for the water bar and the
window board are ploughed, and the throating L is formed by means of
the throating or round plane (8 and L, Fig. 154, *Carpentry*). The round
plane is also used for forming the grooves or throatings J and K.

The sill, with its face edge inwards, is laid on the width rod (see B,
Fig. 89) and the *clearance lines* J and K are squared up, as shown. These
lines are then squared over on the top and bottom. The setting out of
the mortices at each end of the sill to receive the haunched tenons of the
stiles is indicated at A and B.

The head is set out by placing it on the sill (or below it) and marking
the clearance lines L and M, as shown at C, Fig. 89; these lines are squared
over the top and bottom faces. The mortices for the haunched tenons
(see A, B and C, Fig. 82), in addition to the rebate, are set out (see C and
D, Fig. 89).

The projecting ends of the sill and head (called *horns* or *joggles*) are
not cut off until the frame is ready for fixing.

In a similar manner, the stiles are set out from the height rod, both
stiles being placed on the rod, and the sill and head *shoulder lines* N and
P are marked, as indicated at E, Fig. 89. *Note that the lines squared up
from the rod are called* CLEARANCE *lines when associated with members
that are to be morticed (such as a head) and* SHOULDER *lines when the
ends of the members are to be tenoned (as stiles). It is also important
to observe that members, such as stiles, are laid down and marked in*
PAIRS. The ends of the stiles are gauged for the tenons (see F and H,
and p. 89, and the rebates are marked. In marking the bottom of each
stile, care should be taken to allow for the scribing of the foot to con-

form to the weathering of the sill (see B and C, Fig. 82, and G, Fig. 89). A sketch of a completed stile is shown at G, Fig. 89.

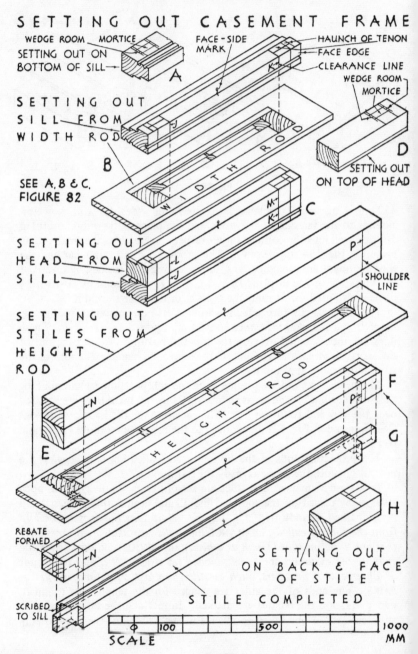

SETTING OUT CASEMENT FRAME

WEDGE ROOM MORTICE
SETTING OUT ON
BOTTOM OF SILL → A

FACE-SIDE MARK

HAUNCH OF TENON
FACE EDGE
CLEARANCE LINE
WEDGE ROOM
MORTICE

SETTING OUT
SILL FROM
WIDTH ROD B

WIDTH ROD

SETTING OUT
ON TOP OF HEAD D

SEE A, B & C.
FIGURE 82

C

SETTING OUT
HEAD FROM
SILL

SHOULDER LINE

SETTING OUT
STILES FROM
HEIGHT
ROD

HEIGHT ROD

F

E

G

H

REBATE
FORMED

SETTING OUT
ON BACK & FACE
OF STILE

SCRIBED
TO SILL

STILE COMPLETED

SCALE
0 100 500 1000
MM

Fig. 89

The mortices and tenons, rebates, etc. are formed (see p. 89), and the members are assembled and corrections made. The frame is then glued, wedged and cramped. Care should be taken to test for squareness by checking the diagonals (which should be equal) and sighting through from one stile to the other to ensure that they are not in twist or winding; any adjustments are made during the wedging operation. When satisfied that the frame is square, the joints are pinned (p. 123). Frames may also be jointed in red lead mastic.

The setting out of the sash is illustrated in Fig. 90. As shown at C, the pair of stiles is placed on the height rod, and the clearance or *sight* lines (those of the top and bottom rails and the glazing bars) are squared up. The mortices and rebates are set out, as shown at B. A completed stile is shown at A.

The top and bottom rails and the horizontal glazing bars are set out from the width rod, as illustrated at G. The ends of the rails and bars are gauged (see D, E and F, and p. 89). When, as in this example, the members are not moulded (which mouldings would be scribed—see p. 63), the top and bottom rail tenons should be haunched (note the haunching of the mortices at J and K at A); otherwise the sash tends to twist. As stated on p. 126, the horizontal glazing bars of a casement are continuous and morticed to receive the ends of the vertical bars (unless the halved joint shown at M, Fig. 96, is adopted, when both vertical and horizontal bars are continuous). Accordingly, the clearance lines are set out on these horizontal bars from the width rod and squared over. The setting out of the short vertical glazing bars is done in the following manner: One of the pieces of glazing bar to be set out is placed on the height rod with its ends lying equally over two of the bar sections marked on the setting out rod; the first shoulder lines are marked and squared over; the depth of the rebate is added to each end and marked as a second shoulder line on the opposite edge of the bar; the tenon lines are next gauged on the ends and down each face as far as the shoulder lines, the shoulders are cut, the rebates are worked and, finally, the tenons are cut. If the joint between glazing bars is halved (as shown at M, Fig. 96), the continuous vertical glazing bar would be set out from the height rod at the same time as the stiles. The joint between a glazing bar and stile is shown at H, Fig. 90, and the halved joint between glazing bars (see D) is shown at M, Fig. 96. When setting out the bottom rail, allowance must be made for the splayed bottom edge (see M, Fig. 83). The joints between the rails and stiles are illustrated at H, J and K, Fig. 82; the working of these joints will be understood from the description already given. Capillary grooves of the type shown in the details in Fig. 83 are formed by the plane; those indicated in the details in Fig. 84 are ploughed.

The assembling, gluing, wedging and cramping of a casement (sash) are carried out in the following order: Firstly, the tenons of the various members are placed in their respective mortices, and any errors are corrected to ensure a tight fit at the shoulders, etc. Next, one of the stiles is placed on the bench ready to receive the bars and rails. The tenons on the horizontal glazing bars are glued and inserted in the mortices (also glued) provided for them; the tenons are pushed well home. If

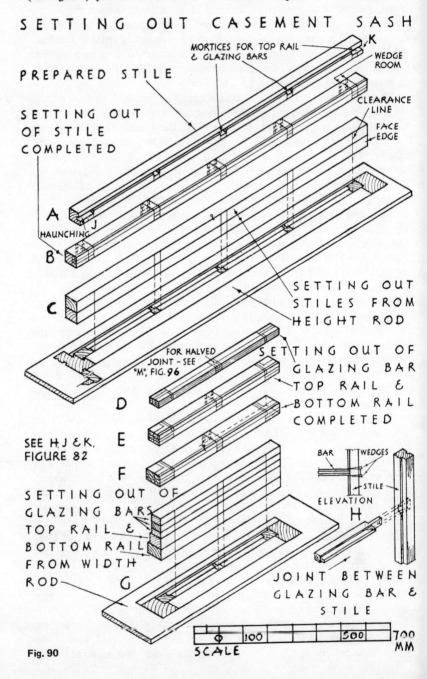

SETTING OUT CASEMENT SASH

MORTICES FOR TOP RAIL
& GLAZING BARS

K

WEDGE ROOM

PREPARED STILE

CLEARANCE LINE

SETTING OUT
OF STILE
COMPLETED

FACE EDGE

A

HAUNCHING   J

B

C

SETTING OUT
STILES FROM
HEIGHT ROD

FOR HALVED
JOINT – SEE
"M", FIG. 96

SETTING OUT OF
GLAZING BAR
TOP RAIL &
BOTTOM RAIL
COMPLETED

D

E

SEE H, J & K,
FIGURE 82

F

BAR   WEDGES

STILE

ELEVATION

SETTING OUT OF
GLAZING BARS
TOP RAIL &
BOTTOM RAIL
FROM WIDTH
ROD   G

H

JOINT BETWEEN
GLAZING BAR &
STILE

SCALE   0   100   500   700 MM

Fig. 90

the short vertical glazing bars are tenoned into the horizontal ones, it is not usual to glue the tenons, they being inserted in the mortices dry. These short lengths of glazing bars are fixed in turn, those between the horizontal bars being placed in position after the latter have been spread out slightly to permit of this. When all the vertical lengths of glazing bars have been positioned, the top and bottom rails are inserted in the mortices in the stile and the tenons of the vertical glazing bars are fitted into the mortices in these rails. The second stile is now fixed; it is some-times necessary to exert pressure, by means of a cramp placed in line with the vertical glazing bars and bearing on the top and bottom rails, to enable the rail tenons to enter the mortices provided in this second stile. In a well-made casement light, the vertical bars, although not wedged in the rail mortices, will be sufficiently tight to prevent any move-ment when the pressure is taken off. The sash is now cramped and wedged up, and the tenons on the rails should be pinned with 6 or 8 mm square section metal pins driven into round holes; before driving home the last of the wedges and pins, the sash must be tested for squareness (by checking the diagonals). The sash should be left until the glue is dry before the surfaces are cleaned up, and the joggles (projecting ends of the rails) should not be cut off until the sash is to be fixed to the frame. Again it is emphasized that all windows (and other framework) must be lying out of twist or winding when wedged up.

Whilst the above method of assembling sashes is best, another method, largely adopted in mass-production factories, is as follows: All the tenons of the rails and bars are inserted in the mortices dry, but with their shoulders left open. The whole of the exposed tenons are glued in one operation, and the sash is then cramped, wedged up and pinned.

FIXED SASHES OR DEAD LIGHTS.—In a window which consists of a single fixed light only, the glass is usually let into the frame, there being no sash.

If, however, as shown at B, Fig. 81, one of the lights is made to open and the other is fixed, the latter should be a fixed sash, well bedded in lead mastic and screwed to the frame. It is a common practice in cheap work to dispense with a sash for the fixed light and to fix the glass directly to the frame, the mullion, jamb, head and sill being rebated for this pur-pose. This completely spoils the appearance of the window, as the "sight lines" of the top and bottom rails of the casement do not "line through" with the top and bottom sight lines of the fixed light, the upper and lower panes of the fixed lights are higher than the intermediates, and, in addition, the sheets are wider than those in the hinged sash.

WINDOWS WITH SOLID FRAMES AND CASEMENTS OPENING INWARDS.—This type of window is not recommended, as it is almost impossible to make it weather-proof. A detailed description is therefore not given. The frame is rebated on the inside to receive the sash(es) which swings inwards. The interference with curtains, etc. caused when the sash is open provides an additional objection.

CHAPTER TEN

CASED FRAME WINDOWS

Windows with cased frames and vertical sliding sashes having square, segmental and semicircular heads. Three-light cased window. Manufacture, including setting out; hanging of sashes. Hardware.

SQUARE HEADED CASED WINDOW WITH VERTICAL SLIDING SASHES

THIS window is illustrated in Fig. 92. It has a pair of sashes, both of which should be made to open for the purposes of ventilation and to facilitate cleaning. The sashes slide vertically within shallow recesses formed in the frame which is built-up with comparatively thin members. The jambs of the frame are in the form of boxes or cases, hence the terms *boxed frame* and *cased frame* which are applied to it. A pair of metal weights contained within the frame are connected to each sash by means of cords or chains after being passed over pulleys fixed to the frame (see also sash balances on p. 153). Without the weights, the top sash when lowered and the bottom sash when raised would drop to the bottom immediately the sashes were released. The sashes of some windows, especially those, for example, that are to be fixed in large stone buildings of the commercial or factory type, are not divided by glazing bars into relatively small panes, but each sash is glazed with a single sheet. When glazing bars are provided, a satisfactory appearance is obtained if the proportion of the panes is as indicated in Fig. 91 (see also p. 106) and if the

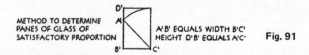

METHOD TO DETERMINE PANES OF GLASS OF SATISFACTORY PROPORTION — A'B' EQUALS WIDTH B'C' HEIGHT D'B' EQUALS A'C'   **Fig. 91**

window is three or four panes wide and four panes high. Both sashes are usually equal in size, although it is sometimes desirable to increase the height of the window when the upper and lower sashes may be two and three panes high respectively.

FRAME.—This consists of two vertical jambs, a head and a sill.

As shown at N, Fig. 93, and S, Fig. 94 (being alternative details), a jamb comprises an *inner* or *inside lining,* an *outer* or *outside lining,* a *pulley stile* (so called because the pulleys are screwed to them), and a *back lining* (often omitted in cheap work); in addition, a thin piece of wood, called a *parting* SLIP or *mid-feather*, is used to separate the two weights, a small *parting* BEAD is provided to separate the two sashes, and an *inner bead* (also called a *staff bead, fixing bead* or *guard bead*) is fixed to complete the shallow recess for the inner or lower sash.

140

The head (see alternative details at K, Fig. 93, and O, Fig. 94) consists of an inner and an outer lining, a *head* or *soffit lining,* an inner bead and a parting bead. The latter bead and the inner lining are sometimes omitted.

WINDOW WITH CASED FRAME & SLIDING SASHES

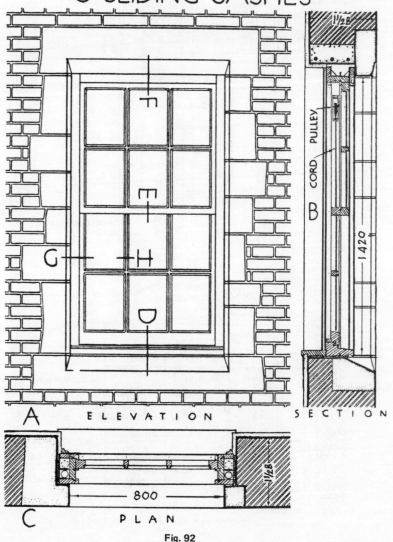

Fig. 92

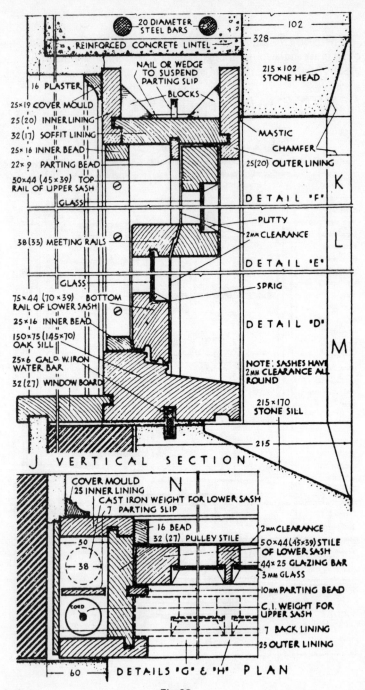

20 DIAMETER STEEL BARS

REINFORCED CONCRETE LINTEL

102

328

215×102 STONE HEAD

NAIL OR WEDGE TO SUSPEND PARTING SLIP

BLOCKS

16 PLASTER

25×19 COVER MOULD

25 (20) INNER LINING

32 (17) SOFFIT LINING

25×16 INNER BEAD

22×9 PARTING BEAD

50×44 (45×39) TOP RAIL OF UPPER SASH

GLASS

MASTIC

CHAMFER

25 (20) OUTER LINING

K

DETAIL "F"

PUTTY

2mm CLEARANCE

38 (33) MEETING RAILS

L

DETAIL "E"

GLASS

75×44 (70×39) BOTTOM RAIL OF LOWER SASH

25×16 INNER BEAD

150×75 (145×70) OAK SILL

25×6 GALD. W. IRON WATER BAR

32 (27) WINDOW BOARD

SPRIG

DETAIL "D"

M

NOTE: SASHES HAVE 2mm CLEARANCE ALL ROUND

215×170 STONE SILL

215

J VERTICAL SECTION

COVER MOULD

25 INNER LINING

CAST IRON WEIGHT FOR LOWER SASH

7 PARTING SLIP

N

16 BEAD

32 (27) PULLEY STILE

50

38

CORD

2mm CLEARANCE

50×44 (45×39) STILE OF LOWER SASH

44×25 GLAZING BAR

3mm GLASS

10mm PARTING BEAD

C.I. WEIGHT FOR UPPER SASH

7 BACK LINING

25 OUTER LINING

60

DETAILS 'G' & 'H' PLAN

Fig. 93

142

The solid sill, with staff bead, completes the frame.

Several methods are adopted for joining together the members of the jambs. Thus, as shown at N, Fig. 93, and S, Fig. 94, the inner and outer lining are each ploughed with a 10 mm square groove to receive the tongues formed on the pulley stile. Alternatively, the pulley stile is housed (let in for its full thickness) 3 mm into the outer lining, and the inner lining is rebated to receive the opposite square edge of the pulley stile. Sometimes the pulley stile is simply butt-jointed (neither tongued nor housed) and well nailed to the outer lining. The edges of the pulley stiles, grooves, rebates, etc., should be painted (and thus preserved) before the members are assembled. In each case the outer lining projects 16 mm to 19 mm beyond the face of the stile, and the edge of the inner lining is flush with the outer face of the stile (except that shown at S, Fig. 94).

The upper end of the pulley stile is either housed or tongued to the soffit lining, and its bottom end is housed and wedged to the wood sill (see A, B, D and E, Fig. 95, and L, Fig. 96). As shown at A and B, the lower end of the stile is about 6 mm below the outer edge of the weathering of the sill, and as indicated at L, Fig. 96, the wedge is driven in from the inside between the stile and the vertical cut of the housing, and this wedge is securely nailed to the stile.

The inner and outer jamb linings extend the full height of the frame (see B, Fig. 95), the inner and outer soffit linings butt against the jamb linings at X and Y (see D, Fig. 95), and as shown at B and E, the oak sill is cut back at each side to receive the lower ends of the inner and outer jamb linings which are nailed to the sill, pulley stile throughout its length, soffit linings along the tongued and grooved (or housed and rebated) joints and at the butt joints X and Y.

The parting slip extends to within 100 mm (approximately) of the top of the sill (if less than this it is difficult to remove the weights if the cords break) and is suspended from the soffit lining (see A and B, Fig. 95). A slot is formed in the latter, the slip is passed through it and either a nail or wood wedge is driven through it, as shown at K, Fig. 93, O, Fig. 94, and A, B and D, Fig. 95. The centre line of the parting slip coincides with that of the parting bead.

The back lining extends from the soffit lining to the upper surface of the sill and is nailed to the jamb linings (see A and C, Fig. 95, and N, Fig. 93); sometimes one edge is housed into the outer jamb lining (see S, Fig. 94), or alternatively, it is housed into the inner jamb lining and secured to the square edge of the outer lining (i.e., the opposite to that shown at S). As shown at N, Fig. 93, the clear space between the pulley stile and the back lining must be 50 mm, as the diameter of the weights is usually 32 mm.

As the equivalent to a back lining is not provided at the head, the necessary stiffness is imparted by the use of 75 or 100 mm long triangular wood blocks spaced along the internal angles between the soffit lining and the inner and outer linings at intervals of from 75 to 150 mm, with one placed across each butt joint between the jamb and soffit linings (see K,

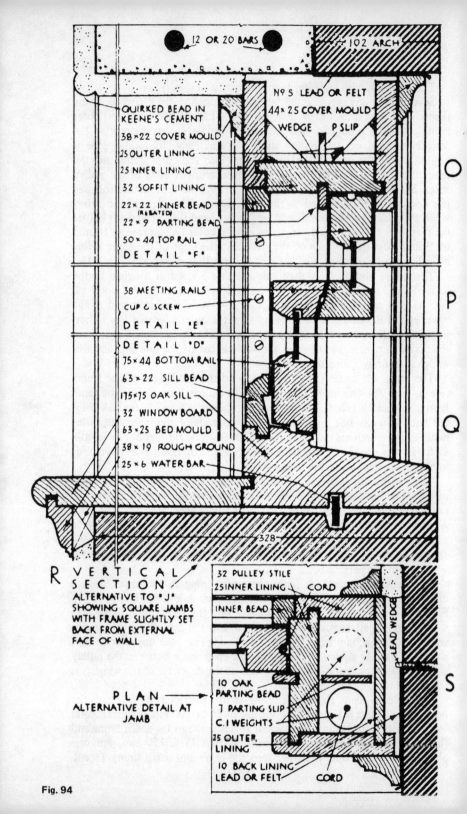

12 OR 20 BARS

102 ARCH

Nº 5 LEAD OR FELT
44 × 25 COVER MOULD
WEDGE   P SLIP

QUIRKED BEAD IN
KEENE'S CEMENT

38 × 22 COVER MOULD
25 OUTER LINING
25 INNER LINING
32 SOFFIT LINING
22 × 22 INNER BEAD (REBATED)
22 × 9 PARTING BEAD
50 × 44 TOP RAIL

DETAIL "F"

O

38 MEETING RAILS
CUP & SCREW

DETAIL "E"

P

DETAIL "D"

75 × 44 BOTTOM RAIL
63 × 22 SILL BEAD
175 × 75 OAK SILL
32 WINDOW BOARD
63 × 25 BED MOULD
38 × 19 ROUGH GROUND
25 × 6 WATER BAR

Q

─328─

R VERTICAL
SECTION
ALTERNATIVE TO "J"
SHOWING SQUARE JAMBS
WITH FRAME SLIGHTLY SET
BACK FROM EXTERNAL
FACE OF WALL

32 PULLEY STILE
25 INNER LINING   CORD

INNER BEAD

LEAD WEDGE

PLAN
ALTERNATIVE DETAIL AT
JAMB

10 OAK
PARTING BEAD
7 PARTING SLIP
C.I WEIGHTS
25 OUTER
LINING
10 BACK LINING
LEAD OR FELT   CORD

S

Fig. 94

Fig. 93, O, Fig. 94, and A, B and D, Fig. 95). These blocks are glued to the linings. If, as mentioned on p. 141, the inner lining is omitted at the head, the construction is greatly simplified, as the outer lining (only 75 by 25 mm is nailed to the square edge of the soffit lining (increased in thickness from 32 to 50 mm); blocks are not, therefore, required; this is a cheap but effective alternative detail, and is equivalent to a solid head.

The inner bead is fixed all round the frame. This bead covers the joint between the inner lining and the pulley stile or soffit lining. In first class work, the inner beads are sometimes rebated, as shown at O and S, Fig. 94; the inner lining is cut back 6 mm from the face of the pulley stile to permit of this; such beads, if they have to be removed (as when broken sash cords require attention), are more readily replaced in correct position than are non-rebated beads. Usually, however, even in good work, these beads are not rebated and are as shown at K and N, Fig. 93. These inner beads are moulded as required (see also those in Figs. 103 and 111), and the ends of each length are mitred. A slightly wider and bevelled inner or staff bead is fixed to the sill; the bottom rail of the sash is also bevelled to ensure a reasonably tight fit which prevents the sashes from rattling (see M, Fig. 93). Alternatively, a deeper *sill bead* (see Q, Fig. 94) is recommended (see also Fig. 112). This allows the lower sash to be raised slightly to permit air to enter between the meeting rails (see p. 147) of the sashes; this incoming air is deflected upwards to minimize draughts, and the latter are not caused at the sill level. This is sometimes called a *ventilating piece* or *draught bead*. Inner beads should be fixed with brass cups and screws (N and O, Fig. 149, *Carpentry*) to permit of their ready removal when required, although they are more often just bradded (nailed).

The parting bead is fitted tightly into a 9 mm square groove ploughed in the stile and nailed. The details show a similar bead at the soffit, although this is often omitted in common work; when provided, it assists in excluding rain and draughts.

Access for Weights.—Provision must be made in each pulley stile for fixing weights. Such is called a *pocket,* and is situated just below the meeting rails of the sashes and extends to about 150 mm above the sill. Two forms of pockets are shown at A, B, E, F and K, Fig. 95.

Side Pocket.—The sketch at F shows this type which is indicated at A, B and C. The plan shows the width to extend from the back of the inner lining to the groove for the parting head, which it includes. Long pockets are preferred; they are about 380 mm long for average-sized sashes and must be at least equal to the length of the weights. The bottom end of the pocket is bevelled at 60°, and the top end is vee-shaped and bevelled at 60° in both directions; the cuts made to form these bevels are made by the *pocket chisel* (described in Chapter X, *Carpentry*); the vee-shaped top end is formed by making a second cut, and the small triangular piece which is removed is glued and nailed to the back of the stile (see section XX, Fig. 95) to form an abutment or cleat for the *pocket-piece*. The latter

146

is secured to the stile by a screw at the bottom end, in addition to the parting bead which is fixed subsequently. The lower sash and parting

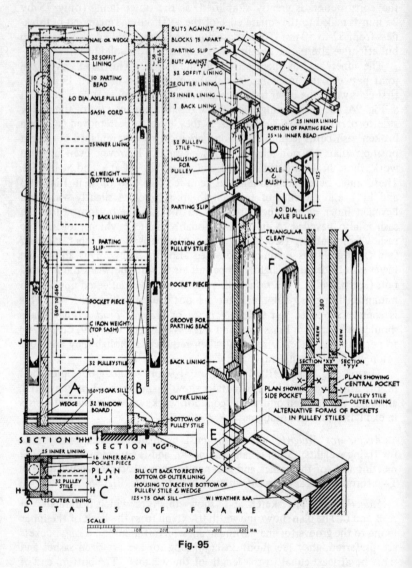

Fig. 95

bead completely cover the pocket and, therefore, any damaged caused when the piece is removed for sash cord renewals is effectively concealed. Pulley stiles should be of even straight-grained stuff to facilitate cutting and removal of the pockets.

Central Pocket.—This is a less satisfactory form and is shown at K, Fig. 95; it has a rebated joint at the bottom end, and a rebated and bevelled joint at the top. This is not so good as the type shown at F, as the outer vertical joint and portions of the horizontal cuts are exposed, and any damage caused to them on removal is conspicuous.

Sills.—The several forms of sills should be noted. That at Q, Fig. 94, is wider than the sill at M, Fig. 93, to allow the external *cover mould* to finish on it. The water bar at Q is shown at the centre of the sill; as implied on p. 124, this is preferably fixed with the outside of the groove in line with the back of the outer lining (see Fig. 112) so that the bar will arrest any water before it has travelled more than 25 mm. A sill with a single weathering and comparatively deep sinking (i.e., somewhat similar to that shown at D, Fig. 85) is often preferred to the double weathered sill, with small sinkings, shown at M, Fig. 93.

Scantlings of Frame.—As the weight of the sashes is transmitted directly to the pulley stiles, it is customary to prepare the stiles out of thicker stuff than that for the inner and outer linings. The nominal thickness of pulley stiles and soffit linings is usually 32 mm (or 25 mm for small frames), and that of inner and outer linings is generally 25 mm (or 19 mm for small frames). The sizes of the various members are figured upon the drawings. Note that full-size details should be drawn to the *finished* dimensions and that these are 5 mm less than the nominal sizes (see p. 67); some of these finished sizes are indicated in brackets in the details (e.g., Fig. 93). It should be observed, however, that the members of the frame are often only planed on their exposed faces, and thus the loss in dressing is reduced to about 4 mm; the back lining is usually just dressed along its edges.

SASHES.—The upper sash slides in the recess formed in the frame by the pulley stile, outer lining and parting bead, and the lower sash is accommodated in the recess formed by the pulley stile, inner bead and parting bead (see Figs. 92, 93, 94 and 95). Each sash consists of two stiles, a top rail and a bottom rail, but as the bottom rail of the upper sash meets the top rail of the lower sash when the window is closed, these two members are called *meeting rails.* A minimum clearance of 1 mm should be allowed all round the sashes to permit of easy movement for polished work, and this is increased to 2 mm when the window is to be painted; rattling of the sashes will result if this clearance is excessive.

Joint between Stile and Top Rail of Upper Sash (see H, Fig. 82, and R, Fig. 96).—The construction at H is usually adopted if the members are moulded, the scribing of the moulds preventing twisting of the sash. The alternative detail at R shows the top rail haunched tenoned (like a door) at each end, and each stile suitably morticed to receive the tenon and wedges. Glued wedges (waterproof glue being used) and a hardwood pin or dowel (see p. 57) or metal pin (p. 139) complete the joint. The methods of securing the sash cord are described on p. 153.

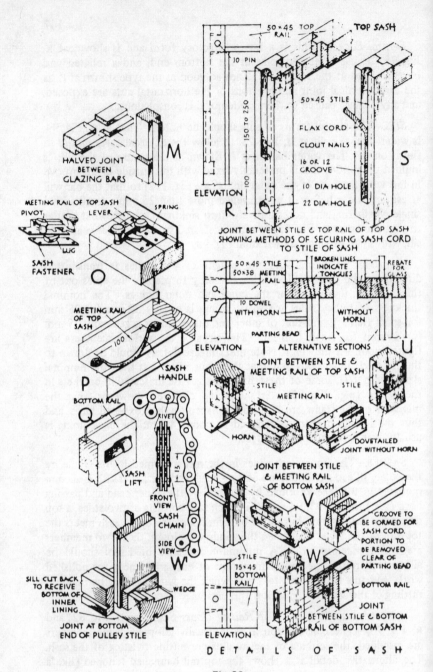

HALVED JOINT BETWEEN GLAZING BARS   M

ELEVATION   R

50×45 TOP RAIL   TOP SASH

10 PIN
150 TO 250
100

50×45 STILE
FLAX CORD
CLOUT NAILS
16 OR 12 GROOVE
10 DIA HOLE
22 DIA HOLE   S

JOINT BETWEEN STILE & TOP RAIL OF TOP SASH
SHOWING METHODS OF SECURING SASH CORD
TO STILE OF SASH

MEETING RAIL OF TOP SASH
PIVOT   LEVER   SPRING
SASH FASTENER
LUG   O

MEETING RAIL OF TOP SASH
100
SASH HANDLE   P

BOTTOM RAIL   Q
SASH LIFT

RIVET
15
FRONT VIEW
SASH CHAIN
SIDE VIEW   W

50×45 STILE
50×38 MEETING RAIL
10 DOWEL
PARTING BEAD
ELEVATION   T

BROKEN LINES INDICATE TONGUES
WITH HORN   WITHOUT HORN
REBATE FOR GLASS
ALTERNATIVE SECTIONS   U

JOINT BETWEEN STILE & MEETING RAIL OF TOP SASH

STILE   STILE
MEETING RAIL
HORN
DOVETAILED JOINT WITHOUT HORN

JOINT BETWEEN STILE & MEETING RAIL OF BOTTOM SASH

STILE
75×45 BOTTOM RAIL
ELEVATION

GROOVE TO BE FORMED FOR SASH CORD. PORTION TO BE REMOVED CLEAR OF PARTING BEAD
BOTTOM RAIL
JOINT BETWEEN STILE & BOTTOM RAIL OF BOTTOM SASH   W

SILL CUT BACK TO RECEIVE BOTTOM OF INNER LINING
WEDGE
JOINT AT BOTTOM END OF PULLEY STILE   L

DETAILS OF SASH

Fig. 96

148

Joint between Stile and Meeting Rail of Upper Sash (see T, Fig. 96).
—The bottom of the meeting rail of the top sash and the top of the meeting rail of the bottom sash are at least 9 mm wider (or the width of the parting bead) than the thickness of the stiles, otherwise a gap equal to the thickness of the parting bead (plus clearance) would be left (see L, Fig. 93, and P, Fig. 94). The joints between the meeting rails are either just bevelled or, as shown, are *bevel rebated*; the latter joint is preferred, for it assists in preventing the sashes rattling, effectively increases the difficulty of gaining access to the sash fastener (see O, Fig. 96) from the outside and enables the rails to separate easily when the sashes are opened.

The stiles of the sashes may extend from 38 to 75 mm beyond the meeting rails, and these projections are shaped as required to form *horns* (or *brackets* or *joggles*); horns are often omitted, however, as they are considered to detract from the appearance. The details at T and U, Fig. 96, show both types. The horned form at T shows a mortice and tenon joint (called a *fork tenon*) with the bevelled portion of the rail passing over the inner face of the stile, which latter is dovetailed to receive it (see section and the isometric sketch); the central tongue is wedged (see elevation); it is usual to leave the upper edge of the bevelled portion projecting slightly beyond the face of the stile, and this may be afterwards dressed down to the stile when the meeting rails are fitted together. In the second or hornless type at U, a dovetailed joint must be adopted, otherwise the joint would readily become loosened when the sash handles (see P, Fig. 96) are pulled downwards whilst the sash is being opened. Note the shaped end of the stile in the isometric sketch and the broken lines in the alternative section which indicate the dovetailed tongue and bevelled portion. The joint is either screwed or pinned or dowelled, as shown at T.

Joint between Stile and Meeting Rail of Lower Sash (see V, Fig. 96).
—Like the top sash, the stiles of the bottom sash may be provided with horns, but in first-class work these are omitted and a dovetailed joint between the meeting rail and each stile is adopted, as shown at V, which indicates the upper end of the stile shaped to receive the dovetailed tenon and bevelled portion of the meeting rail; the latter portion passes over the outer face of the stile, and its lower edge is usually left slightly proud of this face until both meeting rails are finally fitted together.[1] This joint is also pinned or screwed. A groove is formed down the edge of sash stile to accommodate the sash cord; this is similar to that shown at R and S, Fig. 96, and is indicated by broken lines at V (see sketch of the assembled joint). Note the provision made on this meeting rail to receive the glass; as both meeting rails are of the same depth, it is not possible to form the usual rebate on the lower sash meeting rail, and in lieu of it a groove is formed along the underside of the rail (see also L, Fig. 93, and P, Fig. 94).

[1] Students should be careful to show the joint between the meeting rails correctly. Examination scripts and homework sheets frequently show details which indicate the bevel running downwards from the inside to the outside. Movement of the sashes would not, of course, be possible if the meeting rails were constructed to such details.

The ends of the bevelled portions of the meeting rails must be cut away for clearance round the projecting parting beads. The small piece so removed from the bottom sash meeting rail is indicated by broken lines at V. The groove for the cord, the clearance for the parting bead and the dowel holes have been omitted in the sketches so as to render the details less confusing.

Joint between Stile and Bottom Rail of Lower Sash (see W, Fig. 96). —This is an ordinary pinned haunched tenoned joint. The alternative joint shown at J, Fig. 82, is very often adopted (when members are moulded and scribed). The bottom of the rail and the ends of the stiles are shaped as required (examples at D, Fig. 85, M, Fig. 93, and Q, Fig. 94).

Joint between Glazing Bars.—The scribed and franked joints between sash bars are described on p. 126, and the halved joint is shown at M, Fig. 96 (see p. 137). Glue is applied to the joints before assembling and cramping the sashes (see pp. 137—139).

Scantlings of Sashes.—The usual nominal thickness of a sash of average size is 45 mm, but the thickness may be increased to 50 or 58 mm for larger sashes, whilst small sashes may only be 38 mm thick. The common scantlings are: stiles and top rail, 50 by 45 mm thick; meeting rails, 50 mm wide by 38 mm; bottom rail, 75 to 100 mm by 45 mm thick. Glazing bars may be out of 45 mm by 25 mm stuff, but a thickness of 38 mm reduced to 25 mm gives the better appearance.

TIMBER.—The timber employed in the construction of windows of this type are Douglas fir, redwood, oak, pitch pine and teak. Oak, teak or pitch pine are often specified for the sill when the rest of the members are of softwood. Oak or teak are used throughout for first-class work.

HARDWARE.—Although there are many patent devices on the market for use on windows of this description, the following simple fittings have been proved to be quite effective for their purpose. They include sash fasteners, sash lifts, sash handles and pulleys, together with the weights and sash cords or chains.

Sash Fastener (see O, Fig. 96).—This affords an effective security, provided it is of good quality. The fitting is of brass or bronze and comprises two castings, one being screwed at the top and in the centre of the meeting rail of the top sash, and the second (or *lug*) being screwed opposite to it at the top of the meeting rail of the bottom sash; on the former casting there is a lever which is pivoted at one end and has a solid knob at the other. When the lever is rotated, the pivoted end bears against the free end of a strong and highly tempered steel spring which is riveted to a recessed vertical portion of the casting, and the dovetailed notch on the lever engages in the solid curved lug which is riveted to the second fitting. This brings both meeting rails close together and secures the window.

Sash Lift (see Q, Fig. 96).—This is the *hook lift* type, other forms being ring lifts, flush recessed lifts and hinged lifts. One pair of lifts is screwed to the inside of the bottom rail of the lower sash, and at about 150 mm from each end. They are, of course, used to raise the bottom sash and are of brass or bronze.

Sash Handle (see P, Fig. 96).—When a sash is large (and especially when there are no glazing bars to grip when drawing down the sash) a pair of handles may be fixed on the underside of the top sash meeting rail near to the stiles. They are not very convenient, as the lower sash has to be raised before the handles are accessible from the inside.

The following simple expedient for operating a top sash is effective: A pulley is fixed to the soffit lining of the frame immediately over each stile of the upper sash, and an *eye* or ring is screwed into the inner face and near to the top end of each stile of this sash. A piece of cord, of a length equal to about one and a half times the height of the window, is threaded through each eye and passed over each pulley until it is doubled; each cord is knotted immediately above and below the eye; the ends of each double cord are equal and have handles attached. To open the top sash, the required end of each cord is pulled to draw the sash downwards with the top knot bearing upon the eye. The sash is closed by pulling on the other ends of the cords which brings the lower knots against the eyes to lift the sash.

As mentioned on p. 140, in order to conveniently slide the sashes and maintain them in any desired position when open, it is necessary to fix to them sash cords which are fastened to weights situated in the casings after being passed over pulleys fixed to the frame.

Sash Axle Pulleys (see A, B, D and N, Fig. 95).—This type consists of a 58 mm diameter, round grooved, brass pulley (or *sheave*) having 12 mm diameter steel axles which revolve in brass or gunmetal *bushes* 6 mm thick annular bearings) mounted on a metal (iron, gunmetal or rustless steel) case, which is flanged and covered with a brass or bronze face plate; the pulleys may be 45, 50, 58, 63 and 75 mm in diameter. This hollow-rounded grooved type of pulley is suitable for flax cords, copper cords and metal chains of the form shown at W , Fig. 96; square grooved pulleys are adopted for certain heavy chains; the cog wheel type of axle pulley (having a fixed axle with a toothed portion which bears the chain and which revolves on ball bearings) may be selected for extra heavy sashes.

The 125 mm by 28 mm face plate of the pulley is screwed flush with the outer face of a pulley stile, with the top of the plate from 38 to 63 mm down from the head (see A and B); the mortice for the pulley case and the housing for the flange and face plate are shown at D. The pulleys project about 8 mm beyond the outer external face of the pulley stile (see A), and the size of the pulley must be sufficient to allow the weight to hang clear of the frame. Two pulleys per sash are required.

Weights (see N, Fig. 93), S, Fig. 94, and A, B and C, Fig. 95).—These are cylindrical cast iron weights, 38 mm in diameter and of varying length in accordance with their weight; thus, a 2·25 kg weight is about 300 mm long, whilst a 3 kg weight is 380 mm long. The object of these weights is to counterbalance the weight of the sashes. The top of each weight is holed to receive the end of the cord. Lead sash weights, square in section (see Fig. 106), are sometimes used for very heavy sashes, but these must be specially made, whereas the ordinary sizes cf cast iron weights can be obtained from stock varying from 1 to 18 kg.

Opinions differ as to the weight required per sash, but satisfactory results are obtained if *each* of the two weights for the *top* sash is from 0·25 to 0·5 kg *heavier* than *half* the weight of the sash, and if *each* of the two bottom sash weights is from 0·25 to 0·5 kg *lighter* than half the weight of this sash. The weight of each sash is found by means of a spring balance, and due allowance should be made for the weight of the glass to be used and that of the putty and paint.

Sash Cords and Chains.—The weights are secured by either cords or chains which are passed over the pulleys and attached to the sashes.

Best quality stout twisted or braided cotton cord is usually specified for ordinary work. It is obtainable in lengths of 30 mm; its thickness varies from 5 to 9 mm, the former being suitable for weights of less than 2·25 kg, and the latter for weights up to 22·5 kg. The cheaper cord stretches and, therefore, each length should be stretched before being fixed, otherwise it may elongate to such an extent as to limit the movement of the sashes, *i.e.,* the weights of the bottom sash may reach the bottom of the casing before the sash has travelled to its full height (see p. 160). Certain brands of the best quality are waxed and are guaranteed to be stretch proof and damp proof.

The defect of flax cord is that in course of time it frays and ultimately breaks. A stronger and more durable cord is that known as *copper wire cord,* available in 30 mm lengths.

Another form of sash cord consists of a steel wire centre or core which is covered with cotton yarn; the covering prevents the wire from coming into contact with the metal pulley, and thereby reduces the noise when the sashes are moved.

One form of sash chain is shown at W', Fig. 96. This is called the *three-and-two link copper chain,* as it comprises a series of three links or plates (each 1 mm thick) which alternate with a pair of links; the overall thickness of the five links is 6 mm. Each link has two holes, and loose fitting pins or rivets pass through the five links at each connection. The chain can be used in conjunction with the ordinary axle pulley shown at N, Fig. 95, as it readily accommodates itself to the sharpest curve. Special fittings are used for connecting the chain to the weights and sashes. One form of connector to the weight consists of a hook which is simply passed through the eye of the weight. The sash fitting comprises a plate which is screwed to the edge of the sash, and a pin is passed through the brackets on this plate and the holes of the chain links. The chain is an improvement upon, but is more expensive than, the flax cord, and chains have been known to last for more than thirty years before requiring attention. Chains used in conjunction with the cog wheel type of pulley employed for very heavy sashes are of similar construction to the above, but the links are of rust-proofed steel connected by means of phosphor-bronze rivets.

FIXING CORDS TO SASHES AND WEIGHTS.—Both stiles of each sash have to be prepared to receive the cords. Two methods of fixing the cords are shown at R and S, Fig. 96. That shown at S is the most common method, a 12 or 16 mm groove being ploughed 200 to 300 mm down the back edge of each stile and the cord being clout-nailed, as indicated; this groove must be sufficiently wide to clear the protruding pulley at the top of the pulley stile. A better method is shown at R where a similar groove to the above is ploughed to a distance of from 150 to 250 mm (depending upon the size of the sash); this is continued by a 9 mm diameter hole which is bored to a depth of about 100 mm and is terminated by a 25 mm diameter hole formed at the edge. The cord is secured by threading it through the smaller hole, the end being knotted and hammered into the bottom hole.

The sashes are hung as described on p. 160.

Sash Balance.—This fitting, referred to on p. 140, dispenses with weights, cords and pulleys. A cased frame is not necessary, but inner, outer and parting beads must be fixed to the solid frame to form the necessary recesses for the sashes. A sash balance consists of a coiled steel spring tape within a casing to which is attached a face plate. A pair of balances are required per sash. Balances are obtainable in various sizes to suit the weights of the sashes. Mortices are formed in the jambs, just below the head, to receive the casings of the balances. The face plates are screwed to the jambs, and the looped ends of the coiled springs are screwed to the edges of the sashes. When the top sash is pulled down the tapes from the two balances are drawn out, and when the lower sash is raised the tapes in the other two balances are coiled up.

GENERAL.—Windows with cased frames and sliding sashes (often described as "double-hung sashed windows") are most effective in excluding rain and draughts, and are superior to the ordinary casement windows for exposed positions.

The window shown in Fig. 92 and detailed in Fig. 93 is fixed in a recess, the inner face of the pulley stile being in line with the face of the stone outer reveal; if it is a brick wall, the opening may have ½-brick deep recesses, when the outer face of the pulley stile conforms with the face of the outer reveal. Whilst weathertight joints are assured between the frame and wall when the former is built in recesses, the appearance is not so satisfactory, as all but a narrow margin of the frame is concealed; hence, the openings are often provided with square jambs which permit of the whole of the outer face being exposed. The defect of this construction is referred to on p. 127. One of several methods adopted to prevent water gaining access between the frame and wall is shown at O and S, Fig. 94, where a narrow strip of lead (or asphalt felt) is fixed at the jambs and head and covered with a wood moulding. Openings with reversed rebated jambs, similar to that shown at C, Fig. 86, are very suitable for this type of window, as the construction is sound and the appearance satisfactory.

MANUFACTURE.—Most windows are machine made (p. 134), and in the well-equipped workshop few hand labours are necessary in the manufacture of cased framed and vertical sliding sashed windows; even the pockets are machine cut. Nevertheless, the efficient craftsman should be able to prepare windows by hand, as he may be called upon to do this (or at least some of the hand operations) and, further, a knowledge of hand preparation will give him a better understanding of machining. It is unnecessary to give a detailed description of machining this type of window in view of that which appears on pp. 85, 86, 91 and 134. The machined parts are fabricated or assembled on the joiner's bench and finished off by hand according to the standard of finish required.

In the following description it is assumed that the window illustrated in Fig. 92 and detailed in Figs. 93, 95 and 96 is to be prepared by hand. A cutting list will be prepared from the height and width rods.

Fig. 97 illustrates the necessary setting out of the frame. The sill (which should be 3 mm wider than the overall width of the frame to allow for shrinkage) is first set out from the width rod (see B). The clearance lines J and K are marked up and then squared over on the top and bottom. A tapered (on plan) templet, shown at A, is useful for marking on the weathered portions; this is approximately 280 mm long, 100 mm wide, and its thickness is 50 mm at L and 38 mm at M (LM being the width of the sill). As stated on p. 143, the bottom ends of pulley stiles are housed and wedged to the sill (see A, B and E, Fig. 95). Accordingly, the thickness of this templet is equal to the combined thickness of the pulley stile and wedge. The templet is placed on top of the sill against the clearance line J; two lines are then drawn across the sill and against the templet (see B); this is repeated at the other end. The depth of housing of the pulley stile is from 6 to 12 mm below the outer edge of the weathering of the sill (p. 143); therefore, as indicated at N, a line is gauged up from the bottom of the sill and the depth of each housing at ON and PQ is marked; the depth of the housing at JR and KS is also marked. As shown at B and E, Fig. 95, the sill is cut to receive the bottom ends of the inner and outer linings (p. 143); hence at the end of the sill the sinkings for these linings are gauged, and the top lines TU, VW, XY and ZA′ are marked, as shown at B, Fig. 97.

The sill is placed on the soffit lining and the clearance lines at J and K are marked (see C). These are squared across. The depth (9 mm) of the groove to receive the pulley stile tongue (or the housing—see p. 143) is gauged, the width of the groove (9 or 12 mm) or housing (thickness of stile) is marked and squared across, as indicated at B′ and C′. The slot (6 mm wide to receive the end of the parting slip—see A, B and D, Fig. 95 and p. 143) is marked near each end. The groove for the parting bead is gauged (although this is often omitted at the soffit—see p. 145, for ease of working this groove usually extends the full length of the

SETTING OUT CASED FRAME

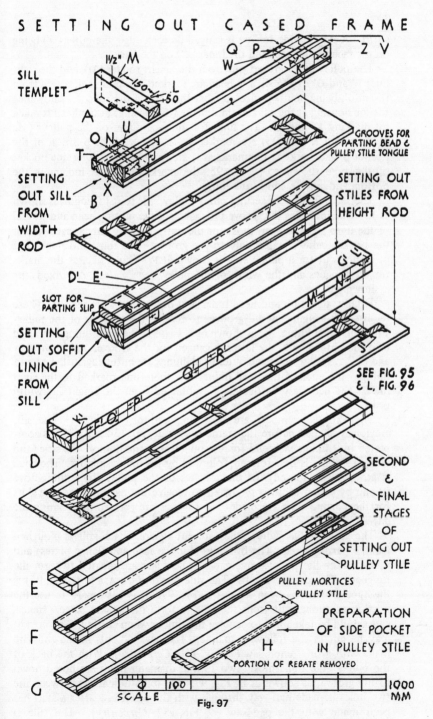

SILL TEMPLET

1½" M

150 50 L

A

GROOVES FOR PARTING BEAD & PULLEY STILE TONGUE

SETTING OUT SILL FROM WIDTH ROD

SETTING OUT STILES FROM HEIGHT ROD

SLOT FOR PARTING SLIP

SETTING OUT SOFFIT LINING FROM SILL

SEE FIG. 95 & L, FIG. 96

SECOND & FINAL STAGES OF SETTING OUT PULLEY STILE

PULLEY MORTICES PULLEY STILE

PREPARATION OF SIDE POCKET IN PULLEY STILE

PORTION OF REBATE REMOVED

0 100 1000 MM

SCALE

Fig. 97

soffit. A 9 mm wide tongue is gauged on each edge, the outer (D') being on the face (underside) and the inner (E') on the back.

The pulley stiles are set out from the height rod (see D), and the sight lines F' and G' of the sill and head are marked. Note that these are from H' and J', being points projected from the edge of the tongue. Allowance for the housing at the sill and the tongue (or housing) at the head is made by marking K' and L'. The lines for the face plates of the pulleys (see A, B, D and N, Fig. 95) are marked at M' and N'. The position of the pocket is also marked; the marks at D are for a 380 mm long side pocket of the type shown at F, Fig. 95, the marks O' and P' indicating the bottom end, and Q' and R' the top.

The second stage of setting out a pulley stile (cut to length) is shown at E. This indicates the groove ploughed for the parting bead and several of the lines squared over, those for the bottom of the cuts at each end of the pocket being squared only to the groove. The third and final stage of setting out for a pulley stile is shown at F. This indicates the marks for the tongues and the width of the pulley face plates. A worked stile is shown at G.

Finally, the jamb and head inner and outer linings are set out. These require the gauging of the grooves to receive the tongues of the pulley stiles and soffit lining. If, as shown at S, Fig. 94, the back lining is housed into the outer lining, the latter is gauged for the groove. As shown at A and D, Fig. 95, the inner and outer head linings are butted against the jamb linings; the ends of the head linings are, therefore, marked to the sight lines. The necessary particulars are obtained from the height and width rods.

The various members are now prepared or "worked". The sill, previously shaped before the frame is set out (pp. 134 and 135), is completed by sinking each end for the pulley stile and linings; the stile (and wedge) sinking is first formed, followed by the lining sinkings. The head is grooved (or housed) for the tongues of the pulley stiles, the groove (9 mm by 6 mm deep) is ploughed to receive the parting bead, the slots for the parting slips are made and tongues formed by rebating the edges.

The ends of the pulley stiles are cut square. Each stile is ploughed for the parting bead. The housings (for the face and flange plates) and mortices for the pulleys are made. The edges are rebated to form the tongues. The pocket is cut. The side pocket (see A and F, Fig. 95) is the type which has been set out in Fig. 97. It is customary to use the portion of timber cut from the stile to form the pocket piece. Hence, care should be taken not to damage the timber when cutting. The pocket may be cut in the following manner: The bevelled cuts at the ends are made with a fine tenon saw (7, Fig. 152, *Carpentry*). With the back of the pulley stile uppermost, two 19 mm diameter holes are bored down to the groove, as shown at H, Fig. 97. The longitudinal cut between the two holes is made half-way through with the panel saw after a start has been made with the pad saw (5, Fig. 152, *Carpentry*). The stile is reversed and a half depth longitudinal cut along the outside of the groove is made with the pad and panel saws. The pocket piece should not be knocked out until later (see below). Alternatively, as stated on p. 145, the length cut of the pocket may be formed by the fine pocket chisel and mallet. The pulleys are fitted and screwed to the stile.

The inner and outer linings are now prepared by ploughing the grooves, and the head inner and outer linings are carefully sawn and planed to butt against the jamb linings.

The following is the usual procedure for assembling the frame: One of the pulley stiles is placed in a housing of the sill (whilst on the bench), wedged and nailed through the wedge and stile. The second stile is fixed in a similar manner, the end being firmly bedded in the housing before wedging; with the sill resting on the floor, the stiles are sighted through from one to the other to see if both are out of winding. The head is positioned and nailed. This skeleton framing, with the inner edges uppermost, is now placed on a pair of winding strips (pieces of wood which have been planed to a true surface) which are temporarily nailed to the bench after their outer edges have been made to coincide with the top and bottom of the frame. A piece of wood, approximately the width of the frame, is temporarily fixed to both sill and winding strip and, after testing the frame for squareness by checking the diagonals, the head is lightly nailed to the winding strip upon which it rests. The projecting ends of the wedges are cut off, the tongue on each pocket piece is sawn off, and the pockets are knocked out by applying a mallet smartly on the back. The edges of the pockets are trimmed (with a chisel on the pulley stile and a plane on the pocket piece). Sometimes pocket pieces are dipped into hot water to "swell the grain" and so ensure a better fit. The vee-shaped top ends are cut off the pocket pieces and glued and nailed to the back of the stiles (see P. 146). The two inner jamb linings are secured by nailing. One end of the head inner lining is accurately sawn square and its edge planed. This lining is then sawn to length by placing its dressed square edge against one of the jamb linings, measuring the length in line with the opposite jamb lining and sawing this end full (on the outside of the pencilled square line). Each end of the head lining is fixed by driving a nail obliquely through the top into the jamb lining. The parting and inner beads are cut to length. The parting beads are fitted tightly into the grooves. The inner beads are mitred at the angles, that at the sill being slightly wider, with its outer edge bevelled (see M, Fig. 93). The inner head lining is fixed. The bottom of the linings are cut flush with the sill. The frame is reversed and again tested to see if it is square. The parting slips (100 mm short of the sill) are secured by passing their heads through the slots in the head lining and nailing or wedging it (see p. 143). The jamb outer linings are fixed. After nailing the back lining, the frame is completed by standing it on the floor and gluing the triangular angle blocks at intervals of from 75 to 150 mm to the linings (see pp. 143 and 145).

The setting out of the sashes is illustrated in Fig. 98. The stiles are set out first, followed by the rails. The two top sash stiles are placed on the height rod and the clearance or sight lines are squared up; the pair of bottom sash stiles is similarly dealt with (see A and B). The mortices for the top and bottom rails and the meeting rails are set out. The complete setting out of a top stile is indicated at C, and for a bottom stile at D. It is assumed that the top sash is to be provided with horns. The required setting out should conform to the details shown at R and T, Fig. 96. Two lines are marked at K and L, Fig. 98, which are 200 and 300 mm respectively from the top of the sash; these indicate the plough groove for the sash cord and the position of the knot hole (see R, Fig. 96, and p. 153. The bottom stiles are marked in a similar manner, M and N being 200 and 300 mm respectively from the top of the bottom sash. The vertical glazing bars, unlike those of the casement sash, are continuous and the horizontal bars are fitted to them (unless the halved joint at M, Fig. 96, is adopted—see pp. 126 and 137); the sight lines for these vertical bars are marked off the stiles, and the ends are gauged (see p. 89).

The top, bottom and meeting rails are set out from the width rod (see E, Fig. 98), all four members being placed together for the squaring of the shoulders or sight lines. These marks are squared over and the ends are gauged for the tenons. The complete setting out is indicated at F, G, H and J. The short horizontal glazing bars are set out in a manner similar to that described on p. 137. Usually a wood templet is prepared and used for marking the dovetailed ends of the stiles and meeting rails (see V, Fig. 96); this is a thin (about 6 mm) piece of hardwood which is cut to the required shape; it is applied in turn at the sides of the stiles and ends of the rails, the dovetails being marked with the marking knife (8, Fig. 151, *Carpentry*). The two top stiles are cramped together when the horns are being moulded to shape.

A description of the preparation or working of a door and a casement sash is given on pp. 85, 89, 134 and 137. Much of this can be applied to sliding sashes. Reference should also be made to the description of the assembling, gluing and wedging up of doors (p. 90) and casements (pp. 137–139), and the forming of the grooves to receive the cords (p. 153).

The sashes are fitted to the frame and any adjustments made. If the sashes are found to be too wide, the stiles are reduced *equally* by planing. The meeting rails should be straight, parallel and level, a reasonably tight fit being provided at the rebates so that when the sash fastener is fixed the sashes lock and do not rattle. Excessive play between the pulley stiles and sash stiles should be avoided (p. 147). The cord grooves on the outside of the sash stiles should also be checked; as stated on p. 153, these should be wide enough to clear the pulleys projecting at the top.

It is the general practice to deliver the sashes and frames, ready fitted, on the site, but without the glass and weights fixed. The latter are usually fixed after the frames have been built into position. Before being fixed

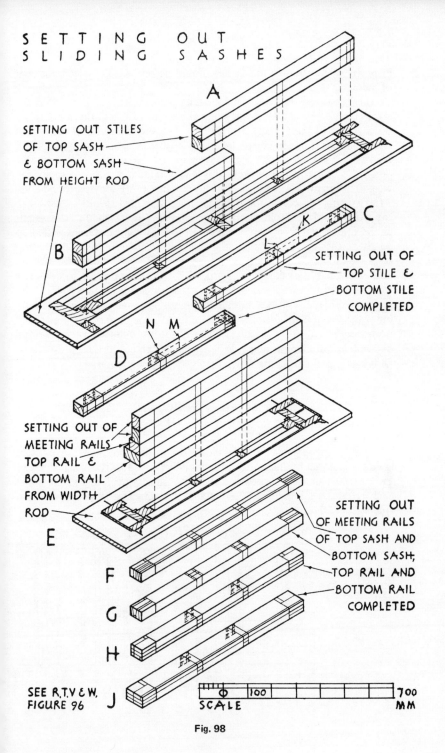

SETTING OUT
SLIDING SASHES

A

SETTING OUT STILES
OF TOP SASH
& BOTTOM SASH
FROM HEIGHT ROD

B

C

K

L

SETTING OUT OF
TOP STILE &
BOTTOM STILE
COMPLETED

N M

D

SETTING OUT OF
MEETING RAILS
TOP RAIL &
BOTTOM RAIL
FROM WIDTH
ROD

E

SETTING OUT
OF MEETING RAILS
OF TOP SASH AND
BOTTOM SASH,
TOP RAIL AND
BOTTOM RAIL
COMPLETED

F

G

H

J

SEE R,T,V & W,
FIGURE 96

SCALE 100 700 MM

Fig. 98

in position, the frames and sashes should be primed, *i.e.*, given one coat of paint.

The sashes are hung in the following manner: It is assumed that the sashes have been weighed, after being glazed (p. 152), and that the correct weights are to hand ready for fixing. The sashes are taken out of the frame, and a further check taken to ensure a satisfactory fit. Both pockets are removed. A cord is taken and threaded over an outer pulley down the frame to the pocket; this is facilitated if a *mouse* (a small lead weight fastened to a length of string) is temporarily secured to the cord. After cutting the cord to length, its end is threaded through the hole in the weight and firmly knotted. A second cord is attached to the weight at the opposite side in a similar manner. Each weight in turn is pulled up nearly to the top of the pulley, the cord is fixed temporarily near the top to the pulley stile and its free end is secured to the stile of the sash by one of the methods explained on p. 153. The temporarily fastenings to the cords are removed and the sash is tried to see if it slides freely. The bottom sash is hung in a similar manner. · The pockets, parting beads, inner beads and sash fastener are then fixed. The cord should have been previously stretched by tugging it after fixing one end (see p. 152). When determining the length of cords, sufficient clearance at the sill should be allowed for any stretching which may occur subsequently.

THREE-LIGHT CASED WINDOW WITH VERTICAL SLIDING SASHES

A wide opening may be divided into two or more lights, or pairs of sashes, separated by mullions. In a three-light window it is usual to make the central pair of sashes wider than the adjacent side lights. In some such windows all the sashes are made to open, and others have fixed side lights with opening central sashes.

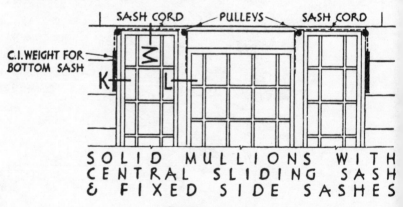

SOLID MULLIONS WITH CENTRAL SLIDING SASH & FIXED SIDE SASHES

Fig. 99

A part elevation of a window having fixed side lights and opening central sashes is shown in Fig. 99. The side lights are screwed to the

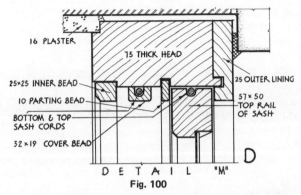

16 PLASTER

75 THICK HEAD

25×25 INNER BEAD

10 PARTING BEAD

BOTTOM & TOP SASH CORDS

32×19 COVER BEAD

25 OUTER LINING

57×50 TOP RAIL OF SASH

D

D E T A I L   "M"

Fig. 100

frame. As shown in the detail at G, Fig. 101, the mullions are solid and, therefore, the weights for the central sashes must be accommodated in the frame at the jambs. Four *pairs* of pulleys are required, *i.e.,* four pulleys for each of the top and bottom hung sashes. Fig. 99 shows the weights in full (to make them conspicuous) and portions of the sash cords are indicated by broken lines. The cords from the sashes to the weights pass over the pulleys fixed at the top of the mullions and those fixed to the head of the pulley stiles at the jambs. The pulleys must be fixed as high as possible, and to permit of this a portion is removed from the top of each pulley face plate. The cords between the pulleys pass immediately under the head of the frame at the side lights, those fixed on the top sash being accommodated in grooves in the top rails of the two upper side sashes, and the other two cords are hidden from view when, as shown in

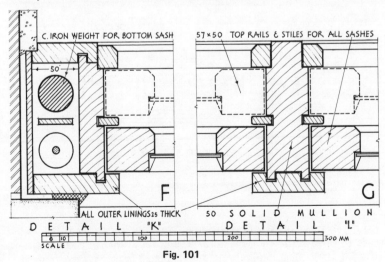

C. IRON WEIGHT FOR BOTTOM SASH

57×50 TOP RAILS & STILES FOR ALL SASHES

50·

F

G

ALL OUTER LININGS 25 THICK

50 S O L I D   M U L L I O N

D E T A I L   "K"

D E T A I L   "L"

SCALE
0 10   100   200   300 MM

Fig. 101

162

Fig. 100, grooved cover beads are screwed (in order that they may be removed readily when broken cords require attention) to the heads of the side lights.

A detail of a solid mullion is given at G, Fig. 101. The mullions vary from 38 to 50 mm in thickness, are double tongued or housed to the outer linings, rebated to receive the inner beads, and grooved for the parting beads.

As shown at F, Fig. 101, the side or jamb boxes are constructed in the usual manner (see also N, Fig. 93 and S, Fig. 94).

The head is usually solid (see Fig. 100) with an outer lining (or it is the full width of the frame and an outer bead is planted on). The mullions are tenoned and wedged to the head, and the pulley stiles are housed into the latter.

An alternative arrangement for hanging the central sashes consists of the provision of cased mullions in lieu of solid mullions, and solid 75 mm thick jamb posts instead of the built-up side boxes. The mullions resemble that shown in Fig. 106, except that the external width need only be 50 mm and the thickness of the stiles next to the fixed side lights may be reduced to 25 mm.

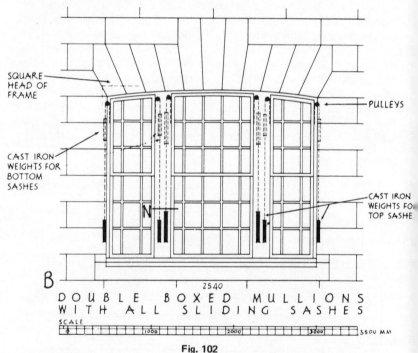

SQUARE HEAD OF FRAME

PULLEYS

CAST IRON WEIGHTS FOR BOTTOM SASHES

CAST IRON WEIGHTS FOR TOP SASHE

N

B

2540

DOUBLE BOXED MULLIONS WITH ALL SLIDING SASHES

SCALE

1000   2000   3000   3500 MM

Fig. 102

An elevation of a three-light cased window having all of its sashes made to open is shown in Fig. 102. The boxes at the jambs are as shown at F, Fig. 101. The mullions are double boxed or cased, *i.e.,* arranged to

accommodate two sets of weights, as indicated in Fig. 102 and detailed
in Fig. 103.   In each mullion the weights of the central sashes are
separated from those of the side sashes by a 12 mm dividing strip, and
the top and bottom weights of each sash are separated by the usual 6 mm
parting slip.   The finished width of the mullions is 200 mm.   This
elevation in Fig. 102 shows a stone arch having a soffit curved to a segment.   As the rise of the curve is small, it is usual to provide the window

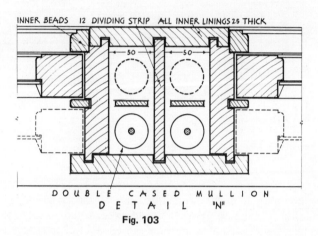

DOUBLE CASED MULLION
DETAIL "N"
Fig. 103

with a square head, as indicated by broken lines in the figure. The construction of the head, with its inner, outer and soffit linings, conforms to
the normal construction (see pp. 141 and 143), except that the *outer*
lining only of the head is of wider stuff and swept to the curve of the
segment. Thus, whereas the external appearance of the head is segmental
(parallel to the curve of the arch), that internally is the same as a square
head. The head of a top sash is as shown in Fig. 104, the lower edge of
the top rail being shaped to the sweep of the outer lining; the rail is
tenoned and wedged to the stiles of the sash, as indicated.

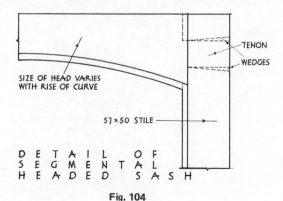

DETAIL OF
SEGMENTAL
HEADED SASH
Fig. 104

164

The part elevation of the window in Fig. 105 also indicates each light to consist of sliding sashes. A detail of one of the cased mullions is given in Fig. 106. It accommodates two large weights, one to balance the sum of half of the weights of the central and side bottom sashes and the other to counterbalance half of the adjacent top sashes (see p. 152 regarding the determination of weights for sashes). A pulley is fixed at the top of each weight, and four pulleys are screwed to, and near the head of, the

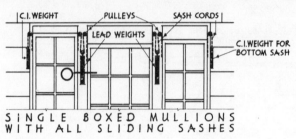

Fig. 105

pulley stiles of each mullion—one for each of the adjacent top and bottom sashes. Each cord passes under the weight pulley, over the two mullion pulleys, and fixed to both of the central and side top (or bottom) sashes (see broken lines in Fig. 105). Cylindrical cast iron weights are preferred, but if heavy weights are unobtainable from stock, specially cast lead weights are employed. This is an alternative arrangement for hanging the sashes to that shown in Figs. 102 and 103, and results in a reduction of 50 mm in the width of the mullions. The construction of the side boxes is as shown at F, Fig. 101.

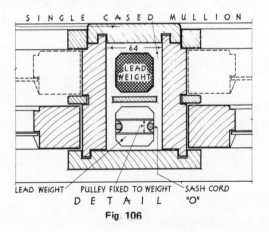

Fig. 106

SEMICIRCULAR HEADED CASED WINDOW WITH VERTICAL SLIDING SASHES

The elevation, section and plan of a large window of this type fixed in an opening in a brick wall with stone dressings are shown in Fig. 107.

FRAME.—With the exception of the head, the construction of the frame is similar to that previously described. The usual construction of a

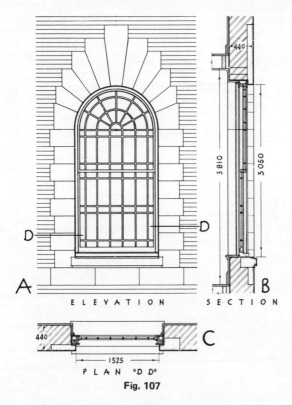

ELEVATION SECTION

PLAN "D D"

Fig. 107

semicircular head is shown in Fig. 108. The soffit lining is built up in two thicknesses of 50 mm thick segments, divided by the parting bead, sawn to the required curve, and glued and screwed together to overlap with joints normal to the curve. The inner and outer linings are glued and blocked to the soffit lining, the tongues and grooves (indicated by broken lines in Fig. 110) being often omitted because of the thickness of the head, which exceeds that of the pulley stiles. The upper ends of the pulley stiles are rebated and continued above the springing line to receive the lower ends of the head. The members are glued, well screwed from the back and blocked. Attention is drawn to the projection of the end of the curved head beyond the face of the pulley stile (see E, Fig. 108). The purpose of this 12 mm stop is to restrict the upward run of the bottom sash and thus prevent it being jammed in the head; it also prevents damage to the glass in the upper sash which may otherwise occur if the latter was forced tightly against the crown of the frame. The joints between the segments of the inner and outer linings are either tongued and grooved or cross tongued and grooved; G shows a t. and g. springing joint in an inner lining; the ends of the wider outer linings are similarly shaped, although the tongues are usually stopped short of the outer edge. The parting slip is suspended from the block shown at E.

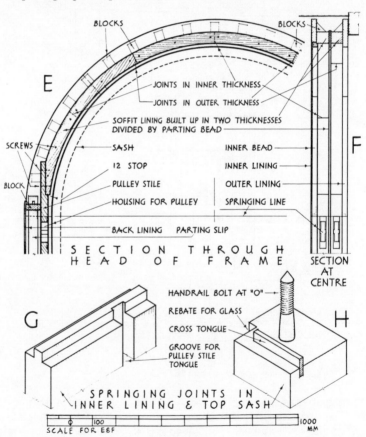

Fig. 108

TOP SASHES.—Details are shown in Fig. 109. The sash, indicated by
thick lines, has a semicircular head in one thickness which comprises two
segments jointed at the crown and either at the springing O or, preferably,
above it (especially if the pulleys are fixed just below the springing line),
as indicated by the broken radial line at P. These butt joints are formed
with *handrail bolts,* so called because they are invariably used to ensure
tight fitting joints between portions of handrails. A handrail bolt is
illustrated at Q, Fig. 109, and consists of a square nut, a round slotted
nut (as it has five or six shallow slots cut in its outer edge) and a washer,
in addition to the bolt which has screwed ends. Details showing the
application of this bolt at the crown joint in the sash are shown at L and
M. A hole, slightly larger than the diameter of the shank, is bored centrally
in each of the adjacent ends of the segments for the bolts. Two holes
are also made from the top, one just sufficiently large to receive the square

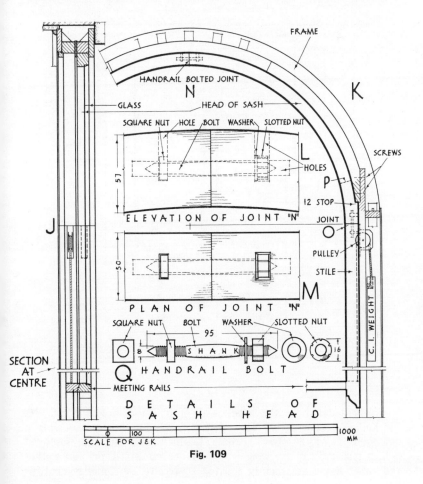

Fig. 109

168

nut, and the other for the washer and slotted nut. The joint is formed in the following manner: The square nut is placed in its hole and the bolt is inserted and screwed on to the nut until half of its length only projects. After gluing the ends, the washer and slotted nut are put into the hole in the other segment, and the free end of the bolt slipped into the drilled hole. The bolt is next tightened by means of a *handrail punch* (a chisel with its edged end slightly curved) or similar tool, which is engaged in the notches of the slotted nut in turn as it is caused to rotate, and this is continued until the ends of the segments are brought together and a tight joint obtained. The joint is strengthened by means of a cross tongue (see p. 119) which is glued into the ends at the rebate side; this prevents the pieces of timber from twisting. Two or three small (5 mm diameter) hardwood dowels serve the same purpose. A sketch of the springing joint with projecting bolt and tongue is shown at H, Fig. 108.

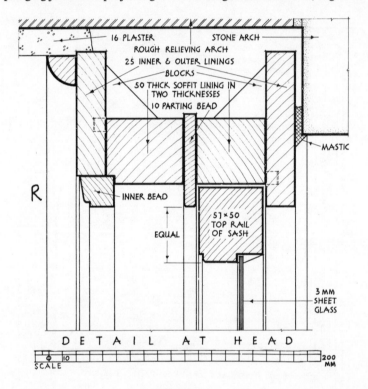

Fig. 110

Enlarged details at the head, jamb and sill are shown in Fig. 110. 111 and 112 respectively. These follow closely the construction already described. It will be observed that: (1) Thick pulley stiles are employed (which take most of the weight of the large sashes), (2) the pulley stiles and soffit lining are slightly rebated to receive the inner beads (this ensures the correct re-fixing of the beads and a free run for the bottom

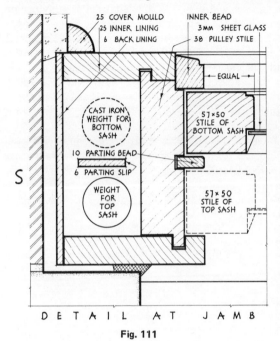

25 COVER MOULD
25 INNER LINING
6 BACK LINING
INNER BEAD
3MM SHEET GLASS
38 PULLEY STILE
EQUAL
CAST IRON WEIGHT FOR BOTTOM SASH
57×50 STILE OF BOTTOM SASH
10 PARTING BEAD
6 PARTING SLIP
WEIGHT FOR TOP SASH
57×50 STILE OF TOP SASH
S

DETAIL AT JAMB

Fig. 111

sash on being replaced after cord replacements, although, as mentioned on p. 145, rebates are often not provided, even in good work), (3) the outside of the groove for the water bar in Fig. 112 is in line with the inside of the outer lining (and thus water passing along a defective bedding joint will only affect a small portion of the wood sill), (4) a deeper draught bead (shown in Fig. 112) than the inner

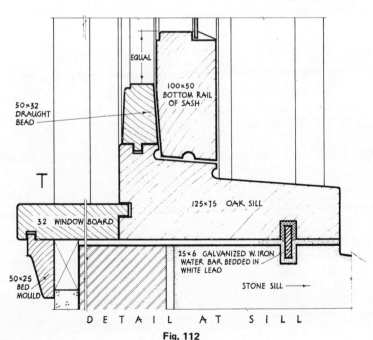

EQUAL
100×50 BOTTOM RAIL OF SASH
50×32 DRAUGHT BEAD
T
32 WINDOW BOARD
125×75 OAK SILL
50×25 BED MOULD
25×6 GALVANIZED W. IRON WATER BAR BEDDED IN WHITE LEAD
STONE SILL

DETAIL AT SILL

Fig. 112

beads enables the lower sash to be raised slightly to permit of ventilation at the meeting rails (if the width of the draught bead is still further increased, the bottom rail of the sash should be correspondingly deeper to ensure, as shown, the margin between the top of the sash and the bead being equal to those indicated in Figs. 110 and 111) and (5) this draught bead and the bottom rail are bevelled to prevent vibration of the sash by ensuring a tight fit between it and the parting bead (the slight clearance shown between the sashes, outer lining and beads is to allow for three coats of paint).

SEGMENTAL-HEADED WINDOWS.—The heads of the frame and sash of a window curved to the form of a segment having a relatively large rise may be constructed as described above, the number of joints depending upon the span and the amount of the rise. If, however, the rise is small, it is usual to provide the window with a square head, as indicated by broken lines in Fig. 102 (see p. 162).

CHAPTER ELEVEN

METAL, ETC. WINDOWS

Metal windows fixed to wood frames. Windows with pivoted sashes and
horizontal sliding sashes. Hardware.

METAL WINDOWS

AN enormous number of metal windows, made of mild steel, bronze and
other alloys, have been employed within recent years. Whilst many of
these are fixed direct to brickwork or stonework, some are required to be
fixed to wood frames; hence the inclusion of this type of window here.

British Standard 990 deals with mass-produced metal windows. It
specifies a Module 100 range of windows which is so named because the
sizes[1] are multiples of 100 mm ranging from 500 mm wide and 200 mm
deep to 1 800 mm wide and 1 500 mm deep. Each window is given an
identification mark which immediately describes its type; this mark has
two numbers, the first of which denotes the width and the last signifies
the height; letters are included in the mark to indicate how the window
opens. When the windows are ordered a final suffix is added (L or R to
determine the "handing" or side at which a side-hung window is hinged).
Thus for example the window in Fig. 113 is type 12FCV9; the first
number shows that it is 1 200 mm wide and the last that it is 900 mm
high, letter F stands for fixed light, C for side-hung open-out vent, and V
for full-width top-hung, open-out vent. When ordering this window the
suffix L would be added to show that the opening light is on the left; if
the opening light were required on the right the suffix R would be used.
Note that in all cases of side-hung vents the hinges are attached to the
outside of the frame. Other letters used in the identification mark are:
B for bottom-hung open-in vent; T for top-hung open-out vent at the
side of C or F; R for horizontally pivoted, fully-reversible vent; S for
fixed sublight, and D for open-out door.

The frame and sash are of 3 mm thick metal and their sections are
identical in size and shape; they are of Z-section (see N, Fig. 113), 26 mm
deep with 20 mm wide flanges, one of the latter having a slight projection
beyond the web to allow the sash and frame to overlap 6 mm both
internally and externally. The sash is connected to the frame by two
extention hinges (see p. 132 and 133); the sketch at M, Fig. 113, shows
the bottom hinge with the sash partly open.

---

[1] The multiple sizes, e.g. 500 mm width and 200 mm depth etc, are the
"coordinating sizes"; the actual manufacturing overall dimensions are 6 mm less
i.e. 494 mm by 194 mm etc.

METAL WINDOW IN WOOD FRAME

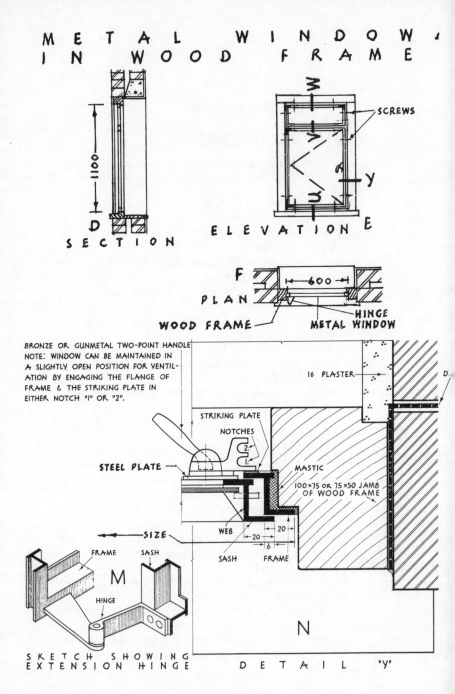

SCREWS

y

SECTION

ELEVATION E

1100

D

F

PLAN

600

WOOD FRAME

HINGE

METAL WINDOW

BRONZE OR GUNMETAL TWO-POINT HANDLE
NOTE: WINDOW CAN BE MAINTAINED IN
A SLIGHTLY OPEN POSITION FOR VENTIL-
ATION BY ENGAGING THE FLANGE OF
FRAME & THE STRIKING PLATE IN
EITHER NOTCH "1" OR "2".

16 PLASTER

D.

STRIKING PLATE

NOTCHES

2
1

STEEL PLATE

MASTIC

100×75 OR 75×50 JAMB
OF WOOD FRAME

SIZE

WEB

20

20

6

SASH

FRAME

FRAME

SASH

M

HINGE

N

SKETCH SHOWING
EXTENSION HINGE

DETAIL "y"

Fig. 113

172

The sash is provided with a casement fastener, or *two-point handle,* and a casement stay. These are of bronze or gunmetal. As indicated at N, Fig. 113, ventilation can be afforded by engaging the flange of the frame (and striking plate attached) in either notch "1" or "2" of the handle; an opening between the sash and frame of up to 25 mm in width can thus be maintained. The casement stay is of the peg type (see p. 134) or the sliding type; the latter has a horizontal arm fixed to the sash which slides through a pivoted fitting at the free end of a rotating bracket fixed to the frame.

On account of the narrow frames, the appearance of these windows when fixed direct to the brickwork or stonework is not always satisfactory. Hence, when used for certain types of buildings, such as houses, the metal windows are often fixed in wood

Fig. 114

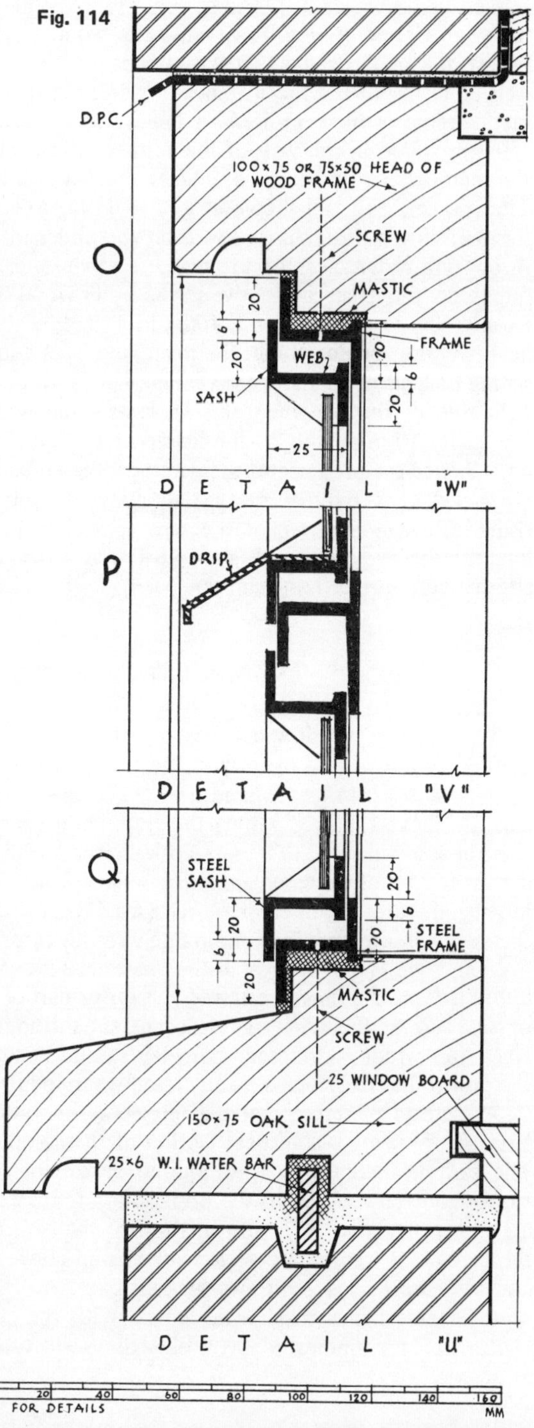

frames, as shown at D, E and F, Fig. 113. The detail at N, Fig. 113, and those at O and R, Fig. 114, show the wood frame double rebated to receive the metal frame. The latter is bedded in mastic, and this must be well done to prevent the entrance of water between the two frames. The metal frame is then screwed to the wood frame, 8 mm diameter holes being provided in the web of the former for this purpose. In good work the members of the frame should be morticed and tenoned (see p. 122). The oak (or teak) sill shown at R, Fig. 114, projects beyond the face of the wall and is throated (grooved on the underside of the projection) to throw rain-water clear of the wall; a stone, etc. sill is not, therefore, required; this is an alternative to the other wood sills shown in Chapters IX and X. As the window is fixed in a cavity wall (see D, Fig. 113), the head of the opening should be protected by a damp-proof course, consisting of lead or asphalt felt, which extends for at least 150 mm beyond each side of the opening; this prevents water which may have entered the cavity from passing to the inside of the building and causing dampness; hence the presence of the damp-proof course at O, Fig. 114.

The glass is fixed with special putty. Small metal dowels (one is shown through the web of the sash at N, Fig. 113) are used to retain temporarily the panes of glass until the putty has set (see p. 126); alternatively spring fixing clips are used.

WOOD WINDOWS WITH PIVOTED SASHES

This type of window consists of a solid frame and a sash which is pivoted to allow it to open with the top rail swinging inwards. It is illustrated in Figs. 115, 116 and 117. The pivots (see p. 176) are fixed slightly above (about 25 mm) the horizontal centre line of the sash so that the sash will tend to be self-closing. The construction of the frame is similar to that of the casement window except that it is not rebated. Both inner and outer beads are required (see Figs. 116 and 117). As shown, the sash is in the middle of the frame with the *upper* portion of the *outer* bead and the *lower* portion of the *inner* bead fixed to the *frame,* and the *upper* half of the *inner* bead and the *lower* half of the *outer* bead nailed or screwed to the *sash.* These beads should appear to be continuous when the window is closed, and they should be cut correctly to enable the sash to be freely opened and closed when required.

A method of setting out the splay-cuts for the beds is shown in Fig. 116. As indicated, a vertical section of the complete window is set up. The sash is inclined to the required maximum opening position (this varies from $10°$ to $20°$ to the horizontal) and the inner and outer beads are drawn. A line "3" is drawn through the centre of the pivots joining the points "1" and "2", which are 12 mm above and below the beads, and two short lines are drawn at right angles to it and across the width of the frame beads to give the cuts. With the centre of the pivots as centre, the arcs indicated by broken lines are drawn to give the corre-

PIVOTED SASH WINDOW

ELEVATION

A

B

D

C

SECTION

11/28

PIVOT "Q"

F

B

1350

TILES

PLAN   Fig. 115

C

328

542

SCALE

0   100   700 MM

sponding points for the splay-cuts on the sash beads. The 12 mm clearance between each of the points "1" and "2" and the sash beads permits of the removal of the sash when required.

The underside of the head of the frame is slightly splayed (about 6 mm), and the top inner bead and the top of the sash are made to conform to it, to allow the sash to clear the frame when being opened. Fig. 117 shows a detail at a jamb of the window.

HARDWARE.—The window fittings consist of pivots, eyelets, cleats, catches and patent ventilating gearing. Some of these are illustrated in Fig. 118.

Sash Pivots or Centres.—Of the various forms, that shown at M consists of a brass, malleable iron or gunmetal pin or stub mounted on a plate screwed to the inner face of the sash, and this engages in a metal

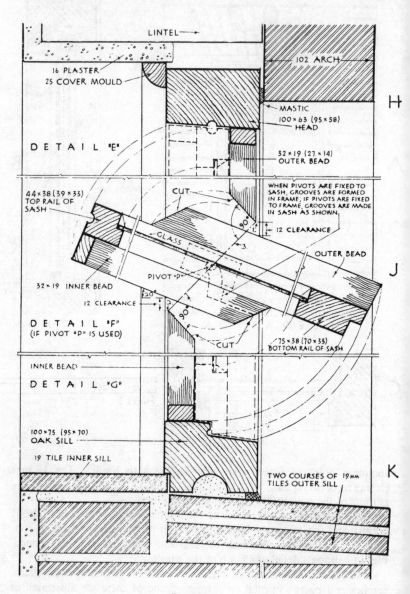

LINTEL →

16 PLASTER
25 COVER MOULD

102 ARCH

H

MASTIC
100×63 (95×58)
HEAD

DETAIL "E"

32×19 (27×14)
OUTER BEAD

WHEN PIVOTS ARE FIXED TO
SASH, GROOVES ARE FORMED
IN FRAME, IF PIVOTS ARE FIXED
TO FRAME, GROOVES ARE MADE
IN SASH AS SHOWN.

44×38 (39×33)
TOP RAIL OF
SASH

CUT

12 CLEARANCE

GLASS

OUTER BEAD

J

32×19 INNER BEAD

PIVOT "P"

12 CLEARANCE

DETAIL "F"
(IF PIVOT "P" IS USED)

CUT

75×38 (70×33)
BOTTOM RAIL OF SASH

INNER BEAD

DETAIL "G"

100×75 (95×70)
OAK SILL

19 TILE INNER SILL

K

TWO COURSES OF 19mm
TILES OUTER SILL

Fig. 116

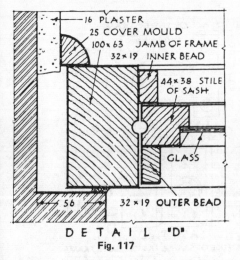

16 PLASTER
25 COVER MOULD
100 × 63 JAMB OF FRAME
32 × 19 INNER BEAD
44 × 38 STILE OF SASH
GLASS
56
32 × 19 OUTER BEAD

D E T A I L "D"
Fig. 117

socket which is screwed to the inner face of the frame. One pair of fittings is required per sash.

The sash pivot shown at P consists of a pin or stub plate and a slotted plate or socket. A pair of these fittings is fixed to the edges of the sash and frame. The pin plate may be fixed either to the frame or to the sash. If the former, each socket plate must be screwed to the edge of the sash with the open end of the slot downwards (not as shown at P) and inwards; a groove for each fitting must also be formed along each inner bead attached to the sash and continued to the slot of the socket plate (see broken lines at J, Fig. 116); when inserting the sash from the inside, the ends of the pivots are engaged in the bottom of the grooves, the sash is pushed downwards and outwards until the slots on the socket plates have been reached. Alternatively, each pin and socket plate may be screwed to the sash and frame respectively; when this is done, the socket plate is fixed with the open end of the slot uppermost (as shown at P, Fig. 118) and the groove is formed in the frame. These pivots are not so readily fixed as the type at M, and if the sash is partially open, it can be easily removed from the outside.

The patent type shown at Q, Fig. 118, is an improvement on pivots M and P. This consists of a gunmetal screw bolt or pivot with three plates T, U and V. A hole is bored through the middle of the sash and frame. As shown at R, plates T and U are screwed to the edges of the stile, and plate V is screwed to the frame. The pin is then inserted by screwing it through the threaded block on plate T. This is an effective fitting, as it can be easily fixed, the sash can be readily removed when required, and it is a secure method of hanging the sash as it cannot be removed from the outside unless the bolts are withdrawn. The size of the bolts varies from 75 to 100 mm long and from 6 to 9 mm diameter. A pair of these fittings is required per sash.

Catches.—A simple form is shown at S, Fig. 118, the latch fitting being fixed in the middle of the inner face of the top rail of the sash, and the striking plate being screwed to the underside of the frame to receive the end of the latch. A spring retains the latch in the fixed position until the sash is required to be opened, when the latch is released by depressing the ring.

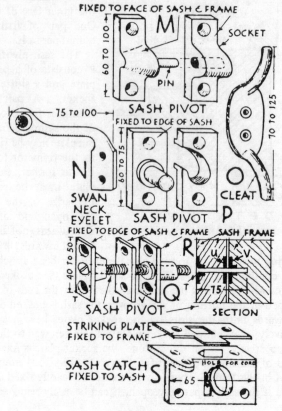

FIXED TO FACE OF SASH & FRAME

M

SOCKET

60 TO 100

PIN

SASH PIVOT

FIXED TO EDGE OF SASH

75 TO 100

70 TO 125

N

SWAN NECK EYELET

60 TO 75

O

CLEAT

SASH PIVOT

P

FIXED TO EDGE OF SASH & FRAME

SASH FRAME

40 TO 50

R

u   v

Q

T

15

SASH PIVOT

SECTION

STRIKING PLATE
FIXED TO FRAME

HOLE FOR CORD

SASH CATCH
FIXED TO SASH   S   65

Fig. 118

Alternatively, the sash may be secured by small barrel or flush bolts, as described for doors.

Eyelets and Cleats.—A simple arrangement which permits of the opening and closing of the sash consists of a length of cord which is attached at each end to brass or bronze eyelets screwed to the inside face of the top and bottom rails. The cord must be of sufficient length to belay it round a metal cleat fixed at a convenient point on the jamb. ˙One form of eyelet is shown at N, Fig. 118, and a cleat is shown at O. If the sash catch S is used, the top end of the cord is fastened through the hole provided for it, and therefore only the eyelet at the bottom rail is required.

There are many patent devices for opening and closing pivoted sashes, one of the simplest consisting of a vertical steel rod which has a hinged arm connected near its upper end, its lower end passing through a gunmetal winding box; the arm is secured to the bottom rail of the sash.

The sash is opened and closed as required by turning the handle of the winding box.

Pivoted sash windows are convenient for lighting and ventilating high rooms, as they can be conveniently opened and closed from the floor level. They are sometimes used for factories, warehouses, laundries, staircases, etc. A pivoted sash is occasionally employed as a fanlight over a door (see pp. 101 and 103).

WINDOWS WITH HORIZONTAL SLIDING SASHES

This form of window, illustrated in Fig. 119, is fairly common, especially in certain of the northern counties. It is generally known as a *Yorkshire Light*, as such windows are a characteristic feature of many of the older stone built houses in that county. Comparatively few are now made, as it is a type which has certain undesirable features, i.e., an unsatisfactory

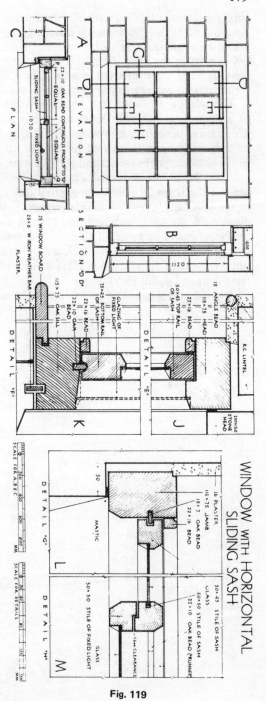

Fig. 119

appearance and a tendency for the sliding sash to jam. As shown in the elevation at A, the appearance is marred on account of the "sight lines" not being continuous, as the top and bottom rails of the sliding sash are not present in the fixed light; this causes each pair of panes in the fixed light to be of three different heights. These windows are still specified for alterations and extensions to buildings, and for replacements.

The window is shown in a regular coursed rubble wall. It consists of a fixed light and a sliding sash. The detail at K shows the method adopted for permitting movement of the sash. An oak bead (or *runner*), with rounded edge, is inserted in the oak sill and extends for the full width between jambs (see C and M); a corresponding but slightly wider groove is formed on the lower edge of the bottom rail of the sash. The head of the frame is rebated throughout its length to receive the top rail of the sash (see J), and the sash is retained in position by an inner bead planted on the jambs and continued round the head and sill. A 2 mm clearance should be provided all round the sash to permit of free movement. Rain and draughts are excluded by letting a bead into the jamb, which engages in a groove in the stile (see L), and rebating the stiles of the fixed light and sliding sash (see M).

A barrel bolt is generally used to secure the sliding sash.

CHAPTER TWELVE

STAIRS

Terms. Essential requirements. Straight flight, dog-leg and open well stairs.
Manufacture, including setting out. Winders. Special steps.

A STAIR is a set of steps leading from one floor to another. A continuous series of steps forms a *flight*, and there may be two or more flights, separated by flat portions called *landings*, between two floors. A stair, together with the part of the building accommodating it, is known as the *staircase*. The horizontal portion of a step, called a *tread*, is connected to a vertical (or almost upright—see F, Fig. 136) *riser*, and these are supported by inclined boards termed *strings*. The Building Regulation requirements for stairs are given on pp. 185—186; they distinguish between a private stairway (one in a dwelling) and a common stairway (one intended for common use in connection with two or more dwellings).

TERMS.—The following definitions of terms are arranged in alphabetical order for ready reference. Some of them are amplified in later paragraphs.

Apron, Apron Lining or Fascia (see G, Fig. 136, and C, Fig. 143) is a board which covers the trimmer joist of a landing, providing a suitable finish to it and the adjacent plaster.

Balusters (see Figs. 133, 135 and 138) are short vertical bars which support the handrail and protect the open side or sides of a stair.

Balustrade or Banister.—An *open* balustrade comprises the balusters, handrail, string and newels (if any) (see Figs. 120, 133, 138 and 144). A *solid* balustrade consists of panelling in lieu of balusters (see Figs. 139, 140, H, Figs. 145 and 146; see also B.R. requirements on pp. 185—186).

Bearers.—Inclined 100 mm by 50 mm or 100 mm by 75 mm members which support the steps and to which the plastered soffit is fixed. Those which serve as intermediate supports are also called *carriage-pieces, rough carriages, rough strings* (as they are not dressed) or *spring-trees* (see Figs. 126, 133 and 143). The short supporting members placed immediately below winders (see p. 186 and Fig. 147) are also called bearers.

Blocks are fixed to the upper edges of bearers and provide additional support of the treads (see Fig. 147). The term is also applied to the small pieces of wood of triangular section which are glued to the inner angles between treads and risers or strings (see D, Fig. 127, F, Fig. 136, etc.).

Brackets or Rough Brackets are more commonly employed and serve the same purpose as bearer blocks, the 25 mm thick pieces of wood being nailed alternately to the sides of the bearers (see Fig. 126, 133 and 143).

Bull-nosed Step.—See "Steps".

Cappings are cover mouldings planted on the upper edges of strings (see F, Fig. 136, and J and K, Fig. 137), handrails (see D, Fig. 141), panelling (see B and C, Fig. 141) and newels.

Caps.—See "Newels".

Carriages.—See "Bearers".

Commode Step.—See "Steps".

Cover Fillets are small members fixed to the underside of outer strings and trimmers to provide a satisfactory finish to the adjacent plaster (see G, Fig. 136, N, Fig. 137, and M and N, Fig. 145).

Curtail Step.—See "Steps".

Dancing or Balancing Steps.—See "Steps".

Dog-leg Stair.—See p. 201.

Drop.—See "Newels".

Easing is a curved upper portion connecting two strings of different inclinations, or a string with a skirting (see C, Fig. 122, and B and G, Fig. 147).

Flier.—See "Steps".

Flight.—A continuous set of steps extending from floor to floor, or floor to landing, or landing to landing.

Going or Run of a step is the horizontal distance between the faces of two consecutive risers (see Figs. 124, D, Fig. 127, and F, Fig. 136) and the going of a flight is the horizontal distance between the face of the bottom riser of the flight and that of the top riser.

Handrails, provided to afford assistance and a safeguard, are fixed at a convenient height to walls (see C, Fig. 122, and H and J, Fig. 128) or at the top of balustrades (see Figs. 133, 135, 137 and F, Fig. 148); they should be of a satisfactory size and shape to enable them being easily grasped by the hand; of the many designs, the simple *mop-stick handrail* illustrated at F, Fig. 148, is one of the most effective (see also B.R. requirements pp. 185–186).

Headroom is the height measured vertically from the line of nosings or pitch line (see B.R. requirements p. 185) to the lower outer edge of the apron (see C, Fig. 122) or to the soffit of a flight immediately above it. This should not be less than 2 m.

Landing is a platform between two flights provided to serve as a rest, and when required, to make effective provision for turning a stair; it also denotes the portion of the floor adjacent to the top of a stair. A *quarter-space landing* is one on which a quarter-turn has to be made between the end of one flight and the beginning of the next (see Figs. 144 and 146). If the landing extends for the combined width of both flights and a complete half-turn is necessary, it is known as a *half-space landing* (see Figs. 133, 138 and 140).

Line of Nosings (or *Pitch Line*) is that drawn to touch the projecting edges or nosings of the treads (see C, Fig. 122 and D, Fig. 127).

Margin is the portion of a close string (see p. 185) between its upper edge and the line of nosings (see D, Fig. 127). This term is also applied to the portions of treads and risers between the strings and the carpet or other covering.

Newels or Newel Posts (see Figs. 133, 135, 137 and 143) are substantial vertical members placed at the ends of flights to support the strings, handrails, trimmers and bearers. The upper moulded end is called the *cap* and the projecting lower end is known as a *drop* (see Fig. 137).

Nosing (see Figs. 124, 127, 136, etc.).–This is the front edge of a tread which projects beyond the face of the riser below it; it is also applied to the projecting upper member of an apron (see G, Fig. 136).

Nosing Line (see H, Fig. 130).–Drawn on a string for setting out the steps and is the line drawn at the required distance from and parallel to its upper edge along which is marked the intersecting points between the treads and vertical faces of the risers (see p. 196). It must not be confused with the "line of nosings" (see p. 182) which is nearer to the upper edge.

Open Well Stair.–See p. 215.

Pitch or Slope is the angle between the line of nosings and the floor or landing, (see p. 185).

Pitch-board or Step-mould is used for setting out the steps on the strings and is a thin wood triangular *templet* (*pattern* or *set square*). One of its sides is equal to the going, that at right angles to this is equal to the rise and the remaining side gives the pitch of the stairs. That shown at E, Fig. 129, has, in addition, a "margin templet" (although its width is actually the distance between the edge of the string and the nosing line, see Fig. 130), and a thin strip at right angles to it is maintained against the edge of the string and assists in ensuring accuracy in setting out. Two additional patterns, called a *tread templet* and a *riser templet,* are required to set out the housings (see p. 196) of the treads and risers respectively (see F and G, Fig. 129); the width of the tread templet equals the thickness of the tread and that of the wedge, whilst the width of the riser templet is equal to the combined thickness of the riser and wedge. The application of these templets is described on pp. 196–201.

Rise of a step is the vertical distance between the tops of two consecutive treads (see Figs. 124, 127 and 136), and the rise of a flight is the total height from floor to floor, or floor to landing, or landing to landing.

Riser is the front member of a step which is connected to the tread (see Figs. 124, D, Fig. 127, F, Fig. 136, etc.).

Run.–See "Going".

Scotia is a concave mould used to provide an additional finish to the nosing of a tread (see D, Fig. 127). A *scotia board* is cut from a relatively wide board and used at nosings of treads forming bull-nosed and similar rounded bottom steps (see Figs. 148).

Soffit or Planceer is the under surface of a stair which is often plastered (see C, Fig. 122, E, Fig. 134, and D, Fig. 144).

Spandrel or Spandril is the triangular surface, either plastered or panelled, between an outer string and the floor (see C, Fig. 133).

Splayed Step.–See "Steps".

Stair.—As stated on p. 181, this consists of a set of steps which lead from one floor to another. Stairs are classified as follows:—

  (*a*) Straight Flight Stairs.
  (*b*) Turning Stairs, including (i) quarter-turn, (ii) half-turn, (iii) three-quarter-turn, (v) newel and (v) geometrical.

  (*a*) *Straight Flight Stair* (see A, Fig. 120 and Fig. 122).—This continues throughout its entire length in one direction, and may consist of a single flight only, or two or more flights in its length which are separated by landings.

  (*b*) (i) *Quarter-turn Stair.*—This type changes its direction either to the left or right, the turn being effected either by a quarter-space landing (Fig. 144) or by winders (Fig. 147).

  (ii) *Half-turn Stair* has its direction reversed either by a half-space landing (as at C, Fig. 120 and D, Fig. 133) or a quarter-space landing and winders (as at B, Fig. 120), or two quarter-space landings and a short flight (as at E, Fig. 143), or completely by winders.

  (iii) *Three-quarter-turn Stair* has its direction changed three times, with its upper flight crossing the bottom one.

  (iv) *Newel Stair* (see B and C, Fig. 120, and Figs. 133, 135, 143 and 146) has a newel at the foot and head of each flight of stair. The newels are therefore a conspicuous feature.

  (v) *Geometrical or Continuous Stair.*—Both the strings and handrails of such a stair are continuous and are set out in accordance with geometrical principles. A newel may, for reasons of design, be introduced at the bottom and top of such a stair, but it is not an essential part of the construction. Geometrical stairs, circular on plan and with the steps radiating from the centre, are called *circular* or *spiral* or *helical* stairs; the wall string of a circular stair may be octagonal on plan as an alternative to the more expensive circular form. An *elliptical stair* is of the geometrical type, the plan of its outer string being in the form of an ellipse with its wall string parallel to it.

Staircase.—This, as previously stated, includes a stair and the part of the building which encloses it.

Stairway is the opening or space occupied by the stair.

Step.—As applied here, it consists of a tread and riser supported by strings. The following are the types of step employed: *Bullnosed step* (see B, G, H and J, Fig. 148) is situated at the bottom of a flight, projects beyond the face of a newel or newels and has one or both ends rounded. A *commode step* has a curved riser and tread nosing. A *curtail, round* or *scroll step* (see C, K, L and M, Fig. 148) has one or both ends which are semicircular or spiral on plan. *Dancing* or *balancing steps* are winders (see below) which do not radiate from a common centre. *Fliers* are those which are chiefly employed, they are of uniform width and are rectangular on plan, *i.e.,* all of those shown in Fig. 122; *diminished fliers* are those immediately adjacent to dancing steps, the width tapering towards the outer string. A *splayed step* is like a bullnosed step but with one or both ends splayed (see A and D, Fig. 148). *Winders* are tapering steps, which usually radiate from a point from the centre of a newel (see Fig. 147); due to its shape the central of three winders is called a *kite winder.*

Storey Rod, Post or Lath is a dressed piece of wood, of approximately 38 mm square, sufficiently long to extend from floor to floor, on which is marked the exact floor to floor height of the part of the building which is to receive the stair; this rod is accurately and equally divided into the requisite number of steps and is then used in their setting out (see p. 196).

Strings or Stringers are the inclined members which support the steps. The following are some of the various forms: A *close* or *housed string* has both top and bottom edges parallel and the treads and risers are housed into it (see Figs. 122, 126, 133, etc.). A *cut* or *open string* or *notch board* has its lower edge parallel to the pitch or the stair and its upper edge is cut or notched to receive the ends of the treads and risers (see N, Fig. 148). A *rough string* is a carriage-piece or bearer. Those fixed to walls are called *wall* or *inner strings* and are usually close strings; those on the outside are known as *outer strings* and may be of either the close or open type.

Tread is the horizontal member which forms the upper surface of a step (see Figs. 124, 127, etc.).

Walking Line represents the average line of travel taken by a person when ascending or descending a stair, and is usually taken to be 450 mm from the centre of the handrail or newel (see D, Fig. 147).

Well or *Well-hole* is the space between the outer strings of the several flights of a stair (see E, Fig. 143) known as an *open well stair.*

*Winders.—*See "Steps".

Several of these definitions are amplified on the following pages.

BUILDING REGULATIONS FOR STAIRS.—The following is a summary of the main provisions in the Regulations which differentiate between a *common stairway* and a *private stairway.* The former is one within a building occupied by more than one family whereas a private stairway is one within a building occupied by one family only.

A private stairway must have: (1) A minimum headroom of 2 m measured vertically above the pitch line and a minimum clearance of 1·5 mm measured at right angles to the pitch line. (2) The tread plus twice the rise between 550 and 700 mm. (3) A maximum of 220 mm per riser with the going not less than 220 mm. (4) A maximum pitch of 42°. (5) Between consecutive floors every step must (a) have an equal going for every parallel step and (b) have an equal rise.

A common stairway must comply with (1), (2) and (5) above and have a maximum of 190 mm per riser with a going not less than 230 mm, a maximum pitch of 38° and not more than 16 risers per flight.

In addition if the stairway rises more than 600 mm both types must be guarded on each side by a wall or balustrade not less than 840 mm vertically above the pitch line with a handrail between 840 mm and 1 m above the pitch line (a) on each side of the stairway if its width is 1 m or more, or (b) on one side in any other case.

Balustrades to landings must be 900 mm (for private stairways) and 1·1 m (for common stairways) above the landing floor.

OTHER ESSENTIAL REQUIREMENTS.—A well designed stair should comply with the following requirements:—

1. It should be constructed of sound materials and workmanship, the treads and risers being properly tongued and grooved together, wedged, glue blocked and adequately supported. The strings should be well secured to walls, newels, trimmers, etc. A bearer or carriage, of sufficient size, should be provided if the stair is over 900 mm wide, with an additional bearer for every 400 mm in width, otherwise excessive deflection will occur and the stair will creak.

2. Its ascent should be relatively easy and the proportions of treads and risers should conform to the B.R. requirement given above. The pitch must also conform to B.R. stipulations to avoid undue fatigue, and it should not be less than 25° in order to prevent a tedious ascent and the occupation of excessive space.

3. The whole of the risers must be of the same height and the treads should be of uniform width if accidents are to be avoided.

4. It should be well lighted, especially at turnings. A solid balustraded stair (see Figs. 139, 140 and 146) requires a larger window than one with balusters, as the former offers a greater obstruction to light. For greater convenience, two-way switches (which enable a light to be controlled from two points) should be provided at the head and foot of the stair.

5. The maximum number of steps in a flight is preferably twelve; this is especially desirable for stairs used by invalids and the aged; stairs in public buildings should conform to this although the B. Regulations allow 16. Such limitation requires the provision of landings.

What would otherwise be a half-space landing should not be divided into two quarter-space landings by a single riser; such an arrangement has been a frequent cause of accidents, especially to unaccustomed users.

6. It must be of adequate width. A satisfactory width for the average-sized house is 900 mm from wall to wall, this is the British Standard width. A narrower stair has a mean appearance and the conveyance of large pieces of furniture, luggage, etc. is likely to damage its balustrade and walls. The width of landings should be at least equal to that of the steps; an increased width is preferable, as the appearance is thereby enhanced and the removal of large objects expedited with less likelihood of damage.

7. Adequate headroom must be provided, see p. 185.

8. Winders may be a source of danger, especially to young children, and they should therefore be avoided. This is not always possible when

the going is greatly restricted and winders may then have to be utilized either at the top or, preferably, at the bottom of a flight; in cramped positions there may be no alternative to the provision of winders at both the head and foot of a flight.

When used, it is usual to divide what would otherwise be a quarter-space landing into three winders, as shown in Fig. 147. If four are used, the average width of each tread is inadequate; if two only are provided, as shown at B', Fig. 121, the average width of the treads is excessive, they are difficult to carpet, and the corner between the riser, lower tread and wall string is not easy to clean.

9. The height of a raking handrail (*i.e.*, parallel to the pitch) should conform to the B.R. requirements (p. 186)

10. A stair should be in such a position that it can be conveniently approached from the lower rooms and afford a ready access to the upper rooms. Doors should be situated at least 300 mm from the head and foot of a stair. A door which opens immediately off a top step is least desirable, as it creates a potential danger, especially to visitors; and there is, of course, less risk of a collision occurring between a person hurriedly descending a stair and one leaving a room through a door which is not directly adjacent to a bottom step.

STEP PROPORTIONS.—A well designed stair, even when the floor space is limited, should entail the minimum expenditure of energy in its ascent, it must therefore be neither steep nor inadequately pitched and must conform to B.R. requirements (p. 185). The step of the average person measures approximately 590 mm and it has been computed that about twice the effort is required in climbing to walking horizontally, hence the B.R. rule.

The nosing is, of course, additional to the going, and the projection of the tread beyond the face of the riser should preferably not exceed the thickness of the tread, as an excessive projection may cause a person to trip when ascending.

A stair with very narrow treads cannot be descended comfortably, as more than the usual care has to be taken to clear the nosing with the heel to obtain adequate foothold on the tread below. For this reason the preferred minimum going is 220 mm. The British Standard domestic stair has a going of 224 mm and rise of 200 mm—see Fig. 122. In public buildings, where the stairs are a prominent feature and ample space is usually available, it is common to employ a 300 mm going and a 140 to 150 mm rise.

STAIR DESIGN.—The essential requirements specified on pp. 185—187 should be kept in mind when designing a stair. The type of stair decided upon depends a good deal upon the size and shape of the stairway, height from floor to floor, etc.

The number of steps to be decided upon is governed to a large extent by the total going available. If the height from floor to floor is fixed, as it usually is, and the going is unrestricted, the number of steps is determined in the following manner: Assuming that the proposed riser is

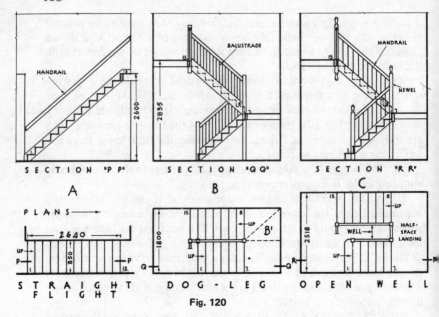

SECTION "P P"   SECTION "QQ"   SECTION "RR"

A   B   C

PLANS —→

STRAIGHT FLIGHT   DOG-LEG   OPEN WELL

Fig. 120

170 mm, the number of risers equals the height divided by 170 mm. Thus, if the floor to floor height is 2 820, the number of steps = $\dfrac{2\,820}{170}$ = 16 or

17. Adopting the latter figure, the exact rise is = $\dfrac{2\,820}{17}$ = $165\frac{15}{17}$ mm. The

going will then = (550 to 700) * $- 2 \times 165\frac{15}{17}$ mm = $218\frac{4}{17}$ to $368\frac{4}{17}$, say

250 mm. It should be noted that the number of treads is one less than that of the risers, as the surface of the upper floor forms the tread for the top step.

If the going of the flight is so restricted that the minimum going of 220 mm (see p. 185) can only be adopted, then the number of steps equals

$2\,820 \div \dfrac{(550 \text{ to } 700) - 220}{2}$ = 11 to 17. Adopting 14 as the number, the

rise of each step = $\dfrac{2\,820}{14}$ = $201\frac{6}{14}$. This will be satisfactory, as it conforms

to the rule 220 + (2 x $201\frac{6}{14}$) = $622\frac{6}{7}$

The types of stairs which are usually employed are the straight flight, dog-leg and open well. A quick comparison between these can be made on reference to Fig. 120, which shows in outline all three types. The construction of these will now be considered in detail.

*See B.R. requirement p. 185.

In the British Standard for stairs a number of standard flights are specified; one of these, a straight flight is detailed in Fig. 122.

The ground floor and first floor plans of a small house are shown at A and B, Fig. 121. Owing to the restricted width available, the straight flight stair shown is the only type which can be adopted; an excess in the preferred maximum number of steps in a flight (see requirement 5, p. 186) is unavoidable. Useful storage accommodation is afforded when, as shown, the space under the stairs is utilized as a cupboard. The foot and head of the stair are approximately 300 mm from the living-room and bedroom No. 1 doors respectively (see requirement 10, p. 000).

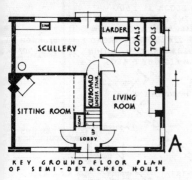

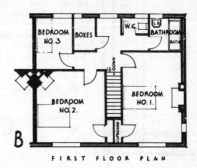

Fig. 121

Enlarged plan, longitudinal and cross-sectional elevations of the stair are shown at D and C, Fig. 122 and Fig. 123.

CONSTRUCTION OF STEPS.—Owing to the limited going of the flight, the minimum width of tread (220 mm going, see p. 185) has been adopted, and it will be seen that only 13 steps can be provided if requirement 10 is complied with. As the height from floor to floor is 2600 mm (see

c), the rise of step $= \dfrac{2\,600}{13} = 200$ mm. This proportion of step agrees

with rule 1 (on p. 185), *i.e.*, 220 mm + (2 x 200) = 620 mm.

The nominal thickness of the treads should not be less than 32 mm* and that of the risers is usually 25 mm. The enlarged detail in Fig. 124 shows one good method of connecting the treads to the risers, both edges of the latter being tongued into the grooved treads and well screwed (preferably) as shown, or nailed; secure fixing is essential, otherwise the tread will leave the riser and a creaky stair will result. The nosing, as previously explained (p. 187), should not project more than the

*Wood treads of stairs for offices, etc. subjected to heavy traffic are sometimes 38 to 50 mm thick.

thickness of the tread. This simple nosing—the square edges are just sand-papered—is all that is necessary for this type of stair; if the stair, having

STRAIGHT FLIGHT STAI

Fig. 122

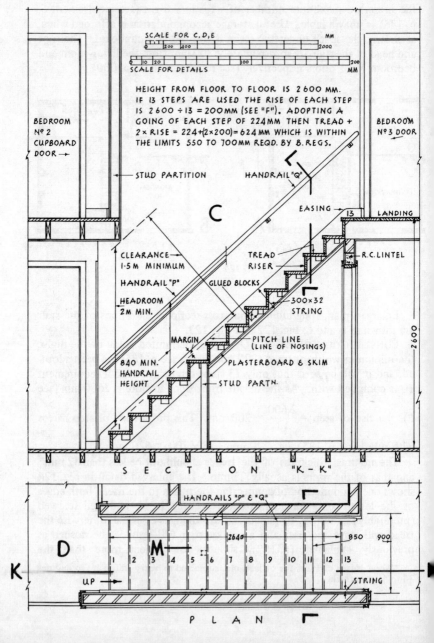

SCALE FOR C, D, E

SCALE FOR DETAILS

HEIGHT FROM FLOOR TO FLOOR IS 2600 MM.
IF 13 STEPS ARE USED THE RISE OF EACH STEP
IS 2600 ÷ 13 = 200MM (SEE "F"). ADOPTING A
GOING OF EACH STEP OF 224MM THEN TREAD +
2 × RISE = 224+(2×200)=624 MM WHICH IS WITHIN
THE LIMITS 550 TO 700MM REQD. BY B.REGS.

BEDROOM
Nº 2
CUPBOARD
DOOR →

BEDROOM
Nº 3 DOOR

STUD PARTITION

HANDRAIL "Q"

EASING

13 LANDING

CLEARANCE→
1·5 M MINIMUM

TREAD

RISER

R.C.LINTEL

HANDRAIL "P"

GLUED BLOCKS

HEADROOM
2M MIN.

300×32
STRING

2600

MARGIN

PITCH LINE
(LINE OF NOSINGS)

840 MIN.
HANDRAIL
HEIGHT

PLASTERBOARD & SKIM

STUD PARTN.

S E C T I O N   "K–K"

HANDRAILS "P" & "Q"

D

M →

2640

850

900

K

1   2   3   4   5   6   7   8   9   10   11   12   13

STRING

UP →

P L A N

nosings as shown, is not to be carpeted, it is advisable for the treads to be of hardwood (such as teak or oak) and not softwood, as the edges are apt

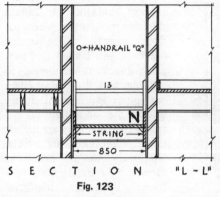

SECTION "L – L"

Fig. 123

to be damaged; incidentally, as felt pads are usually used to protect a carpet, such relatively sharp upper edges do not damage a carpet. Another good (and preferred) method of jointing treads and risers is shown at E, Fig. 141, where the treads are tongued at their inner edges into the risers; this also shows an alternative simple nosing. Another nosing is shown at D, Fig. 127, a scotia or cavetto mould being used; as this moulding is fitted into the grooved tread, there is no need for the riser to be tongued; alternatively, the top outer edge of the riser is tongued to fit the grooved tread, and the moulding is just glued and sprigged to the tread. A common nosing is the half-round, such as is indicated in Fig. 148. A cheap and second-rate method of jointing is shown at P, Fig. 122; here the members and just butt-jointed and nailed together, hence any shrinkage of the risers, and especially the treads, results in unsightly gaps occurring, through which dust passes, and creaks develop.

The treads and risers are supported by two 300 by 32 mm wall strings which are securely plugged to the walls (shown in Fig. 125). A 25 to 30 mm wide margin is provided and, as shown in Fig. 125, the upper edge of the string is rounded and rebated to provide a simple but effective finish between it and the plaster. When the stair width exceeds 900 mm, it is desirable to

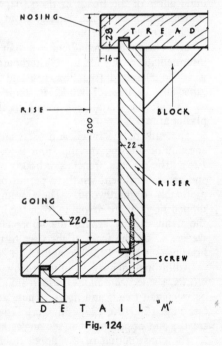

DETAIL "M"

Fig. 124

use an intermediate support in the form of a 100 mm by 75 mm (or 50 mm) bearer or carriage-piece; this is birds-mouth notched and nailed to a short fillet at the foot (or it may be continued through the floor and

192

notched to a deep conveniently placed floor joist) and similarly secured to the wall plate at the head (see C, Fig. 126). In order that the carriage-piece may afford the maximum support, short pieces of 25 mm thick wood (often pieces of floor board), called *rough brackets*, and shaped as shown at C, Fig. 126, are nailed to the sides with their upper edges cut square and brought tightly up to the underside of the treads to which they are nailed; these brackets are fixed alternately to the bearer as shown. As an alternative to these brackets, triangular blocks are nailed on the upper edge of the carriage as shown at C, Fig. 140, and A and G, Fig. 147. In the illustrated examples, the inner edges of the treads or risers (depending upon the type of joint) are shown resting upon the carriages, but sometimes the latter are slightly notched to receive the steps.

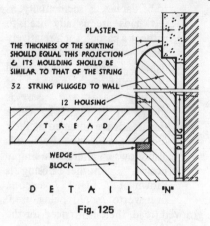

Fig. 125

In addition to strengthening a stair, these carriage-pieces serve as an intermediate fixing for the plasterboard and skim ceiling when, the soffit is to be plastered (see Figs. 134 and 144). It is a common practice, especially in inferior work, to omit these intermediate bearers and as a result the stairs creak owing to the deflection, and defects in the plaster arise.

The ends of the treads and risers are housed into the wall strings, the amount of housing varying from 9 to 16 mm—usually 12 mm (see Fig. 125). The grooves, trenches or housings to receive these ends are tapered and are of sufficient width to permit of the insertion of tapered wedges, preferably of hardwood. These wedges (see L, Fig. 127), after being dipped in glue, are driven in from the back. The tread wedges thus bring the treads tightly against the upper cuts of the housings, and the riser wedges cause the faces of the riser to fit tight against the outer vertical housing (see Figs. 125, 126 and 127, F, Fig. 136, M, Fig. 138, etc.).

Additional rigidity is obtained by the provision of small triangular blocks, termed *glue blocks,* which are glued in at the inner angles formed between the treads and risers. These are spaced at 75 or 100 mm apart (see Figs. 124, 126, 127, 136, etc.). They are also glued to the strings and treads, and occasionally at the angles between the steps and the strings.

The construction of the upper floor at the landing is shown in Figs. 122 and 123. The 32 mm thick nosing forming the top step is either tongued and grooved or splay jointed to the adjacent floor board(s)—see that at G, Fig. 136.

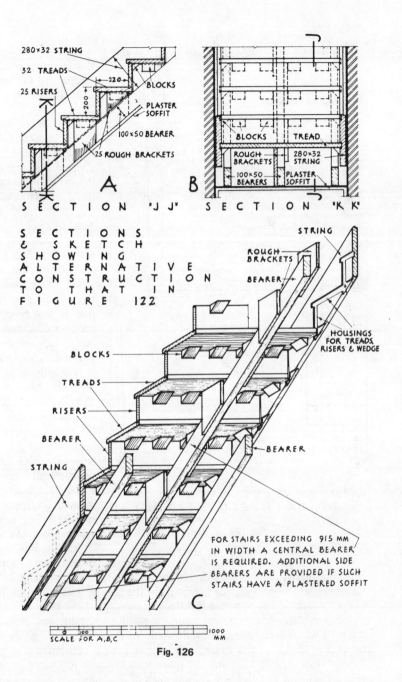

280×32 STRING

32 TREADS

25 RISERS

220

200

BLOCKS

PLASTER SOFFIT

100×50 BEARER

25 ROUGH BRACKETS

A

SECTION "JJ"

BLOCKS   TREAD

ROUGH BRACKETS

280×32 STRING

100×50 BEARERS

PLASTER SOFFIT

B

SECTION "KK"

SECTIONS
& SKETCH
SHOWING
ALTERNATIVE
CONSTRUCTION
TO THAT IN
FIGURE 122

STRING

ROUGH BRACKETS

BEARER

HOUSINGS FOR TREADS, RISERS & WEDGE

BLOCKS

TREADS

RISERS

BEARER

STRING

BEARER

FOR STAIRS EXCEEDING 915 MM IN WIDTH A CENTRAL BEARER IS REQUIRED. ADDITIONAL SIDE BEARERS ARE PROVIDED IF SUCH STAIRS HAVE A PLASTERED SOFFIT

C

100   1000 MM

SCALE FOR A,B,C

Fig. 126

193

HANDRAIL.—A handrail should be of suitable size and shape in order that it may be readily grasped by the hand, and it should be fixed at a convenient height; sharp arrises on a moulded handrail must be avoided to prevent injury to a person's hand, especially during a rapid descent of a stair. Two forms of handrail are shown at C, Fig. 122, and these are detailed at H and J, Fig. 128. The former is a very common wall handrail and is securely plugged to the wall; it is usually of pitch pine or a hardwood. That shown at J is of of hardwood, circular in section, and is screwed to a continuous steel bar which is set-screwed to metal brackets, secured at approximately 1·2 m intervals to plugs. As this latter handrail projects at least 75 mm

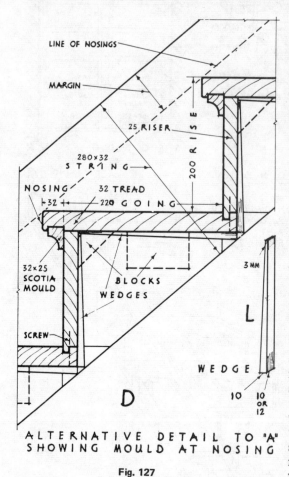

ALTERNATIVE DETAIL TO "A" SHOWING MOULD AT NOSING

Fig. 127

from the plaster, it is not a suitable form for narrow stairs (see p. 211). As shown at C, Fig. 122, the height from the line of nosings to the top of the handrail is 840 mm—see B.R. requirement, pp. 185–186.

HEADROOM.—Adequate headroom is most important, and it is an essential which is occasionally overlooked. As stated on p. 185, it should be at least 2 m. In this example the upper floor is continued over the "lobby" (see A, Fig. 121) and the space thus available is utilized to provide a cupboard or fixed wardrobe to each of the bedrooms Nos. 1 and 2 (see B, Fig. 121). Such provision does not encroach upon the 2 m headroom, (see C, Fig. 122). As shown, the partition across the stair is a stoothing consisting of 100 mm by 50 mm vertical studs, secured to the floor and

195

and ceiling joists, and plasterboarded and skimmed both sides (described on Chap. VI, *Carpentry*); the partition between the cupboards is a similar stoothing, but the studs need only be 75 mm by 50 mm.

CUPBOARD UNDER STAIR.—It is usual to utilize the space under the stair by providing useful storage accommodation as shown in Figs. 121 and 122. The door, of course, opens outwards. The lintel above it is shown supporting brickwork; alternatively, four 100 mm by 50 mm short vertical studs may be used, nailed to the lintel and a wall plate. A low stoothed partition, consisting of three 75 mm by 50 mm studs, is fixed to block out a corner which would be otherwise difficult to keep clean and a portion of the floor which

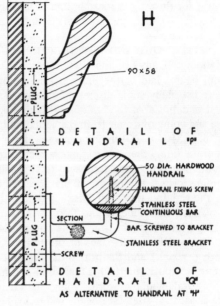

H

90 × 58

DETAIL OF HANDRAIL "P"

J

50 DIA. HARDWOOD HANDRAIL
HANDRAIL FIXING SCREW
STAINLESS STEEL CONTINUOUS BAR
BAR SCREWED TO BRACKET
STAINLESS STEEL BRACKET

SECTION

SCREW

DETAIL OF HANDRAIL "Q"
AS ALTERNATIVE TO HANDRAIL AT "H"

Fig. 128

would serve no useful purpose. Floor boards between this partition and the bottom of the stair may be omitted to provide ventilation to the stair timber. A suitable finish is afforded by plastering the interior or by fixing wall boards to the walls, partition and soffit.

SETTING OUT ON PAPER.—In setting out the stair on paper the student should draw the plan, the nosings (or faces of risers) being accurately spaced by the accurate application of the scale. The longitudinal section is then developed from the plan. The height shown in this section can be expeditiously divided into the requisite number of steps in the following manner: Draw a line representing the landing level at 2 600 mm above the ground floor. Using any convenient scale, place it at an angle on the paper with the zero division intersecting the landing (or ground floor) and the thirteenth division coinciding with the ground floor level (or landing, depending upon the end from which the scale reads), and carefully tick off the intermediate divisions 1 to 12 inclusive. Horizontal lines lightly drawn through these points give the treads, and when connected with the vertical lines developed from the divisions on the plan the required thirteen steps are set out. It is advisable to number each step on plan, as shown in Fig. 122, and also on the section during its development. The direction "up" should be indicated on the plan at the foot of the stairs; this removes ambiguity and facilitates the reading of a drawing, especially when a stair consists of several flights. The rest of the details can be completed without much difficulty, an adjustable set square being useful for drawing the string, line of nosings (to check for accuracy) and handrail. The importance of ensuring adequate headroom is again emphasized.

SETTING OUT AND CONSTRUCTION IN WORKSHOP.—The fixing and trimming (if any) of the floor joists will have been completed and the floor boards laid before the construction of the stairs is commenced. As there is usually some discrepancy between the dimensions taken from a plan and those of the building, it is necessary to obtain the exact total rise and going of a stair from the actual building. A storey rod (described on p. 185) is used for this purpose. To obtain the correct height from floor to floor, the rod, resting on the ground floor, is held vertically (a plumb-bob being used to ensure this) against the end of one of the wall landing joists. The height of the upper floor boards is carefully marked on the rod and the word "rise" is written below it; the point where the suspended bob touches the floor is marked. This height is checked by taking a measurement near to the opposite wall.

The position of the face of the bottom riser is marked on the ground floor (or wall) and the horizontal distance between this and the "bob" point previously marked is measured and marked on another face of the storey rod, and the word "going" is written on it. On being taken to the shop, the "rise" face of the rod is divided by compasses into thirteen equal parts, being the number of risers required. The distance that the face of the top riser is to be from the edge of the landing is marked from one end of the "going" face of the rod, and the net going is then divided into twelve equal parts. The subsequent operations depend upon whether the strings are to be trenched or housed by (a) hand or by (b) machine which is most usual.

(a) Hand Trenching.—A pitch-board, a tread templet and a riser templet are required for setting out a string for the trenchings or housings. One form of pitch-board is shown at E, Fig. 129. It consists of a thin wood set square having a rise and going equal to the dimensions taken from the storey rod; this is tongued into a thicker board of width equal to the required margin and this is housed to a wood base at right angles. A tread templet is shown at F, it is shaped to the required nosing and of a tapered width equal to the thickness of a tread and wedge. Similarly, the riser templet G is equal in width to the combined thickness of a riser and wedge. The length of the strings should be slightly in excess of the *pitch edge* (see E) multiplied by the number of steps, together with the portions required to meet the top and bottom skirtings; the ends of the strings are afterwards trimmed off to accurate length on the job and the skirtings fitted to them.

A brief description of the setting out is given at the top of Fig. 130. After the string has been dressed, the nosing line is pencil marked at the required distance from the upper edge (see Fig. 130). The compasses are set to the length of the pitch edge and thirteen divisions are pricked

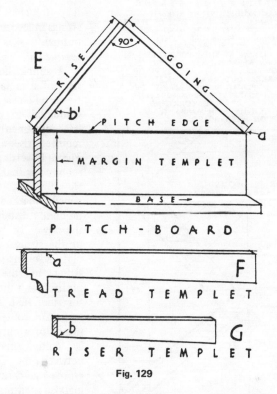

Fig. 129

off along this line. Commencing at one end, and with the base of the pitch-board pressed against this edge of the string, the outside of the first riser and going is *knife* marked along the "rise" and "going" edges. Still maintaining the board in this position, the riser templet is placed against it with the corner of end *b* coinciding with *b'* marked on the board, and the back or wedge-line is marked; the tread templet is then placed as shown against the board with its mark *a* at the *a'* point of the pitch-board, and the nosing and underside or tread wedge-line marked. The pitch-board is then slid along the string and the housing for the next step is marked off in a similar manner.

Three or four holes are sunk with a brace and bit near the nosing of each step and tangential to the outer faces, and the wood between is chiselled out; this permits of the use of the tenon saw for forming cuts along the marked lines, after which the remaining core is removed by a chisel and the bottom of the trenchings finally levelled with a router plane (see *Carpentry*) to give a 12 mm sinking (see Fig. 125). The second string is then set out and the housings formed as described.

(b) *Machine Trenching.*—Simple appliances are now available for the rapid setting out and complete trenching of straight strings. Machines, called stair trenchers, are also obtainable, the latest type of which will cut

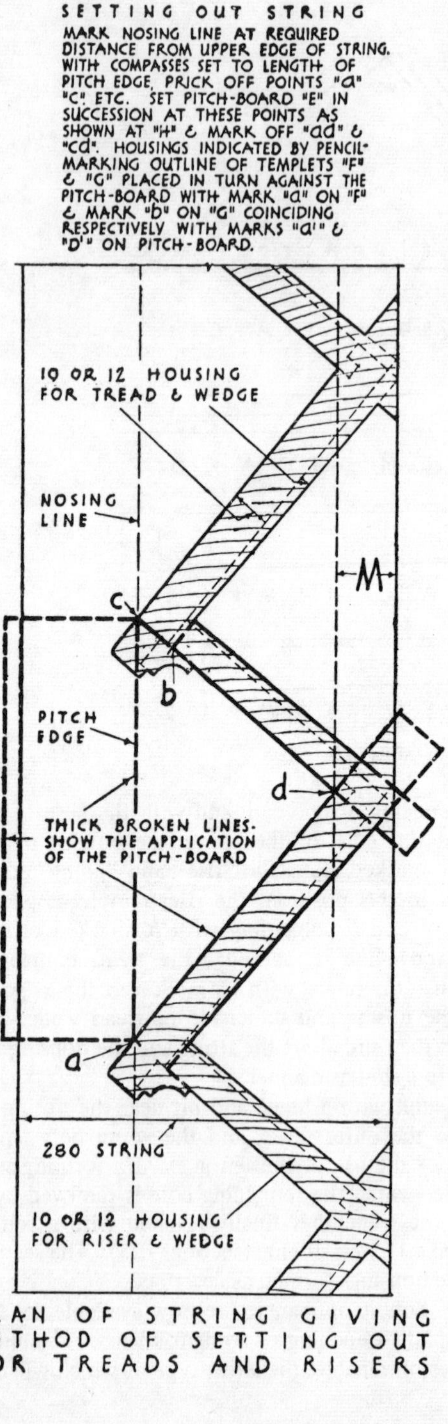

198

SETTING OUT STRING

MARK NOSING LINE AT REQUIRED DISTANCE FROM UPPER EDGE OF STRING. WITH COMPASSES SET TO LENGTH OF PITCH EDGE, PRICK OFF POINTS "a" "c" ETC. SET PITCH-BOARD "E" IN SUCCESSION AT THESE POINTS AS SHOWN AT "H" & MARK OFF "ad" & "cd". HOUSINGS INDICATED BY PENCIL-MARKING OUTLINE OF TEMPLETS "F" & "G" PLACED IN TURN AGAINST THE PITCH-BOARD WITH MARK "a" ON "F" & MARK "b" ON "G" COINCIDING RESPECTIVELY WITH MARKS "a'" & "D'" ON PITCH-BOARD.

10 OR 12 HOUSING FOR TREAD & WEDGE

NOSING LINE

PITCH EDGE

THICK BROKEN LINES SHOW THE APPLICATION OF THE PITCH-BOARD

280 STRING

10 OR 12 HOUSING FOR RISER & WEDGE

PLAN OF STRING GIVING METHOD OF SETTING OUT FOR TREADS AND RISERS

Fig. 130

the trenches of *two* strings in less time than it normally takes a man to *set out one*.

A simple device consists of a metal grooved templet which is graduated to permit of its adjustment to the required rise and going. The only setting out line required is that shown at M, Fig. 130, which is pencil marked at the required distance from the lower or back edge of the string. The templet is clamped to the string in the desired position, and the trenches for the first riser and tread are routed out by means of a cutter which is easily manipulated between the slotted or grooved guides. A pencil mark is then made at the intersection between the gauge line M and the top of the tread cut, the templet is slid along until the outside of the riser guide intersects this mark, the appliance is again clamped and the trenches for the riser and tread of the second step are routed. This is repeated until the trenching of the string is completed.

A similar device can be attached to a spindle moulder (Fig. 7) and the trenching of a string can be automatically completed at one setting.

The stair trencher referred to on p. 197 consists, briefly, of a vertical cutter spindle, the cutter of which travels within guides (adjusted to the required going and rise) as it forms the trenches in both strings during a continuous operation.

There are several methods employed in assembling the various parts of a stair, depending upon local practice, if mass-produced, etc. In one method all the treads are first fixed to the strings, followed by the risers. In another each step, with its tread and riser, is framed together; the steps are then fitted in the trenches of one string, after which the second string is fitted and cramped.

Briefly, the sequence of operations in the first method are: After the strings have been trenched and the treads and risers have been prepared (*i.e.,* tongued, grooved, nosed, cut square to correct length and dressed), the first and last treads are housed into the corresponding trenches of both strings, cramped after being tested for squareness, nailed and wedged. The strings are now placed with their front or upper edges resting on the bench, and the remaining treads are inserted between the trenches, each being tested, cramped and glue wedged in turn. After the outer ends of the wedges have been removed as required, the risers are inserted and wedged. The treads and risers are then screwed (in best work) or nailed (see Fig. 124) and glue blocks are fitted to the inner angles. The treads may also be skew screwed or nailed to the string. Scotia mouldings, if required, are glued and sprigged to the trenches.

In the second method the steps are made separately before being fixed to the strings. One simple appliance, called a *cradle,* which is employed to ensure that the riser is fitted at right angles to the tread, is illustrated in Fig. 131; as shown, its consists of two angle brackets each comprising a bearer to which a leg is firmly fixed. Each upright or leg is notched on its inner edge where it joins the horizontal bearer, the size and shape of the notch being similar to the nosing of the tread (and scotia, if needed). The brackets are screwed to the top of the bench, at about 600 mm apart, the horizontal members being parallel to each other and at right angles to the base of a try square used for ensuring squareness. The tread, outer face downwards, is placed on the bearers with the nosing engaged in the notches of the uprights. The upper tongued edge of the riser is glued and fitted into the groove of the tread as the riser is held against the uprights. The blocks are then glued and fitted to the inner angle. If required, the scotia is glued and inserted before the riser is fitted. The sketch shows the tread, riser and scotia in position. The scotia and the nosing of the tread are subsequently worked to the desired mouldings. When the glue is sufficiently dry, the step is carefully removed and allowed to set. After all the steps have been formed in this manner, and the nosings and sections have been moulded, the next operation is to fix them to the strings. A string, with its trenched face uppermost, is placed on the bench and each step is placed vertically with its lower end fitted into the trench. When all the steps have been housed, the second string is placed in position with the upper ends of the steps

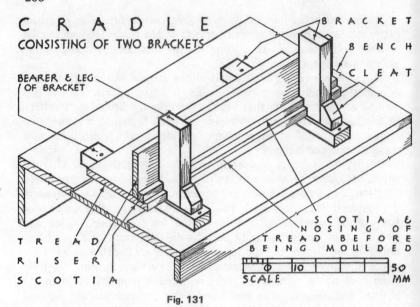

CRADLE

CONSISTING OF TWO BRACKETS

BRACKET

BENCH

CLEAT

BEARER & LEG OF BRACKET

SCOTIA & NOSING OF TREAD BEFORE BEING MOULDED

TREAD

RISER

SCOTIA

SCALE

Fig. 131

engaging in the trenches. The stair is then cramped; if the flight is assembled on a bench specially equipped for this purpose the cramps employed will be of the overhead, type; otherwise ordinary T-cramps (Fig. 58) are used. The treads and risers are now wedged, care being taken to see that each tread is driven tightly against the trench nosing before the tread wedge, well glued, is driven home. To ensure that none of the nosings is out of winding, a straight-edge is applied to them and and any nosing not touching it is driven tighter as required. Glue blocks are fitted between the treads and strings, and treads are screwed to risers, etc., as described above. The top nosing is neatly tongued and grooved or splay jointed to the adjacent floor boards after the stair has been fixed.

As previously mentioned, the stair is well secured by nailing the strings to plugs which have been driven into the joints of the brickwork. The 100 mm by 75 mm bearer or carriage (see C, Fig. 126, if required) is then birdsmouthed and securely nailed to the fillet at the foot and the wall plate at the head. The 25 mm rough brackets are sawn to shape and each is well spiked to the side of the bearer after its upper edge has been glued and fitted to the underside of the tread.

The ends of the strings are cut to the required length—any easings having been previously formed—and the skirtings are neatly fitted to them. Attention is drawn to the note on Fig. 125 to the effect that the moulding on the skirting should conform to that on the string, and its thickness should be equal to the projection of the string beyond the face of the plaster. A clumsy finish frequently results because of inattention to this detail.

Fixing of the handrail to the wall, at the required height, completes the stair.

DOG-LEG STAIR

This is so called because of its appearance in sectional elevation. The outer strings of both flights are in the same vertical plane (see D, Fig. 133). It is a convenient form when the going is restricted and sufficient space equal to the combined width of two flights only is available. It is illustrated at B, Fig. 120, and in Figs. 133–141 (inclusive).

Small scale plans of a house showing the application of this type of stair are given at A and B, Fig. 132, and a larger scale plan and sections are shown in Figs. 133 and 134. Reference to the isometric sketch of this stair in Fig. 138 will give a better idea of its appearance. It will be seen that the balustrade of the upper flight is immediately over that of the lower.

STEPS.—A detail of the steps if given at F, Fig. 136; the height from floor to floor is 2 835 mm (see C, Fig. 133) and if fifteen steps are employed the rise of each is 2 835 mm ÷ 15 = 189 mm (see F). As shown at F, the going is 225 mm and this conforms to the rule "going plus twice rise equals 550 to 700 mm" (p. 185). The inclined risers are an alternative to the more usual vertical form already described and give an attractive appearance to the stair, especially if a simple nosing is employed. The edge of that nosing is parallel to the riser, the slope of which should not be too flat, otherwise the projection of the nosing beyond the bottom of the face of the riser will be excessive (see p. 187). The jointing, housing, wedging, blocking and bracketing of the steps are as described for the straight flight stairs; if the treads are grooved by machinery (the spindle moulder), the grooves will be rectangular and not as shown. The bottom splayed step is detailed at D and E, Fig. 148.

STRINGS and NEWELS.—The outer ends of the steps are housed into the outer strings, the thickness of which is usually 12 mm more than that of the wall strings, i.e., 50 mm. As the stair is 865 mm wide and the upper flight at least has a plastered soffit, the upper string is necessarily wide (see L, Fig. 137), but the lower outer string need only be 250 mm (nominal) wide (see F, Fig. 136) as the spandrel is panelled (see C, Fig. 133). This outer string of the upper flight may be in one piece, 378 mm wide (see M, Fig. 137), or it may consist of two tongued and grooved pieces (see L, Fig. 137 and Fig. 138); for narrower stairs, when a rough carriage is not required, the laths of the plastered soffit may be nailed direct to the steps and parallel to the pitch (shown by broken lines in the detail in Fig. 135). Both outer strings are secured to 100 mm by 100 mm newels placed at the foot and head of each flight. The strength of the stair depends a good deal upon the rigidity of these newels and the method of jointing the strings to them. The bottom newel is continued through the floor and well nailed or bolted to a 75 mm thick joist

202

(see C, Figs. 133 and 143). The central newel is continued to the floor (see C, Fig. 133) to which it is nailed; whilst this is a common practice, greater rigidity is obtained if it is continued through the floor and

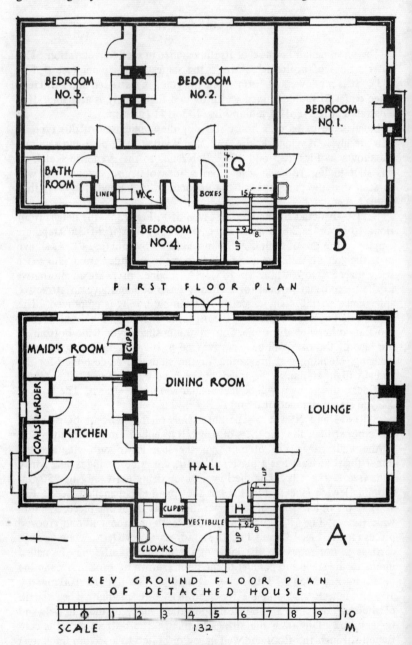

FIRST FLOOR PLAN

KEY GROUND FLOOR PLAN
OF DETACHED HOUSE

SCALE 132 M

Fig. 132

secured to a convenient joist, as shown at C, Fig. 143; this newel iş also notched to the trimmer joist to which it is securely nailed or bolted (see also Fig. 135). The upper newel is also notched to the 225 mm by 75 mm trimmer (see C, Fig. 133, and G, Fig. 136).

Details of the draw-pinned joints between the newel and the strings at B, Fig. 138, are given in Fig. 135. These show two oblique haunch tenons at the end of each string which are fitted into mortices formed in the newel and secured by a pin or hardwood dowel at each tenon. The tenons are formed in the centre of the strings (see sketch in Fig. 135), and if the tenon holes for the dowels are bored slightly nearer to the shoulders than the distance the newel holes are from the edge of the newel, a tight fit between the shoulders and the newel wil be assured when the slightly tapered glued dowels are driven in. An alternative but inferior joint, adopted in cheap work, is to form barefaced tenons on the outside of the strings with shoulders on the inside.

Note that the nosings of the treads are set slightly back from the edges of the newels.

LANDINGS.—The half-space landing is constructed of 100 mm by 50 mm joists, supported by the wall at one end and dovetail housed at the other to a 175 mm by 75 mm trimmer which spans the opening and is carried by the walls (see Figs. 133, 135 and 138), the narrow top tread of the lower flight is rebated over the trimmer and is tongued and grooved to the floor board. The construction at the top landing is similar (see Figs. 133, 134 and G, Fig. 136), but one end of the 225 mm by 75 mm trimmer joist is tusk tenoned into a 225 mm by 100 mm joist (see Q at B, Fig. 132) supported on the wall between the dining-room and hall and that dividing the vestibule and stair; this latter joist also supports the 100 mm by 50 mm vertical studs forming the small box-room partition (see also Fig. 138). The 100 mm by 50 mm bearer or rough carriage of the lower flight is well nailed at the foot to the floor and joist below, and its upper end is birdsmouthed and nailed to a 100 mm by 75 mm *pitching piece* or trimmer which is tenoned to the newel at one end and supported by the wall at the other (see C, Fig. 133). The upper carriage is well secured to the trimmers.

HANDRAIL.—The handrail for the upper flight is housed, tenoned and dowelled (draw-pinned) to the two newels (see C, Fig. 133, and Fig. 135). The interception of the top end of the lower handrail by the upper outer string is unavoidable unless a wider (say 200 mm) newel is employed (but then the stair is not a true dog-leg, as the outer strings are not in the same vertical plane—see p. 201). Besides the unsatisfactory appearance thus presented, the absence of a handrail at the top of this flight is inconvenient, if not dangerous, and therefore an additional handrail (similar to that shown at H, Fig. 128) is sometimes fixed to the wall at the lower flight. The handrail of the balustrade provided at the top of the landing is 915 mm high (see p. 186) and is fixed between a 100 mm by 100 mm newel and a 100 mm by 50 mm newel (known as a *half-newel*) plugged to the wall (see C, Fig. 133 and E, Fig. 134).

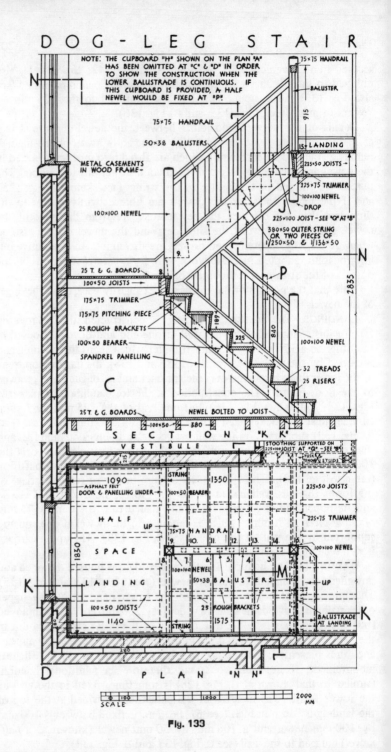

DOG-LEG STAIR

NOTE: THE CUPBOARD "H" SHOWN ON THE PLAN "A" HAS BEEN OMITTED AT "C" & "D" IN ORDER TO SHOW THE CONSTRUCTION WHEN THE LOWER BALUSTRADE IS CONTINUOUS. IF THIS CUPBOARD IS PROVIDED, A HALF NEWEL WOULD BE FIXED AT "P".

75×75 HANDRAIL

BALUSTER

915

LANDING

225×50 JOISTS

225×75 TRIMMER

100×100 NEWEL

DROP

225×100 JOIST – SEE "G" AT "B"

380×50 OUTER STRING OR TWO PIECES OF 1/250×50 & 1/136×50

50×38 BALUSTERS

75×75 HANDRAIL

METAL CASEMENTS IN WOOD FRAME–

100×100 NEWEL

2835

25 T. & G. BOARDS

100×50 JOISTS

175×75 TRIMMER

175×75 PITCHING PIECE

25 ROUGH BRACKETS

100×50 BEARER

SPANDREL PANELLING

1897

225

840

100×100 NEWEL

32 TREADS

25 RISERS

25 T. & G. BOARDS

NEWEL BOLTED TO JOIST

C

100×50   380

SECTION "KK"

VESTIBULE

STOOTHING SUPPORTED ON 225×100 JOIST AT "Q" – SEE "B"

215

1090

ASPHALT FELT

DOOR & PANELLING UNDER→

100×50 BEARER

1350

225×50 JOISTS

225×75 TRIMMER

HALF

UP

75×75 HANDRAIL

9. 10. 11. 12. 13. 14. 15.

100×100 NEWEL

1830

SPACE

8   7.   6.   5.   4.   3.

100×100 NEWEL

50×38 BALUSTERS

M

K

LANDING

UP

100×50 JOISTS

25 ROUGH BRACKETS

1140

STRING

1575

BALUSTRADE AT LANDING

K

STRING

1090

D

PLAN "NN"

SCALE

0   100   1000   2000 MM

Fig. 133

204

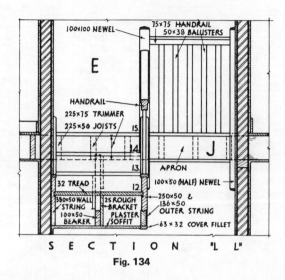

SECTION "L L"

Fig. 134

Alternative details of the balustrade are shown in Fig. 137. Sections through handrails are indicated at E and F. The strings at L and M have already been referred to; the cover fillet at the lower edge of the string at L provides a suitable finish to the plaster, this has a better appearance than the cheaper alternative at M, where the string is grooved to receive the plasterboard and plaster. An alternative finish, suitable when the plasterboard are fixed direct to the steps, is shown in section in Fig. 135. The appearance is also improved if a capping is fixed to the upper edge of each string; two simple cappings are shown at J and K, Fig. 137; the strings shown in Fig. 135 are without cappings.

It will be noted that in all of these details no unsightly gaps will be caused if the timber shrinks.

Two plain, but effective, solid moulded caps to the newels are shown at C and D, Fig. 137, and a drop, similar to C, is shown at N.

BALUSTERS.—The 50 mm by 38 mm balusters shown in Fig. 133 are detailed at G and H, Fig. 137. They are usually spaced at 75 to 100 mm apart and arranged so that one is central at the intersection between the lower handrail and the upper string. If square balusters are used, they should be out of not less than 32 mm stuff (see A and B, Fig. 147) as 25 mm square balusters look spindly when dressed. Balusters may be either housed (as at E, Fig. 137), or tenoned (as at F) into handrails, and housed (see J) or tenoned (see K, Fig. 137) into the cappings or strings (see also Fig. 135). A continuous groove is sometimes formed in the underside of the handrail and the upper ends of the balusters are slid into it. Alternatively, especially when the balustrade is to be painted, a continuous groove is formed in the upper edge of the string; after the balusters have been fixed, the portions of the groove between them are filled in. For inferior work, and owing to the difficulty of housing or

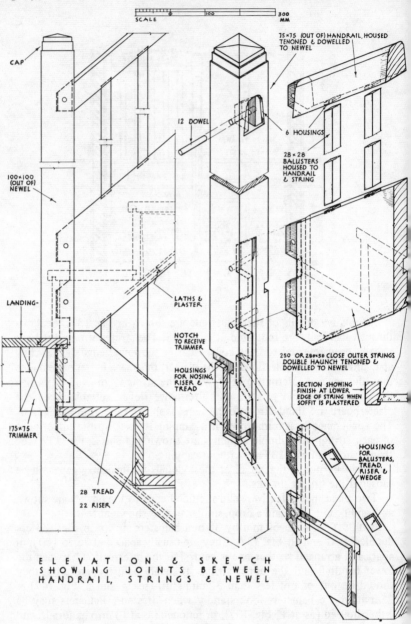

SCALE
100
300
MM

CAP

75×75 (OUT OF) HANDRAIL, HOUSED TENONED & DOWELLED TO NEWEL

12 DOWEL

6 HOUSINGS

28×28 BALUSTERS HOUSED TO HANDRAIL & STRING

100×100 (OUT OF) NEWEL

LATHS & PLASTER

LANDING-

NOTCH TO RECEIVE TRIMMER

250 OR 28×50 CLOSE OUTER STRINGS DOUBLE HAUNCH TENONED & DOWELLED TO NEWEL

HOUSINGS FOR NOSING, RISER & TREAD

SECTION SHOWING FINISH AT LOWER EDGE OF STRING WHEN SOFFIT IS PLASTERED

175×75 TRIMMER

HOUSINGS FOR BALUSTERS, TREAD, RISER & WEDGE

28 TREAD

22 RISER

E L E V A T I O N   &   S K E T C H
SHOWING JOINTS BETWEEN
HANDRAIL, STRINGS & NEWEL

Fig. 135

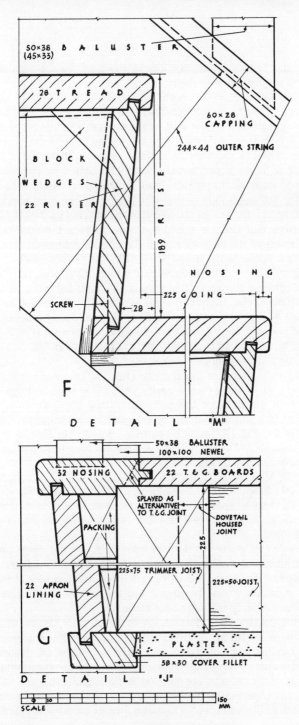

50×38 BALUSTER
(45×33)

28 TREAD

60×28 CAPPING

244×44 OUTER STRING

BLOCK

WEDGES

22 RISER

189 RISE

NOSING

225 GOING

SCREW

28

F

DETAIL "M"

50×38 BALUSTER
100×100 NEWEL

32 NOSING   22 T. & G. BOARDS

SPLAYED AS
ALTERNATIVE
TO T. & G. JOINT

DOVETAIL
HOUSED
JOINT

PACKING

225

225×75 TRIMMER JOIST

225×50 JOIST

22 APRON
LINING

PLASTER

G

58×30 COVER FILLET

DETAIL "J"

0   10   150
SCALE   MM

Fig. 136

207

tenoning the balusters, they are cut to the pitch of the handrails and strings and simply nailed to them.

Additional balustrade details are illustrated in Figs. 141, 145 and 148.

A detail showing a suitable finish to the upper floor, where the balustrade is returned to the wall, is shown at G, Fig. 136. The trimmer is covered with an apron lining, which is sloped to conform to the risers, and tongued and grooved to the nosing and cover fillet; the lining may be of 3-ply. As the nosing is only slightly set back from the edge of the newel, it is advisable to provide small packing pieces as shown; a solid bearing for the balustrade is thus afforded. The nosing is rebated over the trimmer and either tongued and grooved or splay jointed to the floor board. Note that there is a slight margin between the edge (adjacent to the plaster) of the cover fillet and the edge of the newel. Alternative apron details are shown at M and N, Fig. 145.

The spandrel and the area between the long newel, wall, floor and the plastered soffit of the upper flight are shown panelled (see C and D, Fig. 133). Alternatively, these two areas may be filled in with coke breeze blocks (see F, Fig. 144) and plastered, or they may be stoothed (vertical studs and plaster). If an access door is provided (see note at D, Fig. 133), the space under the stair can be used to accommodate gas and electric meters, fuse and switchboards, boxes, etc.

The isometric sketch of this staircase (Fig. 138) shows a portion of the window placed in the external cavity wall. This must be large enough to light both the staircase and hall. Additional lighting to the latter is provided by the glazed door and screen, and, if necessary, the door into the kitchen (A, Fig. 132) may be partially glazed with figured or similar glass. The cupboard H (at A, Fig. 132) has been omitted for the reason stated below the title of Fig. 133

SETTING OUT AND CONSTRUCTION.—Much of the description on pp. 196—201 is applicable. In addition to the net height and going, the position of the half-space landing trimmer will be noted on the storey rod, the width of stairway will be taken and the angles between the walls will be checked.

If a cradle (see p. 199) is used to frame together the treads and risers which are shown at F, Fig. 136, the two legs will be inclined to conform to the slope of the risers. The strings are fitted to the newels at the shop, they are then dissembled, transported to the job and finally fixed after any necessary adjustments have been made.

CONTEMPORARY TREATMENT.—A more modern treatment of this dog-leg stair is shown in the isometric sketch, Fig. 139. The balustrades illustrated in the previous figures are of the *open* type, *i.e.,* balusters are employed. These open balustrades are not always favoured, principally on account of the extra labour entailed in dusting, cleaning and polishing. To meet this objection an increasing number of stairs is constructed with *solid* or panelled balustrades.[1] This latter form of balustrade is particularly

[1] Solid balustrades may also be constructed of 75 mm by 50 mm studs fixed at 400 mm centres and covered with plasterboard and plaster.

ALTERNATE DETAILS
OF BALUSTRADE

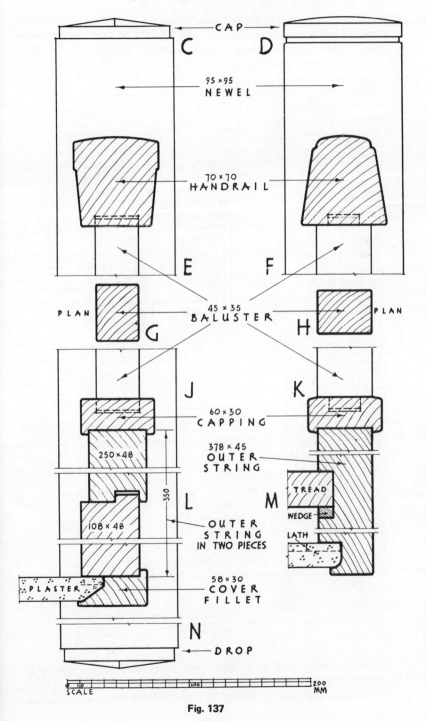

CAP

C   D

95 × 95
NEWEL

70 × 70
HANDRAIL

E   F

PLAN   45 × 35   PLAN
BALUSTER

G   H

J   K

60 × 30
CAPPING

378 × 45
OUTER
STRING

250 × 48

TREAD

350   L   M

WEDGE

108 × 48

OUTER
STRING
IN TWO PIECES

LATH

PLASTER   58 × 30
COVER
FILLET

N

DROP

SCALE   MM

Fig. 137

210

effective when applied to dog-leg stairs because of its improved appearance compared with the somewhat ugly effect produced by the upper outer string intercepting the lower open balustrade. As this is a matter of

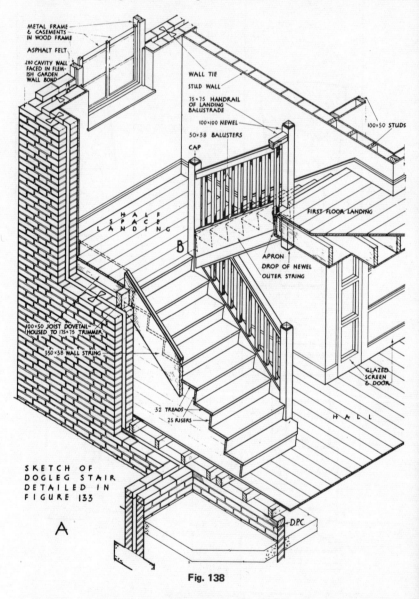

METAL FRAME
& CASEMENTS
IN WOOD FRAME

ASPHALT FELT

280 CAVITY WALL
FACED IN FLEM-
ISH GARDEN
WALL BOND

WALL TIE

STUD WALL

75×75 HANDRAIL
OF LANDING
BALUSTRADE

100×100 NEWEL

50×38 BALUSTERS

CAP

100×50 STUDS

HALF SPACE LANDING

B

FIRST FLOOR LANDING

APRON
DROP OF NEWEL
OUTER STRING

100×50 JOIST DOVETAIL-
HOUSED TO 175×75 TRIMMER

350×38 WALL STRING

GLAZED
SCREEN
& DOOR

32 TREADS

25 RISERS

HALL

SKETCH OF
DOGLEG STAIR
DETAILED IN
FIGURE 133

A

D.P.C.

Fig. 138

opinion, students may draw their own conclusions by comparing the sketch of the open-balustraded dog-leg stair in Fig. 138 with that of the solid-balustraded type illustrated in Fig. 139. It must be emphasized, however, that solid balustrades obstruct a good deal of natural light and will cause the interior of a building (especially the hall) to be dark unless larger windows are provided than those which are adequate when open balustrades are employed.

A plan and longitudinal section of the stair shown in Fig. 139 are provided in Fig. 140. Details are given in Fig. 141. The whole treatment is simple and therefore elaborately moulded nosings, handrails, etc. must be avoided. The steps may be constructed as shown at F, Fig. 136, or as illustrated at E, Fig. 141, where two alternative nosings are indicated. They are housed and wedged in the usual manner (see F, Fig. 141). The strings, which are undressed, are secured to two rough 100 mm by 75 mm posts which are continued and securely fixed to the ground floor and landing trimmers. The ends of the strings are barefaced tenoned to the posts (see J, Fig. 141). Note at F that the outer strings are not in the same vertical plane, the inner faces being flush with those of the posts to provide fixings for the boards of 3-ply. The posts are connected at the top by a 75 mm by 75 mm head (see Figs. 139 and 140 and D, Fig. 141). Two vertical 75 mm by 75 mm studs are stub-tenoned to the head and strings. Both sides of this framing are covered with 3-ply (see Figs. 139 and 140, and D, F and J, Fig. 141). The manufacture and characteristics of this material are described in Chapter II, *Carpentry*. Two alternative joints between the plywood boards are shown at G and H, Fig. 141. The former shows the boards to be butt or square jointed; the thin wood strip which covers the joint is secured by panel pins which are punched and the holes made good with suitably coloured wood mastic or stopping to render them inconspicuous. When chamfer jointed (H) the boards are panel pinned, and these fixings are concealed in a similar manner; this joint can be safely employed under normal conditions as the better graded plywoods shrink very little.

The handrail at the top flight is shown at D, Fig. 141. Whilst this simple treatment is effective in appearance, it is rather wide, and therefore a tapering handrail, such as that at F, Fig. 137, is sometimes adopted; alternatively, a chromium plated circular tube, or one similar to J, Fig. 128, secured by short vertical standards to the rail at D, may be used. The handrail for the lower flight, indicated in Fig. 139, is of circular section as described; this is bent at the ends and screwed to the posts; two additional intermediate brackets would be required. As shown in Fig. 139, the rail at D, Fig. 141, is continued down the post at the half-space landing, and a similar edging is fixed to the longer post (see J, Fig. 141) in order to protect the edges of the plywood and provide a suitable finish.

The difficulty of making a good finish between the plywood and the steps is overcome if thin, narrow *margin fillets* are planted on the face, and these short horizontal and vertical pieces are mitred (see Figs. 139 and 140, and E and F, Fig. 141).

The bottom step is bull-nosed (as shown) or splayed (see Fig. 148).

212

If desired, the walls of the stairway may be panelled to conform with this balustrading. As shown in Fig. 139, the height of this dado panelling

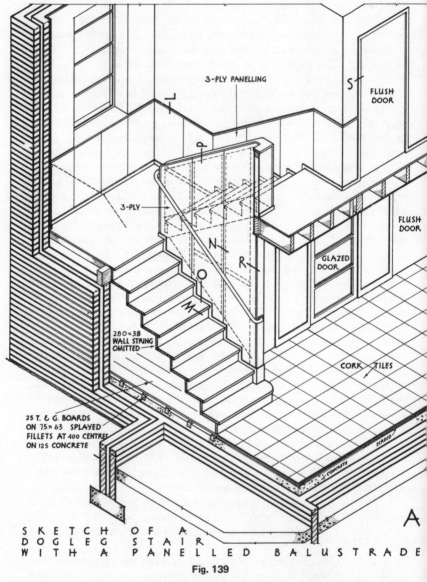

3-PLY PANELLING

FLUSH DOOR

3-PLY

FLUSH DOOR

GLAZED DOOR

CORK TILES

280×38 WALL STRING OMITTED

25 T. & G. BOARDS ON 75×63 SPLAYED FILLETS AT 400 CENTRES ON 125 CONCRETE

SCREED

CONCRETE

A

S K E T C H   O F   A
D O G L E G   S T A I R
W I T H   A   P A N E L L E D   B A L U S T R A D E

Fig. 139

is the same as that of the handrail, the capping (see detail at B, Fig. 141), of similar projection and depth as the handrail, lining through with the window board. This detail shows the plywood and capping to be fixed to 50 mm by 19 mm grounds plugged to the wall. The skirting is of the same size and section as the margin fillets.

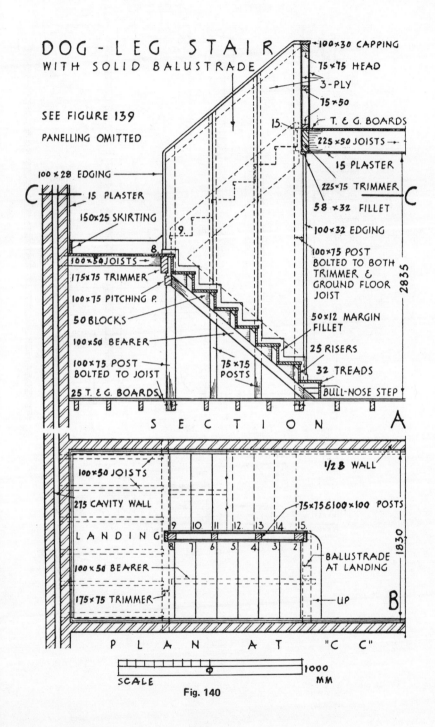

DOG-LEG STAIR
WITH SOLID BALUSTRADE

SEE FIGURE 139
PANELLING OMITTED

100×30 CAPPING
75×75 HEAD
3-PLY
75×50
T. & G. BOARDS
225×50 JOISTS →
15 PLASTER
225×75 TRIMMER
58×32 FILLET
100×32 EDGING
100×75 POST BOLTED TO BOTH TRIMMER & GROUND FLOOR JOIST
50×12 MARGIN FILLET
25 RISERS
32 TREADS
BULL-NOSE STEP

100×28 EDGING
15 PLASTER
150×25 SKIRTING
100×50 JOISTS →
175×75 TRIMMER
100×75 PITCHING P.
50 BLOCKS
100×50 BEARER
100×75 POST BOLTED TO JOIST
25 T. & G. BOARDS
75×75 POSTS

C   C

15

2835

S E C T I O N   A

100×50 JOISTS
275 CAVITY WALL
L A N D I N G
100×50 BEARER
175×75 TRIMMER

1/2 B WALL
75×75 & 100×100 POSTS
BALUSTRADE AT LANDING
UP

9 10 11 12 13 14 15
8   7   6   5   4   3   2   1

1830

B

P L A N   A T   "C C"

SCALE   1000
Fig. 140   MM

213

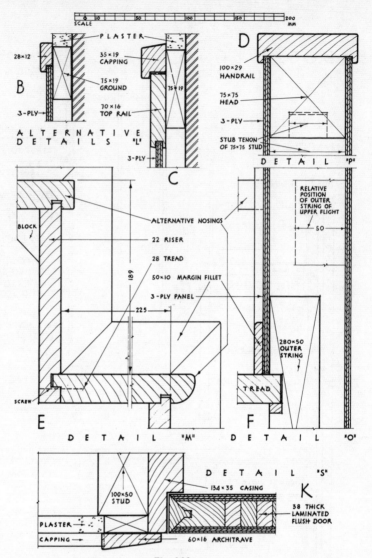

SCALE
0 10   50   100   150   200
                                          MM

B
28×12
3-PLY

PLASTER
35×19
CAPPING
75×19
GROUND
70×16
TOP RAIL

75×19

3-PLY

C

ALTERNATIVE
DETAILS "L"

D
100×29
HANDRAIL
75×75
HEAD
3-PLY
STUB TENON
OF 75×75 STUD

DETAIL "P"

BLOCK

ALTERNATIVE NOSINGS
22 RISER
28 TREAD
50×10 MARGIN FILLET
3-PLY PANEL

189

225

SCREW

E

DETAIL "M"

RELATIVE
POSITION
OF OUTER
STRING OF
UPPER FLIGHT

50

280×50
OUTER
STRING

TREAD

F

DETAIL "O"

DETAIL "S"

100×50
STUD

134×35 CASING

K

38 THICK
LAMINATED
FLUSH DOOR

PLASTER

CAPPING

60×16 ARCHITRAVE

Fig. 141

214

An alternative detail to B is shown at C, Fig. 141. Here the panelling consists of 3-ply panels with top and bottom rails and stiles, the top rail being finished with a plain splayed capping. The balustrade should be similarly treated to conform (see Fig. 146.

The sketch in Fig. 139 shows that the flush door is in keeping with the general design. A detail of a laminated core flush door (see p. 113) is given at K, Fig. 141. The architrave may be as shown or, alternatively, the section may be the same as that of the simple skirting.

OPEN WELL STAIR

The open well stair has a space or well between the outer strings and in this respect it differs from the dog-leg stair. This separation of the strings greatly enhances the appearance of the stair. More space, of course, is needed to accommodate it, but the extra width over that required for the dog-leg stair need not exceed 150 mm, and when planning a staircase it is well worth while trying to obtain this additional width because of the satisfactory results which can be achieved.

It is shown in outline at C, Fig. 120. Key plans of a house showing the application of an open well stair appear at A and B, Fig. 142. Enlarged plans and sections of the stair are illustrated in Figs. 143 and 144.

Much of the construction is similar to that already described. The plan at E, Fig. 143, shows three flights, each 914 mm wide, with two quarter-space landings.

The going of each step is 228 mm. As the height from floor to floor is 2 896 mm (see D, Fig. 144) and there are sixteen steps, the rise of each equals 2 896 ÷ 16 = 181 mm. Thus the going, plus twice the rise, equals 590 mm (see Building Regulation requirement, p. 185).

Three of the newels are bolted to joists at the ground level, and the balustrade is continued at the first floor to two newels and a half newel having shaped drops similar to the caps. The headroom is approximately 2 235 mm if, as shown at C, Fig. 144, the balustrade is returned with the newels in line with the centre of the dining-room door. Although the soffits of the middle and top flights are plastered (see D, Fig. 144), only 250 mm wide outer strings need be used, provided three bearers are employed at each short flight (see C, Fig. 143, and D, Fig. 144). A simple but satisfactory treatment results (see O, Fig. 145), which detail shows a slight projection of the string beyond the face of the plaster; wider strings would give a less effective appearance. One rough carriage or bearer is only required at the bottom flight as this soffit is not plastered.

Details of the balustrade are shown at J, M and O, Fig. 145. Note the simple treatment of the handrail consisting of two members. A rail to which the balusters are tenoned is also fixed to the floor of the landing (see M), and a 50 mm by 16 mm fillet is used to cover the edges of floor

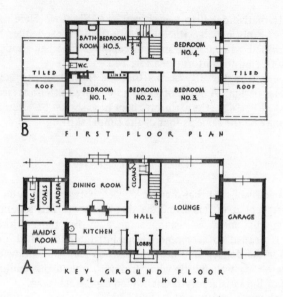

Fig. 142

boards, etc. The newel caps and drops are octagonal shaped out of the solid.

CLOAKROOM.—The plans at A, Fig. 142, and F, Fig. 144, show that some of the space under the stair has been utilized to form a cloakroom in which there is a lavatory basin and a water closet. The partitions consist of 50 mm thick concrete or 38 or 50 mm thick plaster slabs which are jointed in mortar and nailed to the floor, newels, etc.; stoothings (Chap. VI, *Carpentry*) may be used as an alternative. A metal window provides the necessary lighting and ventilation (see also Fig. 146).

The open balustrades illustrated in these sections and in previous figures show plain vertical balusters, spaced at 75 and 100 mm apart. Whilst such simple treatment of this type of balustrade is generally preferred, the balusters can be arranged to give a big variety in design. One design is shown at G, Fig. 145, and this is an alternative to the elevation of the balustrade at T (see D, Fig. 144). Details of this alternative balustrade are given at K and N, Fig. 145; with the exception of that housed into the moulded handrail, the whole of the balusters are out of 32 mm square stuff, the vertical members being stub-tenoned into the horizontal members.

The application of a solid panelled balustrade to this open well stair is shown at H, Fig. 145. This is an example of framed panelling and is an alternative to the type illustrated in Figs. 139 and 140. It shows the balustrade at T, Fig. 144, divided into three panels. A detail is given at L, Fig. 145; the 9 mm thick panels (which may also be of plywood) are framed to top and bottom rails, in addition to vertical members called stiles; the handrail consists of a moulded member surmounting a rail into which the top rail of the panelling is housed. The caps and drops of the newels, moulded from the solid, are more elaborate than those shown hitherto, but a simpler design may, of course, be adopted if preferred.

Some idea of the general appearance of the open well stair detailed in Figs. 143 and 144, but with a solid balustrade conforming to the detail at L, Fig. 145, may be obtained by reference to the axonometric sketch shown in Fig. 146. When designing a balustrade of this type, it is sometimes difficult to obtain panels of uniform width, although a slight readjustment of the position of the newels will assist in avoiding a big variation. Note that a portion of the large window is shown. The need for increased natural lighting when a stair has a solid balustrade is stated on p. 211.

The use of laminboard (Chap. II, *Carpentry*) for the construction of solid balustrades is likely to increase. A detail incorporating this convenient material is shown at F, Fig. 148. The old-fashioned plain mop-stick handrail has been included, as this affords a firm grip; a moulded rail similar to that at L, Fig. 145, would be equally suitable. The laminboard would be housed into the newels and string.

WINDERS

Attention is drawn to the references to winders on pp. 185 and 186. The plan of a portion of a stair, having three winders at the foot, is shown at D, Fig. 147. Two sections, an elevation developed from the plan, and a sketch of the necessary framing are also shown.

Treads should be of uniform width, and the going at the "walking line" (which is usually taken to be along an arc struck from the centre of the newel at 450 mm radius) should be at least equal to that of the fliers, *i.e.,* 225 mm. One method of setting out the winders on plan is briefly described below D.

It will be seen at G that the 100 mm by 50 mm bearer or carriage cannot be continued to the floor but is supported by a trimmer which is secured to the newel and built into the wall. Therefore, other means of support must be obtained for the winders, and hence the provision of a bearer immediately below each of the risers of the second and third steps. As shown at A, C and D, a 75 mm (or 100 mm) by 50 mm bearer, marked "1", is housed into the newel and wall string, and its outer face is in line with that of the riser of step "2" immediately above it (see also G). Similarly, the outer face of bearer "2" is directly below that of the third riser. The treads, because of their maximum width, have to be jointed; these are preferably ploughed and tongued (known also as "cross-tongued") joints and are shown at A and C and by faint lines at D; they are similar to those detailed at D and E, Fig. 148. The short

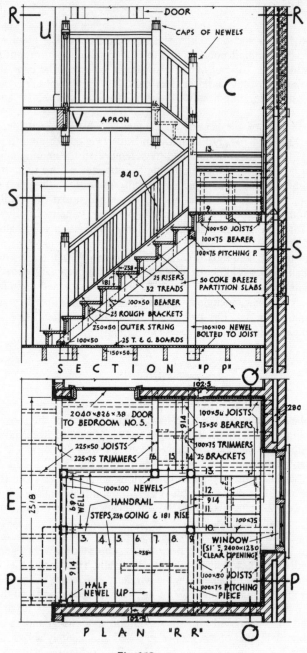

R— R

U

DOOR

CAPS OF NEWELS

C

V APRON

16

13

S

840

9

100×50 JOISTS
100×75 BEARER

100×75 PITCHING P.

S— S

238

25 RISERS
32 TREADS

181

50 COKE BREEZE
PARTITION SLABS

100×50 BEARER
25 ROUGH BRACKETS

250×50 OUTER STRING

100×50

100×100 NEWEL
BOLTED TO JOIST

25 T. & G. BOARDS

150×50

SECTION "P P"

102·5

2040×826×38 DOOR
TO BEDROOM NO. 5.

100×50 JOISTS
75×50 BEARERS

914

225×50 JOISTS
225×75 TRIMMERS

16   15

100×75 TRIMMERS
25 BRACKETS

14

13

100×100 NEWELS

HANDRAIL

12.
914
11.

E

25/8

690
WELL

STEPS, 238 GOING & 181 RISE

10.

100×75

280

3.   4.   5.   6.   7.   8.   9

238

WINDOW
(S 2400×1230
CLEAR OPENING)

914

P— P

HALF
NEWEL UP

100×50 JOISTS
100×75 PITCHING
PIECE

102·5

PLAN "R R"

Fig. 143

218

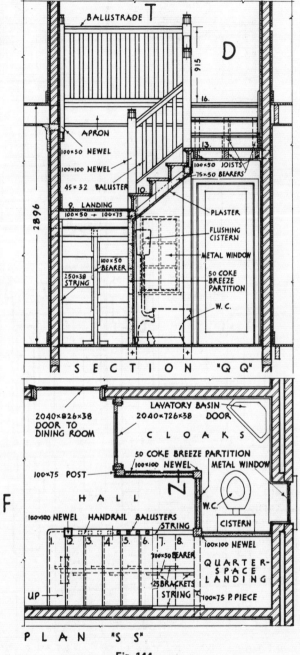

BALUSTRADE

T

D

915

16.

APRON

100×50 NEWEL

100×100 NEWEL

45×32 BALUSTER

2896

9. LANDING
100×50 → 100×75

13.
100×50 JOISTS
75×50 BEARERS

PLASTER

FLUSHING
CISTERN

METAL WINDOW

50 COKE
BREEZE
PARTITION

W. C.

250×38
STRING

100×50
BEARER

10.

S E C T I O N "Q Q"

2040×826×38
DOOR TO
DINING ROOM

LAVATORY BASIN

2040×726×38 DOOR

C L O A K S

50 COKE BREEZE PARTITION

100×100 NEWEL

METAL WINDOW

100×75 POST

H A L L

N

W.C.

F

100×100 NEWEL HANDRAIL BALUSTERS

STRING

CISTERN

1. 2. 3. 4. 5. 6. 7. 8.

100×100 NEWEL

100×50 BEARER

QUARTER-
SPACE
LANDING

UP

25 BRACKETS
STRING

100×75 P. PIECE

P L A N "S S"

Fig. 144

219

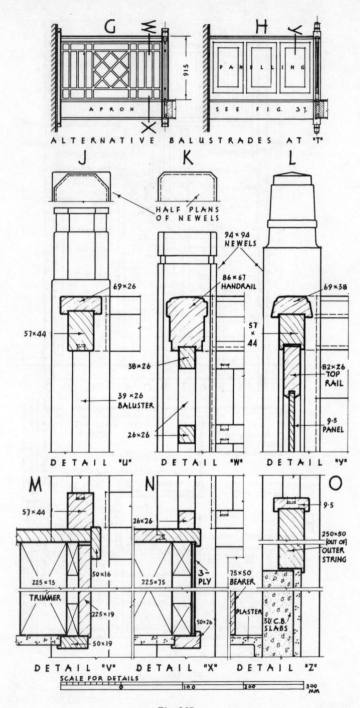

G W

915

APRON

X

H V

PANELLING

SEE FIG. 37.

ALTERNATIVE BALUSTRADES AT "T"

J   K   L

HALF PLANS
OF NEWELS

94 × 94
NEWELS

86 × 67
HANDRAIL

69 × 26

57 × 44

57
×
44

69 × 38

38 × 26

82 × 26
TOP
RAIL

39 × 26
BALUSTER

9.5
PANEL

26 × 26

DETAIL "U"   DETAIL "W"   DETAIL "Y"

M   N   O

57 × 44

26 × 26

9.5

250 × 50
[OUT OF]
OUTER
STRING

225 × 75

50 × 16

3-
PLY

75 × 50
BEARER

TRIMMER

225 × 75

225 × 19

PLASTER

50 × 26

50 C.B.
SLABS

50 × 19

DETAIL "V"   DETAIL "X"   DETAIL "Z"

SCALE FOR DETAILS
100   200   300 MM

Fig. 145

220

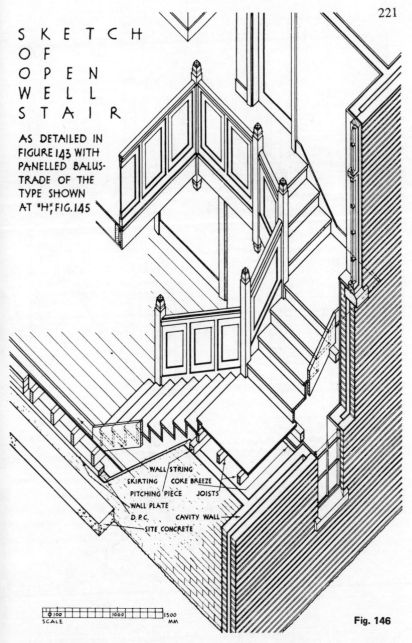

S K E T C H
O F
O P E N
W E L L
S T A I R

AS DETAILED IN
FIGURE 143 WITH
PANELLED BALUS-
TRADE OF THE
TYPE SHOWN
AT "H", FIG. 145

WALL STRING
SKIRTING   COKE BREEZE
PITCHING PIECE   JOISTS
WALL PLATE
D.P.C.   CAVITY WALL
SITE CONCRETE

0 100   1000   1500
SCALE   MM

Fig. 146

returned wall string is tongued and grooved and nailed to the main wall
string, the upper edge of which is cut to a curve or easing. These strings
must be increased in width to accommodate the winder treads, and the
joints between the boards used to build up the string are also ploughed
and tongued (see B, C and G).

W I N D E R S

222

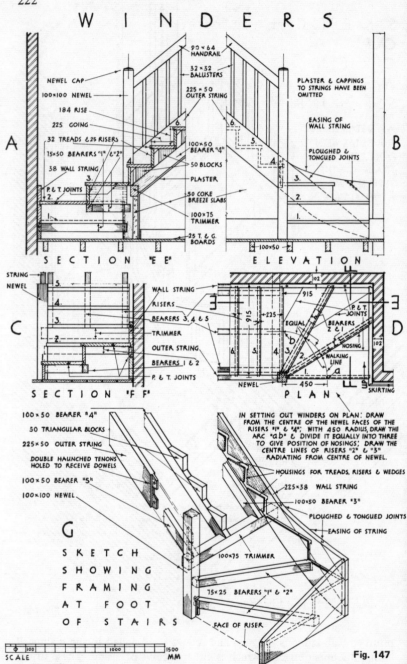

A

NEWEL CAP
100×100 NEWEL
184 RISE
225 GOING
32 TREADS & 25 RISERS
75×50 BEARERS "1" & "2"
38 WALL STRING
P. & T. JOINTS

90×64 HANDRAIL
32×32 BALUSTERS
225×50 OUTER STRING
100×50 BEARER "4"
50 BLOCKS
PLASTER
50 COKE BREEZE SLABS
100×75 TRIMMER
25 T. & G. BOARDS

B

PLASTER & CAPPINGS TO STRINGS HAVE BEEN OMITTED
EASING OF WALL STRING
PLOUGHED & TONGUED JOINTS

100×50

S E C T I O N "E E"

E L E V A T I O N

C

STRING
NEWEL

WALL STRING
RISERS
BEARERS 3, 4 & 5
TRIMMER
OUTER STRING
BEARERS 1 & 2
P. & T. JOINTS

S E C T I O N "F F"

D

102
915
915
225
EQUAL
P. & T. JOINTS
BEARERS 2 & 1
NOSING
102
WALKING LINE
450
NEWEL
SKIRTING

P L A N

G

100×50 BEARER "4"
50 TRIANGULAR BLOCKS
225×50 OUTER STRING
DOUBLE HAUNCHED TENONS HOLED TO RECEIVE DOWELS
100×50 BEARER "5"
100×100 NEWEL

IN SETTING OUT WINDERS ON PLAN: DRAW FROM THE CENTRE OF THE NEWEL FACES OF THE RISERS "1" & "4", WITH 450 RADIUS, DRAW THE ARC "ab" & DIVIDE IT EQUALLY INTO THREE TO GIVE POSITION OF NOSINGS; DRAW THE CENTRE LINES OF RISERS "2" & "3" RADIATING FROM CENTRE OF NEWEL.

HOUSINGS FOR TREADS, RISERS & WEDGES
225×38 WALL STRING
100×50 BEARER "3"
PLOUGHED & TONGUED JOINTS
EASING OF STRING

100×75 TRIMMER
75×25 BEARERS "1" & "2"
FACE OF RISER

S K E T C H
S H O W I N G
F R A M I N G
A T   F O O T
O F   S T A I R S

SCALE
MM

Fig. 147

    The bottom step at least of a stair is often specially shaped. This adds greatly to its appearance. Several of these finishes are illustrated in Fig. 148.

SPLAYED STEP.—The application of this step is shown in the part plan and elevation at A and is detailed at D and E. The bottom step projects beyond the newel. Its riser is in three pieces, the vertical edges of which are mitred, ploughed (grooved) and glued hardwood tongued. The nosing of the tread is shaped to conform. The outer end of the bottom step at D, Fig. 133, and Fig. 138 are splayed and constructed in this manner.

A splayed step may also be formed by constructing the riser as described below.

BULLNOSED STEP (see part plan and elevations at B and the details at G, H and J).—The round end of the step consists of the riser (which is in one piece and has its thickness reduced near the end to enable it to be bent round a wood block shaped to the required (quadrant curve), a shaped scotia board (if required) and the tread shaped at the end to conform. The curved portion of the riser is called a *veneer* as it serves as a thin covering to the block. Its reduced thickness depends upon the curve, the sharper the curve, the thinner the veneer; in the given example the thickness is approximately 2 mm, although for clarity this has been exaggerated in the details. The block strengthens the riser and prevents the veneer from being damaged. This block must not be in one piece only, as this would tend to shrink to such an extent as to leave a space between it and the veneer; the latter would then be readily damaged because of lack of support. Accordingly, the block is built up of three or more pieces, and, in order to reduce still further the liability to shrinkage, the pieces are arranged "cross-grained", *i.e.,* the grain of one is opposite to that of the adjacent piece.

The step is constructed in the following manner: The block is built up to the required height by gluing and screwing or nailing the pieces together, the top and bottom surfaces are planed flat and the block is cut to shape, as shown at H and J, the block is double rebated, one edge being square cut and the opposite edge (nearest to the newel) being bevelled cut or dovetailed. The riser (which should be of carefully selected straight-grained timber, free from knots) is then prepared by marking off the position of the bevelled and square cuts, the length of the veneer being found by placing the dovetailed edge of the block opposite to the corresponding mark on the riser and revolving the block on the back of the riser until the square edge of the block rebate touches the riser, which position is then marked; an extra 19 mm is measured on the riser to provide room for the pair of folding wedges. A marking gauge (4, Fig. 151, *Carpentry*) is now used and the thickness of the veneer marked on the riser. Cuts are made across the back of the riser to form the shoulders, and the chisel and router plane are used to remove the core and form the veneer. The cutting of the veneer is often done on the circular saw (Fig. 1) and sometimes on the band saw (Fig. 4). The shape of the veneered end of the riser, before it has been fixed to the block, is shown by broken lines at J. The back of the veneer and the outer face of the block are then roughened by the toothing plane (Chap.X, *Carpentry*) or file

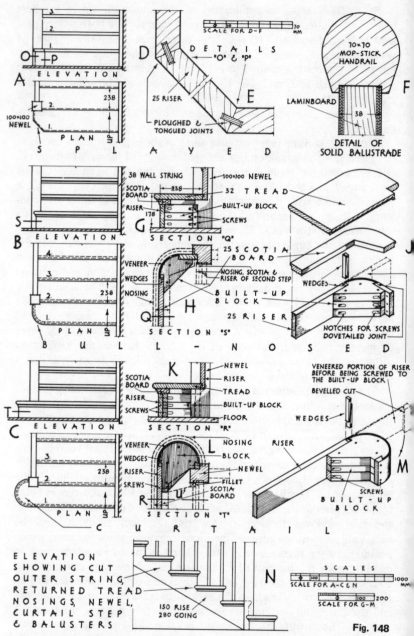

Fig. 148

to give a key for the glue. The latter is now liberally applied to the back of the veneer (after its face has been wetted with boiling water) and the face of the block. With the dovetailed shoulder of the veneer engaging in the dovetailed rebate on the block, the riser is pressed against the block;

the glued wedges are inserted and driven home in order to bed the veneer tightly on the block which is secured to the riser by means of screws screws from the back, the notches for these having been previously prepared.

The scotia board, after being reduced in width and shaped, is screwed to the riser and tread.

The foot of the newel is notched out, as shown, and the riser is screwed to it.

A bullnosed step is also illustrated at B, Fig. 140, and F, Fig. 144.

CURTAIL STEP (see C, K, L and M).—The construction of this semi-circular ended step is similar to that of the bullnosed step. The back of the block is sometimes shaped as shown at U (see L), and a vertical fillet (shown crossed by diagonals) is screwed to it and the newel. The end of a curtail step may also be of a spiral form. This step, because of the side projection, should not be used if the width of the floor at the side is restricted.

CUT STRING (see N).—This has been included to show the difference between it and all the close strings illustrated. The upper edge of the string is notched out to receive the treads, the risers mitre with the vertical cuts on the string, and the moulded nosings are returned. There are usually two balusters per step, with a face of one vertically over a riser.

CHAPTER THIRTEEN

ARCHITRAVES, SKIRTINGS, ETC.

Architraves, skirtings, picture rails and angle beads; methods of fixing.

THE fixing of certain joinery work can only be completed after the walls have been plastered. Architraves, skirtings and picture rails are examples of such work, commonly called "second fixings". A key sketch showing the application of these members is given at A, Fig. 149.

ARCHITRAVES.—These are used at doors (and occasionally windows) for the concealment of the joints between the casings with their grounds and the plaster, and to provide an effective finish.

Casings or linings have been described on p. 73—77 and various sections of architraves are shown in Chapters IV, VI, VII and VIII.

An architrave consists of one horizontal and two vertical members. The size and design of the architrave depend upon the size of the opening, the quality of the timber and the general effect desired. A 100 mm (nominal) wide architrave is usually sufficient for doors up to 900 mm wide; for large openings the width should not exceed 150 mm if in one piece, as it is liable to split when shrinking. Three alternative sections of the architrave at D, Fig. 149, are shown at N, O and P in the same Figure. The plain architrave shown at N, Fig. 149, would be suitable if the door has square or chamfered panels (see J and L, Fig. 39), but a more elaborate architrave would be preferred if, for instance, the panel mouldings were of the section shown at F', Fig. 39. Certain sections, such as those at L, Fig. 50, and P, Fig. 149, should be avoided unless well-seasoned good quality timber (preferably hardwood) is used, otherwise unequal shrinkage will occur, resulting in the members curling or twisting on account of one-half of the section being much thinner than the other. Simplicity in design is a characteristic of modern construction (see also pp. 62 and 65).

The fixing of architraves is described on p. 94.

Some of the joints between the horizontal and vertical members of architraves are shown at A, B and C, Fig. 150. Normally, the angles are mitred (see A), each end being sawn in the mitre block (4, Fig. 158, *Carpentry*) and planed. Several alternative joints are adopted for wide architraves; they include (1) the mitred and stub-tenoned joint shown at B (the mortices and tenons being glued and the latter screwed from

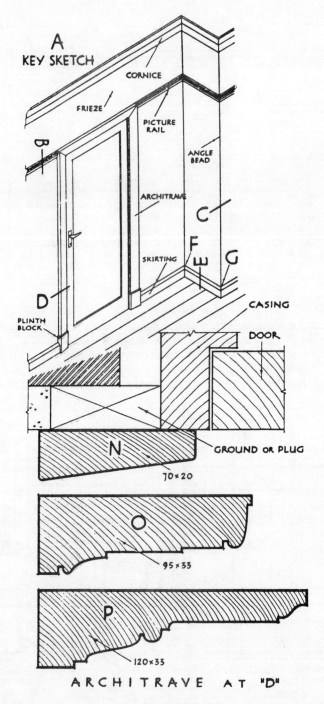

A
KEY SKETCH

CORNICE

FRIEZE

PICTURE RAIL

B

ANGLE BEAD

ARCHITRAVE

C

F
E   **G**

SKIRTING

CASING

D

DOOR

PLINTH BLOCK

N
70 × 20

GROUND OR PLUG

O
95 × 33

P
120 × 33

ARCHITRAVE AT "D"

Fig. 149

227

the back), (2) the mitred and slip-feathered (or ploughed and tongued—
see C, Fig. 150 and D, Fig. 148) and (3) the mitred and hand-rail bolted

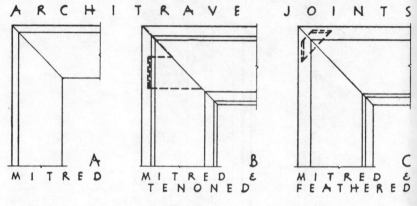

Fig. 150

joint (small bolts of the type shown at Q, Fig. 109, being used, at right
angles to the mitre, to ensure tight joints). Each member is nailed along
both edges to the grounds (or plugs) and edges of the casing.

Usually the feet of the architrave are continued down to the floor to
which they are nailed, but in first-class work they are often finished with
plinth or *foot blocks* (see Fig. 151). These blocks are slightly thicker and

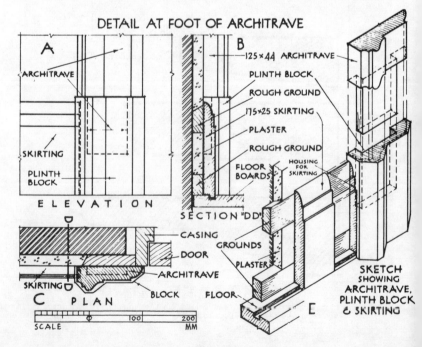

Fig. 151

wider than the architrave and higher than the skirting which is housed into them, and their shape roughly conforms with that of the architrave. A tongue is formed at the foot of the architrave and a mortice is made in the block to receive it; the tongue is glued and securely nailed or screwed to the block from the back. Plinth blocks provide a suitable finish to the architrave and skirting and serve as a protection to the moulded architrave.

SKIRTINGS OR PLINTHS are provided to protect the wall plaster and to cover the joint between the floor boards and plaster. Several sections are shown in Fig. 152. The size varies but the depth nowadays rarely exceeds 100 mm unless for very large rooms.

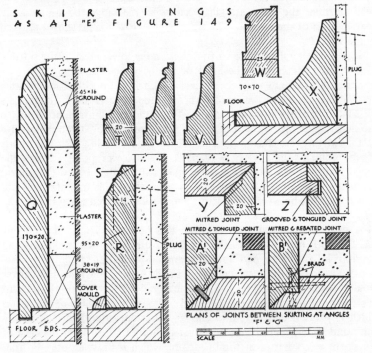

Fig. 152

The best method of securing skirtings as shown at Q, Fig. 152, and B and E, Fig. 151, where horizontal rough grounds are plugged at from 450 to 700 mm intervals in the vertical joints of the brickwork. The grounds must be flush with the face of the plaster and allowance for the thickness of the grounds must therefore be made when chalk lining the plugs (see p. 230). Skirtings which are only 100 mm or less in depth only require one set of grounds. When two rows of grounds are fixed, the space between them is not always filled with plaster, and when it is, care should be taken by the plasterer to ensure that the face of the plaster does not project beyond the grounds.

The cheaper and more usual method of securing skirtings is to fix them direct to plugs which have been driven into the vertical joints of the wall at about 900 mm intervals. After the plugs have been firmly driven into the holes formed in the joints to receive them, a chalked line is applied to ensure that they project in true alignment; each end plug in a wall is marked at a distance from the wall equal to the thickness of the plaster; the chalked line, held on these marks, is stretched tightly and snapped (by being carefully raised near the centre and released); the end of each plug is then sawn squarely off to the white line so formed. For deep skirtings the plugs are staggered, with the plugs fixed alternately near the top of the plinths. The skirting at R, Fig. 152, is shown plugged to the wall.

It is the general practice to fit or *scribe* the lower edge of the skirting to the floor, which might be more or less irregular.

Scribing is done by placing the piece of skirting in position and packing or wedging up the lower end until the top edge is level; compasses (5, Fig. 151, *Carpentry*) are taken and, with the points apart equal to the height that the lowest portion of the floor is below the bottom edge of the skirting, are drawn along the face of the skirting with the points of the compass in a vertical plane; as the lower point follows the irregularities of the floor the other marks a parallel line on the plinth; the lower edge of the skirting is then sawn along this irregular line and thus a tight fit between the skirting and floor is assured when the former is fixed.

A gap invariably appears between this bottom edge of the skirting and the floor boards due to the combined shrinkage of the skirting and the floor joists. This allows both dust and currents of air to enter ground-floor rooms from the space below. A small (9 or 12 mm) quadrant cover mould, as shown at R, Fig. 152, may be bradded to the floor to prevent this; alternatively, the gap may be filled with a material called *plastic wood* which is pressed in whilst in a plastic condition, smoothed over with a knife and sand-papered over when set to bring it flush with the face of the skirting. A better method (but one which is only adopted in first-class work on account of its expense) is shown at Q, Fig. 152, and E, Fig. 151; a tongue is formed on the lower edge of the skirting and this is fitted into a groove formed in the flooring.

Several joints between the ends of skirtings are shown in Fig. 152. The cheapest method is to mitre the ends at both external and internal angles, as shown at Y. Another cheap internal joint consists of scribing one end to the face of the other which has been tightly and squarely fitted into the angle. A better joint for internal angles is shown at Z; one piece of the skirting is grooved from the bottom edge to the bottom of the moulding, the end of the adjacent piece is tongued and the moulded portion is scribed to that of the first piece. A joint used in very good work for both internal and external angles is shown at A'; the thin hard-wood cross-tongue is glued and the joint is assembled before the pieces are fixed to the grounds. The mitred and rebated joint at B' (also called a *lipped* joint) is a good form for external angles; cross-bradding, as shown, is necessary.

As indicated in Fig. 151, skirtings are housed into plinth blocks. If the latter are not provided, the ends of the skirtings should be let into architraves, otherwise gaps will shown when shrinkage occurs.

The designs of skirtings, architraves and panel mouldings when associated together should conform; thus, the skirting at Q, Fig. 152, harmonizes with the architrave shown in Fig. 54 and the panel mouldings N or A', Fig. 39, and the skirting moulding W, Fig. 152, architrave O, Fig. 149, and panel mouldings V or G', Fig. 39, form an agreeable com-bination; the chamfered or bevelled edge shown at R and S, Fig. 152, is preferred when a simple effect is desired. Alternative skirting mouldings are shown at T, U and V, Fig. 152; the cavetto skirting at X, Fig. 152, provides an effective sanitary finish, but the labour in forming the trenching in the floor to receive it is costly.

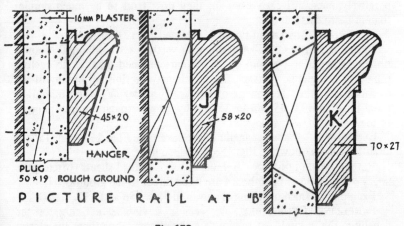

PICTURE RAIL AT "B"

Fig. 153

PICTURE RAILS.—These are often omitted in the modern house. When fixed in rooms, especially in those which may be only 2 400 mm high, they may have the effect of spoiling the proportions by breaking up the wall surfaces and "lowering the ceilings". The use of hooks which are pinned behind the pictures now make unnecessary the provision of picture rails.

When they are required, a satisfactory finish is usually obtained if they are fixed at the level of the top of the door architrave, as shown at B, Fig. 149. Alternative sections through picture rails are given at H, J and K, Fig. 153, and the plug and rough ground (two forms) fixings are included; plugs are generally used and are driven into vertical joints of the walling after the plastering has been completed.

CHAPTER FOURTEEN

PANELLING

Types of panelling. Curved plywood.

FOR centuries timber has been used to provide a durable and attractive internal surface. In earlier days the mouldings used to enrich the panelling were often elaborate and in the British Isles there are many examples which incorporate hand cut skirtings, cornices and other moulds. Although occasions may arise where this highly moulded decorative work is appropriate, it is more usual now to rely upon the self colour of the wood for architectural effect. Expensive timbers, employed relatively cheaply as veneers to plywood, either plain or figured, afford a pleasing surface. Mouldings of any shape can be machined very quickly and comparatively inexpensively; even so, they now tend to be much simpler than in past years.

Panelling is of two main types: (1) framed and (2) flush.

FRAMED PANELLING.—A framing of vertical and horizontal grooved timbers, size 75 or 100 mm by 25 mm, are tenoned together to enclose square or rectangular panels. The panels may be finished by any of the methods given in "Treatment of Panels" (Chapter IV). The framing is fixed to 50 mm by 25 mm or 38 mm by 19 mm rough grounds plugged to the wall.

Examples of framed panelling are given in Figs. 154 and 155; a modified kind is shown in Fig. 158 described later.

FLUSH PANELLING.—No framing is used, instead sheets (often quite large) of plywood or laminboard are fixed direct to the grounds.

Examples of flush panelling are given in Figs. 156 and 157.

PANELLING GENERALLY.—As well as serving as a fixing for the panelling, the grounds act as stops for the plaster; sometimes the plaster is carried behind the panelling.

Fixing is by means of screws or nails placed in unobtrusive positions or where they will be concealed by cappings, etc. Where it is not possible to hide the screws they may be recessed and covered with pellets (carefully selected small pieces of timber), or covered with small turned buttons. Fixing pins or nails should be reasonably small, the finer ones (similar to sewing needles) can be broken off flush with the surface; the larger ones can be punched home and the hole filled with matching stopping. 50 mm or 65 mm oval nails are often used for the heavier mouldings; stopping can be done by the polisher who is able to match the colour accurately. On very expensive work solid timber is still used for the infilling panels; more usually plywood is preferred. In framed panelling the grooves for

232

Fig. 154

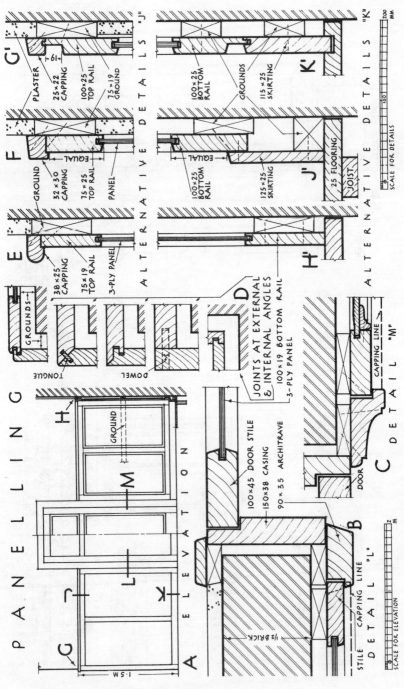

233

Fig. 155

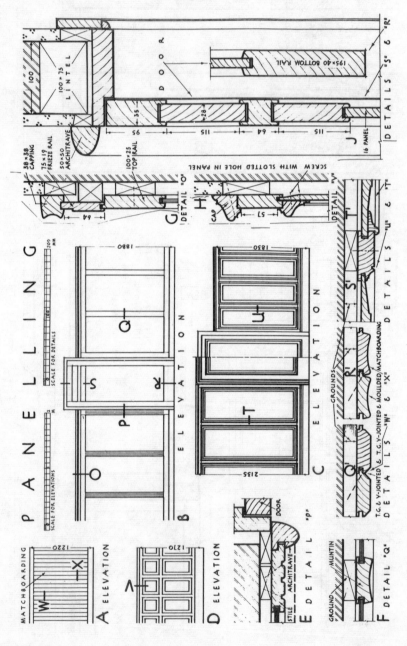

234

the panels are made 3 mm deeper than the panels to allow for movement with changing moisture content (m.c.). Plywood itself moves very little with changing humidity; the m.c. of panelling timber should be about 9 per cent.

The various figures are now described:—

FIG. 154.—The elevation at A, of framed panelling, is of a wall panelled in alternative ways on either side of the central door. The panelling is returned at both the external angle G and at the internal angle H.

Differing angle treatments are shown at D and in Fig. 157 at K.

The plywood panels are set into the vertical members (stiles at the door and muntins intermediately) and horizontal rails. The plan detail at B of the section L at the left hand side of the door shows the very simple arrangement. A slightly more elaborate scheme is given at C where a planted mould is used to the panelling on the right side of the elevation.

Three alternative capping details are given at E, F and G where the top rail, nailed to the rough ground is surmounted by a simple cap.

Three different skirting treatments are shown at H′, J′ and K′.

FIG. 155.—This has four different elevations at A, B, C and D. The one at A has a strong vertical character obtained by the use of match-boarding; alternative details W and X of this are shown at Q′ and R′. The narrow matchboards (about 75 mm wide) are tongued and grooved and can be variously shaped; they are nailed near the tongues into horizontal grounds about 900 mm apart (see also p. 48).

The elevation of rectangular panelling at B shows alternatives on either side of the door. On the left the muntins and stile are grooved on the face as indicated in the detail at E where a relatively bold architrave is adopted. Sections through the door are shown at J and the capping is illustrated at G. The muntins Q, detailed at F, have a slight concave surface.

The elevations at D shows the panelling arranged as upper square panels with rectangular ones below. The capping is enlarged at H, it has a bolection cap with similar mould to the panel below.

A more elaborate elevation drawn at C shows two variations on either side of the centre line. Here solid panels are employed (plywood is more general); the panelling is raised and fielded (see p. 65) and is detailed at S′ and T′.

FIG. 157.—Here in the elevations at A and B flush panelling, not framing, is used; they show larger plywood panels with few mouldings.

The four different joints U between the panels are shown at C. That at 1 is of a direct butt joint, 2 shows a vee-joint and cover fillets are applied in 3 and 4; rough grounds are required behind the joints. Other joint details are given at E, Fig. 157. Two caps are shown at F (1 and 2).

The section N through the recessed door is enlarged at D, it employs a plywood jamb lining grooved into the door frame and 50 mm quadrant architrave.

The built up 200 mm high skirting is detailed at E (1).

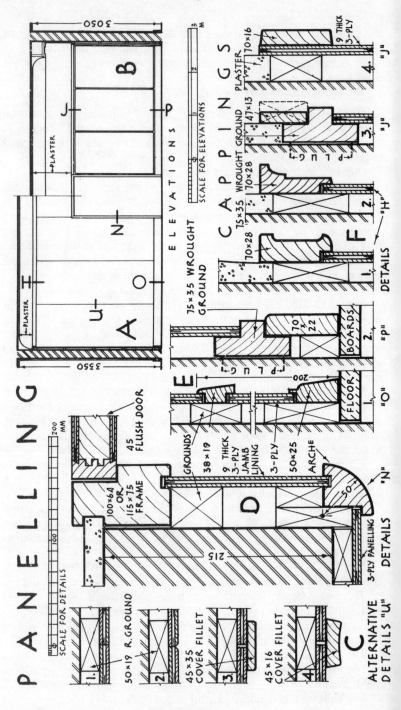

Fig. 156

236

Fig. 157

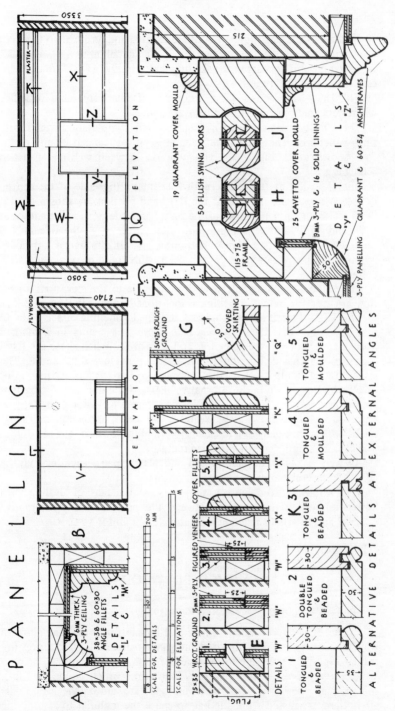

PANELLING

ELEVATION C

ELEVATION D

DETAILS

B

V

PLYWOOD

2740

3050

3350

PLASTER

K

X

Z

Y

W

A

DETAILS "L" & "M"

6mm THICK 3-PLY CEILING

38×38 & 60×30 ANGLE FILLETS

SCALE FOR DETAILS

SCALE FOR ELEVATIONS

200 MM

75×35 WROT GROUND 15mm 5-PLY FIGURED VENEER COVER FILLETS

PLUG

E

1.

2.

3.

4.

5.

"W"

"W"

"V"

"X"

"X"

50×25 ROUGH GROUND

F

G

50 COVED SKIRTING

"K"

"Q"

19 QUADRANT COVER. MOULD

50 FLUSH SWING DOORS

115×75 FRAME

H

J

25 CAVETTO COVER MOULD

9mm 3-PLY & 16 SOLID LININGS

DETAILS "Y" & "Z"

3-PLY PANELLING

QUADRANT & 60×54 ARCHITRAVES

DETAILS

50

215

1 TONGUED & BEADED

2 DOUBLE TONGUED & BEADED

3 TONGUED & BEADED

4 TONGUED & MOULDED

5 TONGUED & MOULDED

K

30

30

30

35

ALTERNATIVE DETAILS AT EXTERNAL ANGLES

237

In the elevation at B the grounds are rebated and wrought so that part of them appears on the surface as in the detail at E (1), Fig. 157. A similar ground appears in the skirting 2 at E in Fig. 156. Two differing caps are drawn at F (3 and 4).

FIG. 157.—This shows more examples of relatively plain panelling where veneered plywood would look attractive.

The elevation at C shows a fireplace wall completely covered with flush panelling. The joint V between adjacent panels can be any of the four shown at C, Fig. 156. The junction between wall and panelled ceiling is given at A.

The elevation at D has alternative schemes either side of the central double swing doors. Details of the left hand portion are shown at B, E (1, 2 and 3), G and H; those of the right hand side portion are shown at E (4 and 5), F and J. Of the joint alternatives at E, the one at 2 is obtained by removing a strip of the outer ply. In the one at 3 the edge has an inlay piece of veneer 25 mm deep; this could be of a contrasting coloured wood.

The external angle details at K do not relate to the elevations above, they are used for framed panelling as mentioned under Fig. 154, p. 235.

FIG. 158.—This is an example of battened panelling and is akin to matchboarding described for Fig. 155 above; it results in a marked horizontal effect by the use of t. and g. boards. When these are fixed together, 38 mm wide horizontal channels are provided; see C and E. The same kind of result is achieved by using plain battens and narrow strips of plywood as shown in the alternative at D. At the doorway the battens are tenoned into the stile as shown in the enlarged elevation C at W.

FIG. 159.—This shows at V, W and L the use of hardwood mouldings on to which thin gauge metal sheet (aluminium, bronze, etc.) is drawn. The caps at X and Y are of extruded metal.

As well as plywood, laminboard and plastic panel sheeting may be adopted; several examples are shown of these.

The details A to F and Z show different means of dealing with horizontal and vertical joints between the panel sheets. Alternative external and internal angles are indicated at H, J and M to O.

CURVED PLYWOOD

The following methods are used to curve plywood:—

Hydraulic pressure.—Shaped male and female forms are used between which successive layers of plywood and glue are placed, hydraulic pressure is then applied to bring the forms together to shape the material.

Vacuum process.—This uses only one form which is enclosed in a rubber bag; the layers of plywood and glue are laid on the form. The air is then exhausted from the bag to cause the material to assume the

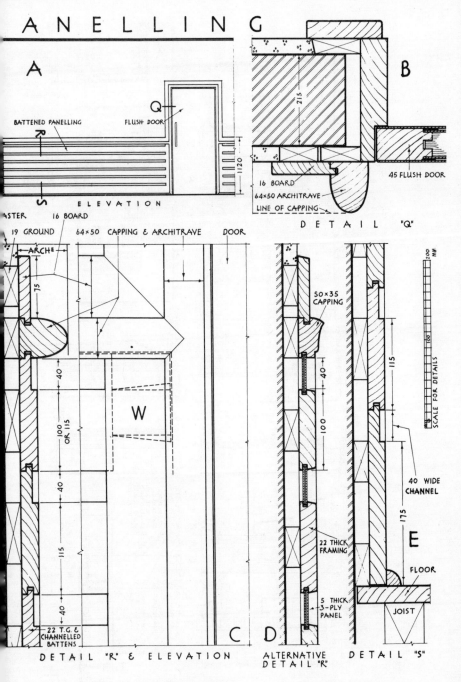

ANELLING

A

BATTENED PANELLING

FLUSH DOOR

Q

R

S

1120

E L E V A T I O N

B

215

16 BOARD

64×50 ARCHITRAVE

LINE OF CAPPING

45 FLUSH DOOR

D E T A I L   "Q"

C

ASTER   16 BOARD

19 GROUND   64×50 CAPPING & ARCHITRAVE   DOOR

ARCH

75

40

100 OR 115

W

40

115

40

22 T.G. & CHANNELLED BATTENS

D E T A I L   "R" & E L E V A T I O N

D

50×35 CAPPING

40

100

22 THICK FRAMING

5 THICK 3-PLY PANEL

A L T E R N A T I V E
D E T A I L "R"

E

115

40 WIDE CHANNEL

175

FLOOR

JOIST

D E T A I L   "S"

200 MM

100

SCALE FOR DETAILS

Fig. 158

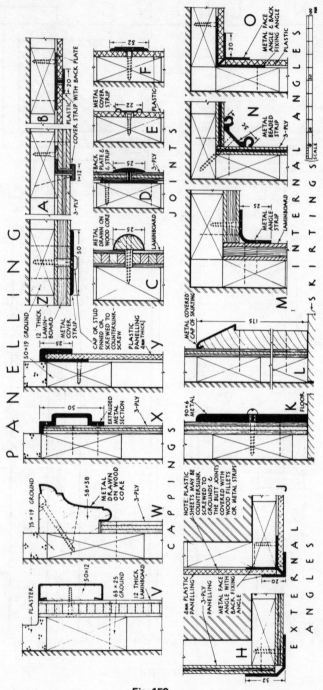

Fig. 159

240

shape of the form; if waterproof glue is used then steam can be admitted to simplify the bending by softening the wood.

Steaming.—The above methods are costly and only used for expensive work. By using a steam hose, plywood can be bent round a timber core of ribs used as permanent groundwork.

Small radius curves can be provided by using canvas backed veneer; or by removing the backing layers of ordinary plywood and easing it round the groundwork. For panels thicker than 6 mm, the back of the plywood can be saw-kerfed. Some of these methods are indicated in Figs. 160 and 161.

FIG. 160.—This shows a plan of a pilaster having a 225 mm radius convex surface. It is built up by means of studs and shaped ribs which form a core for the plywood covering.

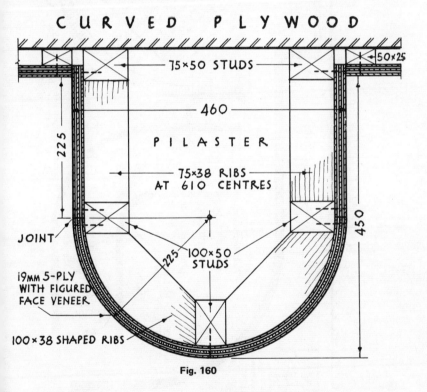

Fig. 160

FIG. 161.—This shows at R an internal corner where the plywood is fixed to studs attached to the wall. A detail of a square corner W is also shown at R, it illustrates how part of the backing plywood is removed to effect the turn. An easier method of making a curved internal angle is drawn at S where the plywood is in two separate thicknesses.

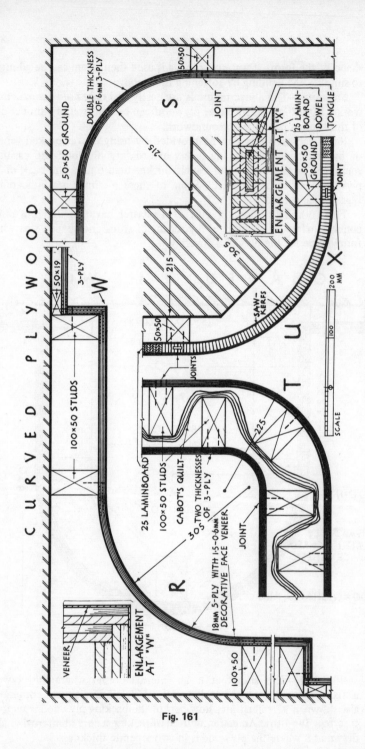

CURVED PLYWOOD

DOUBLE THICKNESS OF 6mm 3-PLY

50×50 GROUND

50×50

JOINT

S

215

ENLARGEMENT AT "X"

25 LAMINBOARD
DOWEL
TONGUE

50×50 GROUND

JOINT

50×19

3-PLY

W

215

305

100×50 STUDS

SAW-KERFS

50×50

X

JOINTS

U

200
MM

100

SCALE
0

T

225

25 LAMINBOARD

100×50 STUDS

CABOT'S QUILT

305 TWO THICKNESSES OF 3-PLY

R

18mm 5-PLY WITH 1·5-0·6mm DECORATIVE FACE VENEER

305

JOINT

100×50

VENEER

ENLARGEMENT AT "W"

100×50

Fig. 161

The plan at U is of a convex curve made with laminboard which has its back surface saw-kerfed to permit bending. The joints X between the curved and adjacent flat parts are made with dowels at 300 mm centres with hardwood tongues between as shown in the inset detail.

The plan at T is of a partition wall with a bullnose angle. It is made with studs between which a sound insulating quilt is draped; the small radius inner curve is made with two thickness of three-ply.

CHAPTER 15

ADHESIVES FOR JOINERY

The main adhesives[1] (known also as glues or cements) used to stick timber parts together are:—

(a) Synthetic Resins
- (1) Phenol/Formaldehyde
- (2) Urea/Formaldehyde (Aminoplastic)
- (3) Resorcinol/Formaldehyde
- (4) Polyvinyl Acetate (PVA)

[1] The following B.S. are available from The British Standards Institution: 745, Animal Glue; 1203, Synthetic Resin Adhesives for Plywood; 1204, Synthetic Resin Adhesives; 1444, Cold Setting Casein Glue.

(b) Casein Glues

(c) Vegetable Glues
- (1) Soya Bean
- (2) Starch Derivatives

(d) Blood Albumin Glues

(e) Animal Glues (Scotch Glue)

Depending on the location, an adhesive will need to satisfy one or more of the following requirements: (1) completely, or (2) partially resistant to wet; withstand (3) heat and (4) mycological attack (m.a.) from micro-organisms which can occur in damp places. Hence it is possible to select a glue for any given purpose[2] but the following other factors have to be considered: (i) The thickness of the "glue-line"; this is dependent on how closely the parts to be joined can be brought together. Accordingly glues are divided into two kinds. *Close-contact* (CC) glues used mainly for plywood manufacture and similar purposes where heavy pressure ensures tight joints and where a glue-line thickness exceeding 0·13 mm can be avoided with certainty; and *gap-filling* (GF) adhesives used for general joinery and large assembly work when a thin glue-line cannot be guaranteed, they are suitable for glue-lines up to 1·3 mm thick. (ii) The ease of preparation and application of the glue; for example, an animal glue has to be heated before use and other kinds require mixing with a hardener before they are ready. (iii) The storage-life and pot-life (the time for which the glue remains usable after it has been prepared); some glues require special storage conditions and must be used within a limited time after mixing. (iv) The length of time for which adequate pressure must be maintained varies with different glues. (v) The resin glues have to be used within prescribed conditions of temperature and humidity. (vi) Some glues stain the timber; this is obviously undesirable for veneers and other exposed work. (vii) Certain resin adhesives have to be used carefully to avoid the risk of skin infections to operatives.

Knowing the degree of exposure of the joined timbers and whether GF or CC types are needed, further valuable advice can be had from the adhesive manufacturer whose instructions for storage and application must be carefully followed.

The following is a brief description of the different kinds of adhesive listed above:

(*a*) (1) *Phenol/Formaldehyde Resin.*—This is a chemically produced resin derived from a reaction between carbolic acid (phenol) and an aldehyde. It is made in WBP, MR and INT grades either GF or CC and is practically indestructible. Both hot and cold-setting types are made, the former for plywood manufacture and the latter for general joinery. It is not liable to m.a., is fire-resisting and does not normally stain the wood. The resin can be had in liquid or powder form and some kinds require mixing with a separate liquid hardener; careful temperature control is needed; the cleaning of tools is difficult it being only soluble in alcohol; there is a danger of dermatitis to operatives.

A similar adhesive is the melamine/formaldehyde type usually obtained as a white powder resin to which water is added; it is normally only suitable for CC work and is weatherproof and resistant to m.a.

(*a*) (2) *Urea/Formaldehyde (Aminoplastic) Resin.*—This is also synthetically produced and made from a reaction between urea and formaldehyde. It is made in all the grades given in (*a*) (1) above; the resin (syrup or powder) and the hardener (liquid or powder) being either combined ready-mixed or available separately for subsequent mixing. The separate application method (both parts being in liquid form) is used for plywood manufacture where the resin is added to one surface and the hardener to the other; the surfaces are then brought together and if a quick-setting hardener is used the work is completed rapidly. Slower-setting types are used for general joinery. Pot-life varies from 20-minutes to 24-hours for the cold and hot-setting types respectively. It does not normally stain timber and is good against m.a. and heat. Care must be taken to use the glue at the temperature stipulated by the maker and within the specified time limits. There is less danger from dermatitis than with the phenolic types; it is water soluble prior to hardening.

(*a*) (3) *Resorcinol/Formaldehyde Resin.*—This is chemically made from resorcinol and formaldehyde; it is more expensive than (*a*) (1) and (2) being less sensitive to temperature, whilst being applied, than these two. A top class cement classed as WBP; is normally GF and so useful for general joinery (also for glued laminated work—see Chapter V, *Carpentry*); proof against m.a. and is water soluble until hardened. The resin is in liquid form requiring the addition of a powder hardener; it has a long storage-life; pot-life is from 1½ to 4-hours.

(*a*) (4) *Polyvinyl Acetate (PVA).*—This is classed as INT; it is a ready-mixed white syrupy liquid being increasingly used by joiners in lieu of the once universal animal glue. It is non-staining, easy to use but must be stored at a temperature above 4°C and not below 16°C. Water soluble and immune to m.a.; it sets within an hour.

(*b*) *Casein Glues.*—Casein is a milk derivative. Rennet, or acids such as hydrochloric, is added to skim milk to hasten the separation and precipitation of the curd. The latter is finely ground after it has been washed, pressed and dried and borax or other chemicals added. Obtained in powder form, to which water is added before use, it is soluble in water. Widely used for general joinery and also for plywood making. It can be described as moderately gap-filling and is satis-factory for glue lines up to 0·8 mm thick. Some caseins are liable to stain certain hardwoods such as oak and mahogany; some have a limited resistance to water and others none; they are susceptible to m.a.

(*c*) (1) *Vegetable Glues.*—The main vegetable used is (1) *Soya Bean* grown in the U.S. and Manchuria for its oil content. Other oil seed residue glues are obtained from ground nuts. They are made as a white powder (some kinds contain caustic soda and other chemicals) requir-ing the addition of water for application. They are moderately moisture-resistant having properties similar to casein; not much used in the U.K. but widely used for the manufacture of Douglas Fir plywood.

(*c*) (2) *Starch Derivative Glues.*—This vegetable glue is derived from cassava (tapioca) flour and incorporates some caustic soda. It is applied cold; has reasonable strength but is only suitable for interior use; liable to stain some woods; seldom used in the U.K.

(*d*) *Blood Albumin Glue.*—Produced from blood obtained from slaughterhouses; some kinds incorporate chemicals like para-formaldehyde. It has fair water-resisting qualities but is subject to m.a. and will stain certain hardwoods. Whilst it is used for the hot-press manufacture of plywood it is seldom encountered in the U.K.

(*e*) *Animal Glues.*—Known also as *Scotch Glue* it is the oldest of adhesives but quite unsuitable for external work; it is non-resistant to heat and m.a. Due to the amount of preparation required before it is ready for use and the fact that it has no gap-filling characteristics it is no longer the most widely used glue although it is very strong It is prepared from the skins and bones of cattle, horses, etc. The skins are steeped in liquid lime for two or three weeks, washed, dried and the glue (glutin) is extracted by boiling. The bones are cracked in a mill, placed in benzol or other solvent to remove the fat, taken to a steam boiler where the glue is extracted, and finally purified by heating with alum, etc. Another kind is *fish glue* obtained from fish offal.

Animal glue is prepared for use by softening it by several hours' immersion in from two or three parts cold water; it is then melted by heating in water-jacketed glue pots and applied hot at an approximate temperature of $60°C$; it should not be boiled. It does not stain the wood, although care has to be taken when applying it to sycamore, maple and similar light coloured woods to prevent discolouration.

[2]In B.S. 1204 the following classification is used: WBP—a weather and boil-proof glue which withstands severe weather exposure, heat and m.a.; it is practically indestructible and more durable than wood. MR—moisture and moderately weather-resistant; not boil-proof or as durable as WBP; withstands full weather exposure for a few years; it resists cold water for a long time and hot water for a limited time; good against m.a. INT—suitable for interior use; not boil-proof nor necessarily resistant to m.a.; it resists damp and cold water for a limited period.

INDEX